THE EVOLUTION OF THE MICROSCOPE

The Powell and Lealand "No. 1" microscope. This instrument represented perhaps the height of microscope design and craftsmanship in this country during the last century.

The Evolution of the
MICROSCOPE

by

S. BRADBURY, M.A., D.Phil., F.R.M.S.

Fellow of Pembroke College,
Lecturer in Human Anatomy,
University of Oxford

1966
THE QUEEN'S AWARD
TO INDUSTRY 1966

PERGAMON PRESS

OXFORD · LONDON · EDINBURGH · NEW YORK

TORONTO · SYDNEY · PARIS · BRAUNSCHWEIG

Pergamon Press Ltd., Headington Hill Hall, Oxford
4 & 5 Fitzroy Square, London W.1
Pergamon Press (Scotland) Ltd., 2 & 3 Teviot Place, Edinburgh 1
Pergamon Press Inc., 44-01 21st Street, Long Island City, New York 11101
Pergamon of Canada Ltd., 207 Queen's Quay West, Toronto 1
Pergamon Press (Aust.) Pty. Ltd., Rushcutters Bay, Sydney, N.S.W.
Pergamon Press S.A.R.L., 24 rue des Écoles, Paris 5e
Vieweg & Sohn GmbH, Burgplatz 1, Braunschweig

First edition 1967
Second Impression 1968

Library of Congress Catalog Card No. 67-18485

Printed in Great Britain by A. Wheaton & Co. Ltd., Exeter
08 003143 9

To my Parents

In commendation of ye Microscope

Of all the Inventions none there is Surpasses
   the Noble Florentine's Dioptrick Glasses
For what a better, fitter guift Could bee
   in this World's Aged Luciosity.
To help our Blindnesse so as to devize
   a paire of new & Artificial eyes
By whose augmenting power wee now see more
   than all the world Has ever doun Before.

HENRY POWERS 1664

CONTENTS

PREFACE

OF ALL the instruments used by the scientist, the microscope is perhaps the one which most aptly symbolizes this profession to the non-scientist. It is a tool which finds application in research (both in biological and non-biological fields), in teaching, and in a multitude of industrial and other applications. In fact wherever there is need to supplement the rather mediocre performance of the human eye, and to make the details in a small object visible, then the microscope in some form or other will be used. One suspects that very few of the many users of this instrument are more than vaguely aware of the interesting stages through which the microscope has passed during the course of its long development. This present book has been written in an attempt to present, in a readable form, some of the features of this history, an acquaintance with which often helps in understanding the rationale of the design features found in current microscopes.

Much more research remains to be carried out into the development of the microscope. It is strange that such an important symbol of our technology has hitherto been very largely overlooked by the historians of science. There are, of course, some notable exceptions to this and I have drawn to a great extent upon their work. In particular for the earlier period the *History of the Microscope* by R. S. Clay and T. H. Court has been invaluable; much help has also been obtained from the Cantor Lectures on the microscope delivered by J. Mayall, and from Harting's classic work *Das Mikroskop*. Later writings on this subject, especially those of A. Hughes and E. Frison, have also been extensively drawn upon. Much of the information concerning the stages in the development of the electron microscope is taken from the work of E. Ruska and T. Mulvey.

Many interesting changes may be discerned in the development of the microscopes used for various specialized purposes, especially in the physical sciences. The story of the polarizing microscope and the metallurgical microscope remain to be told at some future date. In the present book, however, it proved impossible to cover these topics and do them full justice so that, very reluctantly, it was decided to restrict the scope to the microscope as used in biology.

It is probable that some factual errors have been perpetuated, for which I apologize, but whenever possible I have gone back to the original sources, particularly when illustrating a specific point by means of an actual quotation.

Acknowledgments

I am most grateful to G. L'E. Turner of the Museum of the History of Science, Oxford for many helpful discussions, and to Alan Todd of Micro Instruments (Oxford) Ltd. for information on the design features of current microscope stands. I wish to extend my thanks to Miss Christine Court who prepared many of the drawings and to the photographic staff of the Department of Human Anatomy, Oxford for their willing assistance; I am also indebted to Mrs. G. Fodor who typed the final manuscript. Last, but by no means least, I wish to express my thanks to my wife Sheila not only for her forbearance during the writing of this book but also for reading and correcting the first draft of the manuscript.

My thanks are due to Messrs. J. A. Churchill Ltd. for permission to quote extracts from Carpenter and Dallinger's *The Microscope and Its Revelations* and for the use of a figure from this work (Fig. 5.15), and to Dr. S. H. Robinson for permission to quote from his address on Powell and Lealand to the Lincolnshire Natural History Society. I also extend my thanks to the following who supplied illustrations and gave permission for their reproduction: Messrs. A.E.I. Ltd (Figs. 8.6; 8.9; 8.10; 8.12); Messrs. Degenhardt (Fig. 7.7A); Studio Edmark, Oxford (Fig. 4.12); Messrs. Leitz (Fig. 7.15B); The Museum of the History of Science, Oxford (Figs 3.1; 4.12); The Royal Microscopical Society (Figs. 1.11; 1.14; 1.15; 2.11; 3.8; 3.10; 3.12; 4.1; 4.5; 4.8; 4.9; 4.11; 4.14; 5.2; 5.6; 5.7; 5.8; 5.14; 6.2; 6.4); The Science Museum, London (Figs. 2.5; 2.12; 4.2; 4.10; 5.5); Messrs. Siemens, Germany (Figs. 8.8, 8.11A & B); The Wellcome Trustees (Fig. 4.3).

CHAPTER 1

THE FIRST MICROSCOPES

PEOPLE are naturally curious about their surroundings. Their bodies need detailed information about the world around them in order that they may adapt smoothly to the demands and processes of living. More important, in human beings the search for information is carried much further than the bare requirements for existence in order to satisfy our innate desire to understand the world in which we live. We are provided with various receptive mechanisms or senses to help gather such information: of all these senses, the most important by far is that of sight. It is natural, therefore, that we are constantly using our eyes to tell us where we are in relation to obstacles, and to provide us with information about the properties of objects around us. The disabilities suffered by anyone who is blind, such as the difficulty which they experience in carrying out simple everyday tasks, the uncertainties attached to moving around, and the aesthetic losses from which they suffer, bring home the importance of sight to us very forcibly indeed.

It seems natural, therefore, that when we want detailed information about some part of our surroundings we first take a very close look at it. Such visual examinations are normally perfectly adequate for the day to day processes of living, but we must remember that the visual gathering of detailed information relating to our surroundings, and the classification and study of such knowledge forms a large part of the discipline known as "natural science". For such purposes the human eye often proves to be a very inadequate tool indeed, excellent though it may be for the normal needs of existing in our world; this is because the amount of detail which it can reveal to us is very limited.

From the days of the earliest civilizations, such as those of the Babylonians and the Egyptians, through Greek and Roman times up to the so-called "Dark Ages" in Europe, scientists and philosophers, astronomers and medical men have all been observing and collating natural phenomena. Much valuable information was obtained, but the whole world of structure which was smaller than the limits of resolution of

1

the sharpest eyes remained completely unknown, though not unsuspected. During the Dark Ages serious study was almost at a standstill, except for the Arabian world, in which the knowledge of the Ancient scholars was carefully preserved and augmented. When eventually the writings of the Greeks were translated from Arabic into Latin, the European scholars tended to spend their time commenting upon them and attempting to reconcile them with the doctrines of Christianity and the teachings of the Church. Such attitudes proved distinctly discouraging both to the observation of the natural world and to experimental study, although isolated figures such as the Oxford scholar Roger Bacon proved to be notable exceptions to the rule.

With the European Renaissance in the fifteenth century, scholars began to revolt against the dogmatic interpretation of the early writers such as Aristotle and the physician Galen; this change of intellectual climate proved significant, as it led to the stimulation of the processes of observation and experiment, which in turn placed the natural sciences on a sound footing. The development of observation in science gradually led to a dissatisfaction with the relatively poor resolution of the naked eye and this paved the way for the development of optical aids to vision.

The first successes of the new studies were in astronomy and mechanics, but there was soon a spread to the biological and medical fields. One of the landmarks in this latter field was undoubtedly the publication of the superb anatomical studies of Andreas Vesalius, in 1543, which were known under the title *De humani corporis fabrici*. This work, with its accurate illustrations of structures which can be seen with the naked eye, refuted many of the doctrines which had been accepted uncritically since the days of Galen 1300 years before, and it set the standard and provided the inspiration for the future. Scientists, such as Gabriele Fallopio, Bartolommeo Eustachii, Francis Glisson, Thomas Wharton and many others less well known, followed the lead given by Vesalius and began the detailed study of anatomical structures. So far, during all the years from the earliest times up to the end of the sixteenth century, studies of the structure of natural objects had been performed with the unaided eye. Studies of both objects at great distances such as the stars, and very minute objects and structural details of larger objects were limited by the capabilities of the human eye. As more and more scientists took up such studies the need for supplementing the human eye became apparent; when the method of combining lenses to obtain an enlarged image was discovered at the end of the sixteenth century its possibilities were rapidly realised. The needs of the scientists stimulated rapid progress in microscopy and this, in its turn, gave immense benefits and impetus to the work of the scientists. Before the development of the microscope in its early days is described in detail, however, we must see what developments in optics led up to it, and consider what artificial aids to vision were available up to the end of the sixteenth century.

It cannot be decided with certainty whether the ancient world was aware of the magnifying properties of simple convex lenses. From the writings of the Romans it seems that they knew that such lenses could converge the sun's rays and act as a burning glass. Indeed, from the writings of Pliny we have good evidence that this was actually used in medical practice for the cauterization of wounds, when he says

> I find that among doctors it is thought that nothing is better when any part of a body is to be burned than to use a crystalline sphere placed in the sun's rays.

Several other sources confirm that the ancient world was aware of the action of the burning glass, although it is certain that they did not understand how the phenomenon occurred, as at that time the laws of refraction of light by a crystalline sphere were not known.

One famous passage which occurs in the writings of Seneca may be translated as

> Letters, however small and indistinct, are seen enlarged and more clearly through a globe of glass filled with water.

In another chapter of the same work he states that fruit appears larger if it is floating in water. The conclusion is drawn that as all objects seen through water appear larger than they are, the enlargement is due to the water; the geometrical shape of the object containing the water is not involved in the process. One may conclude that although the phenomenon of the refraction or bending of light rays on their passage at an angle from one medium to another had been observed, there was no conception of the action of a lens-shaped transparent body in the production of a magnified image. There is certainly no mention in Pliny's works, or indeed in those of any other writer of this period, of the use of lenses to correct or compensate for defects in the human eye, such as long or short sight. The use of lenses in this way would have certainly been mentioned had their effects been known; references in writings of the fifth century A.D. to short sight (and again as late as the thirteenth century) specifically state that this condition is uncurable. Spectacles appear to date from the last years of the thirteenth century; evidence for their use to correct defects of vision is provided by the writer of a Florentine manuscript dated 1299 in which he says

> I find myself so pressed by age that I can neither read nor write without glasses which they call spectacles, newly invented, for the great advantage of old men when their sight grows weak.

Many examples of engraving on gems and precious stones have survived in our museums; some of these carvings show extremely minute detail which, it has been objected, could not have been executed without some form of magnifier. This has been used as an argument to support the contention that the magnifying action of a convex lens was known to the early engravers. It seems unlikely, however, that this was the case, as no account of the use of artificial aids has survived in any of the classical writers. In particular, Pliny, who was deliberately attempting to chronicle all the existing technological knowledge of his day, would surely have mentioned this important detail had it been a custom. He goes into great detail about gem-engraving, and mentions that the workers looked at or through emeralds or other green stones in order to strengthen or rest their tired eyes, but there is no hint of the use of a glass sphere or any other possible magnifier. Almost certainly the secret of such detailed engraving must have been in the high degree of visual acuity of the workmen. There is much individual variation among different people as to the amount of detail visible in an object; short-sighted people, in particular, when they place an object very close to their eyes can see detail which would be almost invisible to a person with normal sight. Such ability, together with the long and careful training of an engraver could quite well account for the minute detail found in many examples of their work without supposing the availability of any artificial aids to vision.

An interesting example of the exceptional visual acuity of some engravers is furnished by the entry for August 10th, 1664, in the famous diary of Samuel Pepys:

> Abroad to find out one to engrave my tables upon my new sliding rule with silver plates, it being so small that Browne that made it cannot get one to do it. So I find out Cocker, the famous writing master, and get him to do it, and I set an hour by him to see him design it all: and strange it is to see him with his natural eyes to cut so small at his first designing it, and read it all over, without any missing, when for my life I could not,

with my best skill, read one word or letter of it; but it is use. He says the best light for his life to do a very small thing by (contrary to Chaucer's words to the Sun, "that he should lend his light to them that small seals grave") it should be by an artificial light of a candle, set to advantage, as he could do it.

This ability to read and engrave work almost beyond the limits of vision of the majority of people evidently made a considerable impression on Pepys. It should be noted that at this date, although the microscope was well advanced, engravers obviously still preferred to carry out their work with the naked eye.

Probably the first real appreciation of the action of a lens, in particular the ability of a convex form to produce a magnified image of an object appears to be due to the Arabian scholar Ibn al Haitham (962–1038), more commonly known by the Latin form of his name Alhazen. His great work was translated into Latin in the twelfth century, when it became known as the *Opticae Thesaurus Alhazeni Arabis*. It was eventually published four centuries later in Basel. The *Thesaurus*, which is noteworthy for its constant reference to experimental methods in support of the various propositions, contains one of the first anatomical descriptions of the eye. In one proposition of the book, in which Alhazen considers refraction through a sphere in the situation where the eye and the object lie on extensions of the same diameter, he states quite definitely that the image will be larger than the object itself. Alhazen seems to have been mainly interested in refraction at one surface of the sphere only and no practical applications of his observation are considered.

Some two hundred years later, Roger Bacon was obviously familiar with the theoretical and experimental studies of his predecessors, including Alhazen. He applied his knowledge of optics to such practical ends as the design of burning glasses and the devising of paraboloidal mirrors to concentrate the sun's rays to a point for the same purpose. A well-known passage in his *Opus Majus* deals with the production of a magnified image of objects, and is worth quoting here as it appears in Smith's *Opticks*, a standard eighteenth-century treatise on the subject:

> If the letters of a book, or any minute object, be viewed through a lesser segment of a sphere of glass or crystal whose plane base is laid upon them, they will appear far better and larger . . . . And, therefore, this instrument is useful to old men and to those that have weak eyes. For they may see the smallest letters sufficiently magnified.

Although it is clear from this passage that Bacon clearly understood the principle of using a plano-convex lens as a magnifier, it seems most unlikely that he had actually constructed a simple magnifier. The art of grinding and polishing glass for optical purposes would, at that time, still be very rudimentary and practical application of these theories required a much higher standard of skill than is reasonable to attribute to the period of Roger Bacon. It may be that he obtained some experimental confirmation of his ideas from observations made, perhaps, through a broken crystal sphere.

It is a far cry from this early theorizing of Roger Bacon to the optical studies of Giovanni Battista della Porta (1543–1615) who was a versatile man of great intellect and a prolific writer on many subjects. One of his works was a kind of encyclopaedic treatise on popular science and was published in its complete form of twenty separate books in 1589 under the title *Magia Naturalis*, which when later translated into English became known as *Natural Magick*. One of the books comprising this work is entitled *Of Strange Glasses*; in this Porta provides clear evidence of the practical uses to which lenses had been applied in the sixteenth century for the correction of visual defects. Disney Hill, referring to a later work of Porta's states:

> It is noticeable that the *De Refractione* says nothing about lens-combinations but confines itself to single lenses. The time for this particular development had clearly not yet arrived.

On the other hand one passage from Porta's *Magia Naturalis* seems to provide evidence that the knowledge of some kind of lens-combination did in fact exist at this time. He says:

> Concave lenticulars will make one see most clearly things that are far off; but convexes things near at hand; so you may use them as your sight requires. With a concave you will see small things afar off very clearly; with a convex, things neerer to be greater, but more obscurely; if you know how to fit them together you shall see both things afar off and things neer at hand, both greater and clearly. I have much helped some of my friends who saw things afar off, weakly: and what was neer confusedly, that they might see all things clearly.

Some authorities believe that this signified a device for correcting the inherent imperfections of a lens by adding a second to make a doublet; more probably, however, it implies a rudimentary knowledge of the effects of combining more than one lens to form an optical instrument.

From his later work it is apparent that the empirical optics of spectacle lenses were now well understood and that by the sixteenth century lens-making had become established as a definite industry; interest in optics was growing and perhaps there were empirical, rather crude attempts at producing optical combinations. The situation at this time has been well summarized by Disney Hill in his introduction to the catalogue of the collection of the Royal Microscopical Society, in which he writes:

> Much was as yet empiricism and guesswork. The law of refraction still awaited discovery; the compound nature of sunlight was as yet unsuspected; even the rudiments of mathematical optics could scarcely be said to exist. On the other hand, familiarity with lenses must have been considerable, and their application to the infirmities of human vision must have supplied a constant stimulus to their improvement and manufacture.

At this point, before considering various claims to the invention of the microscope it is necessary to digress and consider the capabilities of the unaided human eye and how it may be supplemented by the use of lenses.

The light rays enter the eye through the transparent cornea and are brought to a focus to form a sharp image on the light-sensitive elements of the retina lining the inside of the eyeball. The bending or refraction of the light is caused by the combined action of the corneal/air interface and at the crystalline lens which is situated just behind the coloured iris. Variations in the shape of the lens, caused by the pull of a small muscle, enable the eye to form equally sharp images of objects at different distances; this property is known as accommodation, and enables the normal eye to form sharp images of objects which vary in distance from infinity to about ten inches from the eye itself. This latter distance is usually termed the "least distance of distinct vision" or the "conventional visual distance".

It is a well-known fact that the apparent size of any object varies according to its distance from the observer. If we look at a man who is at the far end of a street he seems to be much smaller than when he is only a few yards away, although quite obviously his size has not changed. The change in the apparent size of the man as he walks towards us is due to the fact that the angle which is subtended by light rays from an object at the optical centre or "nodal point" of the eye increases as the object is brought closer to the eye. This is shown diagramatically in Fig. 1.1; here AB represents an object of constant size which is viewed from three positions in turn. When seen from the farthest point, E, the visual angle AEB is small. At an intermediate position, D, the angle is clearly larger, and when the observer is near to AB, the point C, the visual angle, represented now by ACB, is largest of all.

It is thus obvious that the visual angle subtended at the eye by any object depends on its distance, and it follows that if the object is very

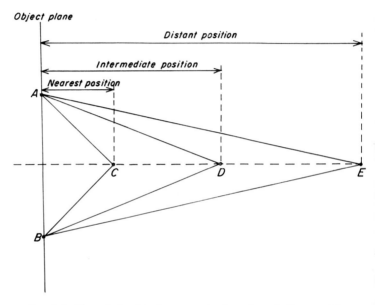

FIG. 1.1. The relationship between visual angle and distance. The angle subtended at the eye of the observer by the object AB increases as one gets nearer to it (represented successively by the positions E, D and C), and the greater the amount of detail which can be resolved in the object.

small, i.e. subtends a very small visual angle, it may be made to appear larger by bringing it closer to the eye. If we think of the printed letters forming a page of newsprint held five feet from the eye, they subtend a very small visual angle and, therefore, the image on the sensitive retina is extremely small; the result is that they cannot be seen distinctly. The larger black type of the main headlines subtends a larger angle at this same distance and hence the retinal image is larger and the letters can be read. By bringing the paper one foot from the eye the angle subtended by the small print increases and these letters in turn become legible.

Experiments and calculation have both shown that when the angle subtended by any object at a given distance falls below one minute of arc it is no longer resolvable by the average human eye. In practice there is some variation according to the nature of the object and tests of visual acuity have to be designed to take this into account. A grating of black and white bars observed at the nearest distance of distinct vision (ten inches) by an average person would be seen resolved into its components when there were about 200 lines in the space of one inch.

Since an object must be magnified so that its image subtends at least one minute of arc at the eye, in order for it to be resolved, it might be supposed that this could be achieved simply by bringing the object nearer to the eye, and so increasing its visual angle. The power of accommodation of the eye is limited, however, and objects cannot be placed nearer than the least distance of distinct vision, if they are to be seen in sharp focus.

With very short-sighted individuals, of course, the nearest distance of distinct vision may be as close as two inches, so that they can increase the apparent size of fine detail by removing their correcting spectacles and bringing the object very close to the eye.

For the majority of observers the visual angle must be increased some other way and it is the microscope which is the tool by which this object can be achieved. It must be stressed at this point that we have been talking about *resolution* rather than *visibility*. Resolution, the ability to distinguish two separate points of light or details on an object as separate points, was clearly understood in the seventeenth century by Robert Hooke, although it was treated in relation to astronomy and the observation of double stars, rather than to microscopy. Hooke was the first to conclude that in order to see the stars as double they must be separated by such a distance that they subtend a visual angle of one minute of arc. If they are closer than this, then to most people the two points of light would appear single, so that the visual angle of one minute of arc represents not the limit of visibility but the limit of resolution. It is this property with which we are largely concerned in microscopy. If an image is merely magnified without resolution having been achieved, the result is a blur, which does not convey any more meaningful information and it is then termed "empty magnification". Most people, when confronted with a microscope usually ask "What is its magnification?", when the question which should be asked is about the resolution of the lenses.

The microscope then serves to increase the visual angle under which the object is seen, thus making it possible, in effect, for the eye to approach very close to the object and still preserve the sharpness of the image thrown on the retina despite the restrictions imposed by the limited powers of accommodation of the eye. Microscopes may increase the visual angle by the use of one or more lenses which enable the eye to form a sharp, spread-out image on the retina, or alternatively by projection of a greatly enlarged real image of the object upon a screen, which is then viewed by the eye in the normal way as though the image were the actual object. Normally when the microscope is mentioned it is an instrument of the first type that is meant, where the image is formed directly in the eye by rays of light from the microscope. The second type — known as a projection microscope — was, however, much used in the eighteenth and early nineteenth centuries in the form of the solar microscope, so called because the illumination was by means of the sun's rays directed into the instrument by means of a special mirror. The projection microscope has recently been revived and is now much used for teaching purposes because the image can be seen easily by several people at once. A modern version of this type of instrument uses a television camera attached to the optical system of the microscope so that the final image may be presented on television monitor screens, which can be seen by large numbers of people.

The increase of visual angle, i.e. the spreading out of the image of the object on the retina of the eye may be achieved either in a single stage by the use of a convex lens (or nowadays a combination of lenses cemented together in order to achieve a more perfect image) or in two stages. In this case the first lens combination, called the objective, furnishes a real enlarged image of the object and this enlarged image is looked at by a further lens system known as the ocular. When only a single lens or combination is used, as in the reading glass or watchmaker's magnifier, it is termed a *simple microscope*; where two or more lens systems are used we have the *compound microscope*.

The action of a simple microscope is shown in Fig. 1.2, in which the visual angle may be compared with that produced by the same size of object placed at the nearest distance of distinct vision shown in Fig. 1.3. In this latter figure the object AB produces an inverted image CD on the retina of the eye. The visual angle is represented by the value *a.* When a simple convex lens is used as a microscope the object AB is placed closer to the eye than before and the lens interposed between it and the eye. The retinal image C'D' is now larger than before and

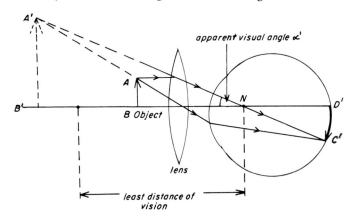

FIG. 1.2. The convex lens acting as a simple microscope. AB is placed nearer to the eye than the least distance of distinct vision and within the focal length of the lens. The virtual image AB appears erect and magnified, and its apparent visual angle (α') is increased.

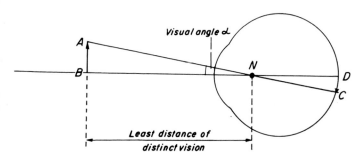

FIG. 1.3. The visual angle (α) subtended by an object AB placed at the least distance of distinct vision is represented diagrammatically in this figure. N represents the nodal point or optical centre of the eye and DC the image of the object on the retina of the eye.

the object appears to be situated at A'B'. This image cannot be projected onto a screen, it does not exist independently of the eye and is said to be "virtual". When a lens is used to throw an image on a screen a picture is formed independently of the eye and in this condition the image is known as a "real" image. From Fig. 1.2 it will be seen that the virtual image produced during the use of a simple microscope is enlarged and the same way up as the object or, as it is termed in optics, "erect". The virtual image of A'B' now subtends an apparent visual angle of α' which is greater than the true visual angle α produced by the viewing of the same object without a lens. The virtual image makes it appear

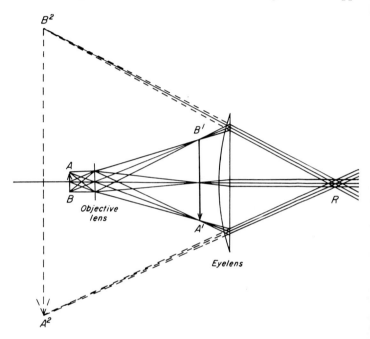

FIG. 1.4. A schematic diagram to show the arrangement of two lenses to form a compound microscope. The real, inverted intermediate image is indicated at A'B' and the final, virtual image at A^2B^2. R represents the "Ramsden circle" where the rays are brought together after passing through the eyelens.

to the eye as if the object itself were situated at A'B' and had that actual size.

The operation of a compound microscope may be shown in a simplified form by a similar type of diagram (Fig. 1.4). Now the object AB is placed just outside the focus of a convex lens or combination of lenses known as the objective. This produces a real, magnified image at A'B', which is seen to be upside down, or "inverted".

This real image is viewed with the aid of a further convex lens (the eye lens or ocular) so arranged as to produce an erect, virtual image of part of the intermediate image A′B′; this virtual image is represented by A²B² and is still further magnified. As the primary or intermediate image is inverted with respect to the object, it follows that the final virtual image produced by the eyepiece will also be inverted with respect to the object and it will be still further magnified by the action of the eyepiece lens.

It will be seen from Fig. 1.4 that in a microscope constructed with only two lenses, the eyelens must be rather large in order to accept the whole cone of rays from the intermediate image A′B′.

The rays are brought together outside the eyepiece at R, which is found a considerable distance from the eyelens. Point R is called the "Ramsden circle" or "eyepoint" and it is at this point that the eye of the observer must be situated. Considerable practical difficulties exist in manufacturing large lenses which have a correspondingly larger radius of curvature; again, the distance of the eyepoint causes considerable inconvenience to the user for unless the whole cone of rays forming the Ramsden circle enters the pupil of the eye, the whole of the field of view is not obtained. It is not easy to achieve this condition when the eyepoint is some distance from the lens surface.

In order to overcome these difficulties the so-called Huygenian eyepiece, which consists of two lenses arranged as in Fig. 1.5, is now largely used. The larger of the two lenses is called the field lens, the smaller and more powerful being the eye lens. It can be seen from the diagram that the intermediate image A′B′, which in the absence of the field lens would have been produced in the position marked by the dotted lines, is now smaller and formed nearer to the objective. The eye lens, which provides most of the magnifying power of the eyepiece, forms a virtual image of this intermediate image in the usual way. It can be seen that the Ramsden circle is now much nearer to the eye lens (compare Figs. 1.4 and 1.5) and that the diameter of the lenses needed to achieve the same area of field of view is now much smaller. In Fig. 1.5 the size of an equivalent single lens is shown by dotted lines on the right hand side of the diagram.

This eyepiece then has important advantages over a single-lens eyepiece in being easier to construct, as it uses small lenses of great curvature, and in possessing a close eyepoint; even more important, the component lenses can be so calculated that their aberrations cancel out some of the residual errors introduced by the incomplete corrections of the microscope objective.

This form of compound microscope having convex lenses in the eyepiece is known as the "Keplerian" type, from the fact that this method of optical construction was first suggested by Kepler in his *Dioptrice* published in 1611. An alternative construction, which substitutes a diverging or concave lens in the eyepiece, is known and is usually called the "Galilean" system, although there is some doubt whether Galileo himself was the inventor.

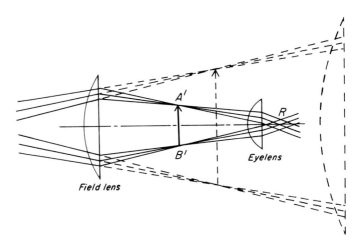

Fig. 1.5. The Huygenian eyepiece. The converging action of the field lens causes the intermediate image (A′B′) to be smaller and situated nearer the objective than would otherwise be the case. The eye lens produces a virtual image of this in the usual way. The size of an equivalent single eye lens is shown dotted in the diagram.

It seems likely that this system originated in Holland and was taken up by Galileo when he made his telescopes in the early part of the seventeenth century. The Galilean telescope can, by extending the distance between its lenses, also be used as a microscope, and undoubtedly Galileo himself discovered this fact. Under such conditions, however, the Galilean system suffers from the severe drawback of having a very restricted field of view; this, together with the inconveniently large amount of separation required between the lenses, no doubt caused it to fall into disuse for microscope systems.

A passage written in 1614 by Giovanni du Pont, Seigneur de Tarde, quoted in Clay & Court's book on the microscope is interesting in this respect. Du Pont says:

> The tube of the telescope for looking at the stars was not more than two feet in length, but to see objects that are very near, but which we could not distinguish on account of their small size, the tubes must be two or three arms' length.

Galileo used his instrument to look at insects and the same author related that Galileo told him that

> With this tube I have seen flies which look as big as lambs.

As a consequence of the limitations mentioned above, the Galilean type of instrument did not figure in the subsequent development of the microscope, although it has had some limited use in the nineteenth century as a simple dissecting microscope — the so-called "Brücke lens". Its main advantage for this purpose lay in the fact that there must be a considerable distance between the object and the front lens of the instrument which allows room to carry out manipulation and dissection.

There has been much confusion over the claims to be regarded as the inventor of the compound microscope built on the Keplerian pattern. It now seems unlikely that we shall ever be able to settle the matter with certainty, largely owing to the difficulties of interpreting the vague descriptions in the early manuscripts and to the lack of authentic early instruments of known date.

An amusing example of the confusion which can arise from studies of these early writings on this strange new instrument is provided by the *Magia Universalis* of Gaspar Schott published in 1677. Figures in this work show what seem to be giant microscopes, which are nearly the size of a man. Some of these figures are reproduced here as Fig. 1.6. Such instruments would be obviously completely impracticable and historians of the microscope dismissed them as mere flights of fancy. Mayall, however, in his Cantor Lectures on the microscope published in 1888 mentions a suggestion by Frank Crisp, the then Secretary of the Royal Microscopical Society, which seems to explain these strange instruments. The suggestion was simply that the mistake is solely due to the engraver when redrawing the figures. Schott in one case gives the original source of his material and in the other cases it has proved possible to trace them in other contemporary accounts; some are taken

A

B

C

FIG. 1.6. "Giant microscopes" from Gaspar Schott's *Magia Universalis* of 1677. Compare these three figures with the corresponding illustrations in Fig. 1.7, which represent the same type of microscope. A false impression of their scale is gained as a result of the engraver's error.

A   B

C

FIG. 1.7.

(a) microscope from Traber's *Nervus Opticus* (1675)

(b) microscope from Kircher's *Ars magna lucis* (1646)

(c) Traber's conception of Divini's microscope.

from a book *Ars Magnis Lucis et Umbrae* published by Kircher in 1646, whilst illustrations of comparable instruments are found in Traber's *Nervus Opticus* of 1675 (Fig. 1.7).

One tends to estimate the size of the instruments by reference to what is drawn with them and as the engraver instead of drawing simply an eye looking through the small tube (Fig. 1.7a and c) pictured a whole man, one gains the impression that the tube is of an appropriate size (Fig. 1.6 a and c). Again the drawing shown as Fig. 1.6(b) would suggest a man looking at a candle flame through an immense convex lens, but on reference to the original source in Kircher (Fig. 1.7 b) one sees that the artist has again converted the representation of an eye into a whole man and that what he has shown as a candle flame was originally meant to represent an insect, impaled on the point of a pin, which is being examined through a lens which must only be a few inches in diameter!

These errors are all the more strange because Schott mentions himself in his text that the tube of one of the instruments

> scarcely exceeds in length and thickness the joint of a finger.

In other cases too he quotes the approximate sizes of the tube of the instrument he is drawing. Perhaps the errors may be due to the still unfamiliar nature of the new instruments and the possibility that the engravings were prepared separately and not seen by Schott. With such hazards abounding in the seventeenth-century literature it is not surprising that doubt still exists as to the early history of the microscope!

In the famous *Dioptrique* published in 1637, Rene Descartes shows two types of simple microscope, one almost certainly the source of Kircher's figure, the other of a plano-convex lens fixed in a central aperture in what was presumably a metal speculum. This instrument (Fig. 1.8) carried the specimen impaled on a metal spike, labelled G, which held the object in the focal plane of the lens. It seems that the instrument was designed to be held up to the sun, which was reflected by the mirror so as to illuminate the opaque object. The reflector, which served to illuminate the object, was later carried on the barrel of the objective of a compound microscope, or was fitted surrounding the mounted lens of a simple microscope and was known, after one of its subsequent inventors, as a "Lieberkühn."

In the same book a few pages later, Descartes introduces a figure (reproduced here as Fig. 1.9) of an instrument which is mounted on a stand in a similar manner to a telescope. Again the figure of a man introduced suggests an instrument built on a gigantic scale. There is nothing in the text to indicate the size of the microscope, but again we are probably dealing with a case of draughtsman's licence; the figure which immediately precedes this in the original shows a

Fig. 1.8. The simple microscope designed by Descartes. The lens is mounted in the centre of a concave mirror which concentrates light upon the specimen impaled upon the spike G.

"perspicillum" mounted on an identical stand, but in this case only an eyeball is drawn at the observer's end. This instrument is obviously a small Galilean telescope and therefore it seems probable that in view of the similarity in mountings, the two instruments would have been of comparable size. The microscope appears to be of the Galilean type, with a bi-convex objective lens, which may not have been of a spherical curvature, and a single concave lens acting as an eyepiece. The object is shown, as in the case of his simple microscope, as being surrounded by a large hyperbolic mirror. Again the idea was to illuminate an opaque object by concentrating the sun's rays onto it. A further very interesting feature, which foreshadows a much later development in illumination technique, is a smaller plano-convex lens (li in the figure) mounted on an arm in such a way as to concentrate a beam of light on

Fig. 1.9. The "giant" microscope of Descartes. Note the "Lieberkühn" type of mirror (CPNC) and the condensing lens (li). The object was placed at Z.

a transparent object placed at the focus. This must be one of the first indications of the method which has come to be universal for studying transparent objects with transmitted light. No indications of the focusing methods are given. Although Descartes directs that both instruments should be used with full sunlight, it seems unlikely that either was ever actually constructed. Mayall thought such an instrument would have proved far beyond the rather slender technological resources of Descartes' times. It must be regarded as an intellectual exercise of some ingenuity, but it does furnish one of the earliest printed representations of the combination of lenses in such a way as to form a compound microscope.

As in the case of many useful instruments, it seems probable that the basic idea of how to combine lenses to form a device for magnifying objects occurred independently, at about the same time, to more than one person. Certainly many opticians were active at the end of the sixteenth century, especially in Holland, in the construction of telescopes, so that it is likely that the idea of the microscope may have occurred to several of them independently. Various authorities give the credit to different people and it is difficult to disentangle the rival claims. In all probability the date may be placed within the period 1590–1609 and the credit should go to three spectacle makers of Middelburg in Holland, any or all of whom may have had some part to play in the inception of the microscope.

Hans Janssen, his son Zacharias and Hans Lippershey have all been cited at various times as deserving of the chief credit. From seventeenth-century writing, especially by Wilhelm Boreel, a member of the Dutch diplomatic service, it would seem that the Janssens, both father and son, are chiefly involved. Boreel affirmed in letters (which were later published) that he had known the Janssens personally for a very long time and that Hans Janssen had told him that they were inventors of the microscope. It seems that they had sent one instrument to Prince Maurice of Orange and another to Archduke Albert of Austria. This latter instrument eventually passed into the hands of Cornelius Drebbel and it was then seen by Wilhelm Boreel himself when the latter was envoy to England around 1619.

From his description we learn that it had a tube about eighteen inches long and two inches in diameter, supported by a stand in the form of three brass dolphins. This was placed on an ebony base so that this instrument would only have been suitable for viewing opaque objects by reflected light.

Hans Lippershey's claim to have constructed a microscope is not so well substantiated; it is certain, however, that he did construct a telescope which was unusual at that time in being a binocular instrument. It was made with lenses ground from rock crystal, because of the generally poor quality of the glass available at that time (which was usually greenish in colour and marred by the presence of air bubbles). It was probably for this reason that one of the best known of the seventeenth-century microscopists — Antoni van Leeuwenhoek —

occasionally ground his lenses from grains of sand which formed a
source of pure quartz.

All these early microscope makers were certainly working quite
empirically; as the manufacture of lenses for spectacles was now
quite widespread it seems likely that the chance combination of two
convex lenses held one above the other in the hand would occur.
In some positions they would act as a crude compound microscope
from which the actual mounting of the lenses in a tube would be a
short step. Whoever took these first steps is not known for certain,
but his invention very soon spread widely. From the letter of Wilhelm
Boreel, which has already been mentioned, we know that Cornelius
Drebbel had a microscope in England in 1619 and other contemporary
accounts indicate that the invention reached Rome a few years later.

Harting, one of the great authorities of the last century, certainly
believed the compound microscope to have been invented in Middelburg by the Janssens around the year 1590. Rooseboom, however,
has recently suggested that this claim cannot be regarded as valid.
Drebbel, if one can believe the testimony of Boreels, actually travelled
to Middelburg to purchase a microscope, which he later copied;
although he cannot be given any credit for the invention, nevertheless
he played an important part in its acceptance as it was instruments
made by Drebbel which circulated widely through Europe. Indeed,
it was one of his microscopes which Galileo, when visiting Rome in
1624, was called upon to explain to its owner who was unable to
make it work. Contemporary letters (later published in the *Journal
of the Royal Microscopical Society*) seem to show that this instrument
or "occhiale", as it was called, was "a new invention, different from
that of Galileo", which showed a flea the size of a locust. Another letter
says that "the effect of the occhiale is to show the object upside down
and to cause the real motion of the little animal to seem contrary;
as for example, if it be going from east to west it will appear to go
from west to east". This makes it likely that the instruments of Drebbel
were of the Keplerian form with a convex or plano-convex eye
lens.

It has already been suggested that Galileo's only contribution to the
microscope was to convert the telescope with a concave eye lens into
a microscope by extending the tube. Once the Dutch Keplerian
microscope became known, the shorter, more manageable body-tube
length and the greatly increased field of view resulted in all subsequent
efforts being channelled into the development of this type. The

Dutch thus seemed to be foremost in the field for both telescopes and microscopes at this time, but it must be remembered that the greater part of the credit for the application of these discoveries should go to the Italians. Galileo, in particular, was studying the moon and recording its craters, and the rings of Saturn, whilst in 1625, very shortly after the introduction of Drebbel's microscopes to Rome, we find Francisco Stelluti using it in what must be one of the first micro-anatomical studies on the structure of the honey-bee.

In the museum of Middelburg there is preserved a very old micro-scope, which is reputed to be an instrument constructed by Zacharias anssen himself although there is no *direct* evidence to link it with him.

Fig. 1.10. A diagrammatic section through the microscope discovered by Harting in Middelburg and believed to be attributable to Janssen. Note that each lens is mounted in a draw tube which can slide in the outer casing. No stand was provided for this instrument, which was apparently held in the hand whilst in use.

It was presented to the museum in 1866 by a private donor, in whose family it had been for several generations. Harting believed this instrument to be a very early compound microscope and it excited much interest in the microscopical world at that time. Since then various copies have been made and a working model may be seen in the Science Museum at South Kensington. The method of construction of this microscope is shown in Fig. 1.10, from which it can be seen that the microscope consists of three tubes, the middle one of which acts as a sleeve to support the outer two, so enabling them to be slid apart. Each of the end tubes contains a lens, that which serves as the objective being plano-convex, whilst the eye lens is bi-convex. The latter lens is loose in the original instrument, but presumably it was once held in place by means of a ring fitted inside the tube. As there is no form of tripod support the instrument was intended for use in the hand.

It is obvious that this microscope differs from the Janssen instrumen
described by Boreel, but as the microscope he was describing was a
presentation model the differences in construction may be explained
again the surviving Middelburg instrument may be an early or
experimental model intended for some special use or the possibility
exists that it is not by Janssen at all.

Fig. 1.11. An early compound
microscope, probably dating
from around 1670, ascribed
to Campani. It shows the
typical, rather crude methods
of construction in vogue at
the period.

Fig. 1.12. Divini's microscope
of 1667. Note the rough tripod mount, the four draw
tubes and the absence of any
mechanical devices for focusing the microscope.

The inner sliding tubes of the instrument enable it to be extended from about ten inches to sixteen inches in length so changing both the focus and the magnification. With the tube pushed right in the power is about three diameters, which rises to nine diameters on full extension of the tubes. Despite its doubtful origin this instrument is of great significance to the development of the microscope and Harting concludes:

> In spite of the fact that all direct proofs fail, I consider it by no means improbable that the tradition is true and that this instrument is one of the oldest microscopes which by Hans and Zacharias Janssen or by the first alone were manufactured long before they brought to a finish instruments more accurate and optically more complete which were destined for Prince Maurice and the Archduke Albert.

When we move on to the latter half of the seventeenth century we find that examples of the microscopes of the period are still preserved in museums, though in many cases with the lenses lacking, or in very poor condition. These instruments show very clearly the rather crude methods of construction at first used and how during the course of a very few years the mechanical parts of the instrument began to assume a fairly standardized form. One early microscope, shown in Fig. 1.11, is attributed by Mayall to the Italian instrument maker and optician Campani, who lived and worked in Bologna at this time. The date of the microscope shown here is doubtful, but it may be thought to represent the state of the art in Italy around the 1670's. As such it is interesting to compare it with the contemporary British microscopes of the same period (see Chapter 2), and note that already there was a considerable divergence in design between the British and the Continental makers, a feature which was to form such a major issue in later nineteenth-century microscopy.

It is obvious that the Continental instrument-makers were content to produce an instrument which was designed solely for the examination of opaque objects which were placed on the table between the tripod feet of the instrument. The tubes are made of cardboard, which was much used in the seventeenth century for optical instrument tube making, and focusing of the lens was effected very simply by sliding the tube within the collar formed by the upper part of the tripod. With the low magnification lenses of rather poor quality in use at this time no very precise focusing mechanism was required and the sliding tube would have served very well and been simple to construct.

A very similar instrument (Fig. 1.12) has been described as the invention of Eustachio Divini around the year 1667. His description appeared in an Italian publication, but a synopsis appeared in the *Philosophical Transactions* for the year 1668 which is worth quoting:

> Eustachio Divini hath made a Microscope of a new Invention, wherein instead of an Eye-glass convex on both sides, there are two plano-convex Glasses, which are so placed, as to touch one another in the middle of their convex surface. This Instrument of which Honoratus Fabri treats largely in his *Opticks* (viz. Prop. 46) hath this peculiar, that it shews the Objects flat and not crooked, and although it takes in much, yet nevertheless magnifieth extraordinarily.
>
> It is almost 16½ inches high, and adjusted at 4 different lengths. In the first, which is the least, it shows lines 41 times bigger than they appear to the naked Eye: In the second 90 times: in the third 111 times: and in the fourth 143 times. Whence one may easily calculate, how much it augments surfaces and solidities. The Diameter of the Field it discovers, or the subtense of the visual angle, measured upon the Object-plate, in the first length is of 8 inches and 7 lines; in the second of 12 inches and 4 lines: in the third of 13 inches: and in the fourth of a little more than 16 inches.
>
> As they viewed with this Microscope the little grains of sand searched, they perceived an Animal with many feet, its back white and scaly, but less than any of those hitherto observed. For, although the Microscope shewed every grain of sand as big as an ordinary Nut, yet this Animal appeared no bigger than one of the grains of sand seen without a Microscope. Whence may be concluded its smallness, which occasioned one of the beholders to give it the name of the Atome of Animals.

Here is a reference which suggests that the early microscope makers were very sensible of two of the great defects of the simple microscope with a convex lens, namely the curvature of the field and its limited extent. Divini obviously produced one of the first doublets which he claimed much improved these particular shortcomings.

The similarity of the microscope to the early model of Campani's is apparent from Fig. 1.11 and 1.12. Again the focusing is by a sliding of the paper-covered cardboard tubes and again the mount is a simple crude type of tripod. The lenses of this early Divini microscope do not seem to have survived.

Bedini has recently published a study of several of the early seventeenth-century Italian microscopes by such makers as Campani and Divini. He shows that it is possible to classify these instruments into three basic types according to the form of their sliding tubes. In the first group (type A) the lowest of the tubes is also the narrowest, and the other tubes fit onto each other, so that the uppermost is also the largest in diameter. A second group (type B) has the opposite form, i.e. the largest diameter tube is the lowest and the topmost tube would be the smallest. The early Campani microscope (Fig. 1.11) belongs to this classification, whereas the instrument usually ascribed to Divini (Fig. 1.12) belongs to type A. The general arrangement of these instruments is shown diagramatically in Fig. 1.13.

Bedini also recognizes the existence of a third or type C instrument which probably developed rather later than the other two variants.

A   B   C

FIG. 1.13. The three types of Italian seventeenth-century microscopes recognized by S. Bedini. For description, see text.

In the type C microscope the body tube had only one draw tube, the objective screwed into a nosepiece at the lower end of the body tube which was supported in a turned wooden socket ring attached to a tripod. Bedini believes that all three types were developed within a short period of each other, before the introduction of the screw-focusing model by Campani (see Fig. 1.15).

Within a very few years of the construction of the instruments of the sliding-tube pattern, which have just been described, great advances were made in the construction of the microscope stand; in particular the tubes were made of brass, the workmanship was of a much higher standard and the crude tripod was often replaced by elaborate scrolled supporting legs. Focusing no longer was by sliding the barrel inside a collar, but by a screwthread device which altered the distance between the eye lens and the objective; this device was often combined with a second screwthread for altering the distance of the microscope body from the object.

Two instruments of this pattern are illustrated in Fig. 1.14. For some considerable time these microscopes were attributed to Galileo,

Fig. 1.14. Two brass microscopes from the late seventeenth century, which were wrongly attributed to Galileo. They have no stage plates but are noteworthy for their high standards of mechanical construction. No lenses have survived.

but this seems unlikely, since their general method of construction places them at the end of the seventeenth century and Galileo died in 1642. Again no provision is made for the examination of objects by transmitted light; one of the first instruments with this feature is again due to Campani (Fig. 1.15).

The method of construction of this instrument is very similar to that of the so-called "Galileo microscopes" mentioned above, especially with respect to the focusing movements. Of particular interest, however, are the two plates forming the base of the microscope. The lower plate has two spring clips attached to it, a device which serves to hold it firmly against the upper plate. The object slide could then be sandwiched between the plates, and the object brought into the field of view by sliding the ivory holder until the object was positioned over the central hole which pierced both plates. This arrangement enabled the user to hold the instrument up to the sky or to a candle

FIG. 1.15. A later microscope of Campani (*ca.* 1686). Note the double screw thread focusing mechanism and the stage plate with clips and a central hole for the observation of objects by transmitted light.

flame and so examine the specimen by transmitted light; alternatively, the microscope could be placed on an opaque object in order to study its surface.

In the "Descriptio Novi Microscopii, Autore Dn. Josepho Campano, ejusque usus", which appeared in the *Acta Eruditorum* (1686), an account of this microscope is reprinted from the Italian *Giornale de Letterati* of the previous year. This contains a plate which shows the instrument in use both for the examination of a transparent specimen and for observing an opaque object, in this case wounds and scars. At least ten of these later Campani screw-barrel microscopes are known to have survived and they all bear a very remarkable resemblance to one another. It is interesting to note that in this instrument Campani has achieved a radical reduction in size, as his microscope is only about five inches when fully extended and three inches when closed, whereas earlier instruments, such as that of Divini which has been described above, were about sixteen inches or so in height.

One further microscope designer of the late seventeenth century is worth mentioning here, in view of the very advanced design features which he incorporated in his instruments. Bonanni, in his book *Micrographia curiosa* published in 1691 and now something of a rarity, described two types of microscopes. One compound microscope of the Campani screw-barrel construction introduced the method of holding the object slide firmly between two brass plates pierced with a central hole and kept pressed tightly together by means of a spiral spring. At this time most microscopic objects were mounted dry between circles of talc which were inserted into holes drilled in an ivory or wooden slider. Bonanni's device served very well to hold these mounts firmly in the focal plane of the microscope and the "spring stage" as it is known became a standard accessory of microscopes until well into the nineteenth century.

Bonanni's other microscope is extremely interesting and was of a completely novel conception. It was a horizontal instrument, mounted on its own baseboard (Fig. 1.16). This instrument was designed by Bonanni to fulfil certain features which are of interest as they show many of the factors which are important in the design of instruments today! Translating freely from his original Latin, his aims may be set out as:

1. Convenience in examining the object,
2. A convenient movement for bringing the instrument to the object (i.e. for focusing),
3. The focusing movement should be gradual and occur without danger of losing the object in the field of view, which often happened when the focusing was effected by rotating a screwed tube,
4. The field of view should be equally illuminated,
5. The illumination should remain constant,

Fig. 1.16. Bonanni's horizontal microscope of 1691. Note the rackwork coarse focus adjustment and the lamp with the substage condenser. The microscope and the lamp are mounted on a single board to ensure that they are in the same relationship at all times.

6. The instrument should be stable, so that the eye could be removed and when it is replaced the image would still be in focus and the field would still be the same so that the object might be drawn easily.

There can be no doubt that this instrument possessed features in advance of its time. It was probably the first instrument to be given a coarse focusing mechanism worked by a rack and pinion, which is shown in exploded view in Bonanni's drawing (Fig. 1.16). Another unusual feature was the provision of a two-lens condenser mounted onto the lamp house. This concentrated light on to the specimen, as indicated in the figure by dotted lines which Bonanni inserted in order to emphasize this feature which was so novel and important for its success. In view of the great interest of this instrument it is worth quoting Bonanni's own description of it, again very freely translated:

> The column or post HK, suitable for supporting the microscope and its parts, is erected vertically at right angles to the horizontal board MN by the skill of an instrument maker. On such a pillar is placed the small box VX, on top of which is placed the toothed runner GR which can be moved freely backwards and forwards by means of a toothed cylinder inserted transversely into the little box. To this runner is attached a pillar Y, made of brass or steel, which holds the microscope AB still. This pillar has been drilled and serves as a socket by means of which different microscopes can be freely inserted and fixed by the little screw Z. Moreover the microscope can be fitted so that it is held in a threaded brass ring and supported by it. At the end of the little box indicated by X, two parallel plates CD are erected vertically, leaving sufficient space between them to receive straight wooden strips with the objects. In between them is inserted under tension the flat spring E so that the said strips are firmly pressed against the plate C next to the microscope which suffices to hold them thus whilst at the same time they may be easily moved in any direction. If the straight wooden strip I with the objects is therefore inserted between the place C and the spring E, which have holes in their middle at the level of the microscope, the holes can be seen by the eye placed at A, and the desired distance from the object to the microscope can be obtained by rotating the toothed cylinder F, which engages in the toothed runner and so will move the microscope constantly in the same straight line. Otherwise the microscope may deflect to any part of the observed object. When, however, you focus the instrument, so that the object appears distinctly, you will be able to draw it easily by placing the eye repeatedly to the microscope without any tedium or noticeable error. Since it is hardly possible to carry out the tasks, however, unless the object

appears clearly illuminated, I placed another pillar on the same board MN, which supported a lantern at the desired distance, so that its light was located in the same horizontal line as the microscope axis. Then I added a tube with two lenses OO, mounted between the light of the lantern and the object by means of a bracket S furnished with screws at R and V so that it was possible to lengthen and elevate it according to the task in hand. The lenses were so arranged that the light was bent and focused onto the place where the object was located for observations.

I cannot describe how distinctly the objects are seen by means of the light, and better by night than by day in bright sunlight: for at night that unsuitable and harmful light which illuminates the object and the object lens from the sides is absent. The exclusion of this light serves to explain the present superiority of this microscope to any other instrument.

As an additional convenience when we are observing objects, we can draw them on a card placed in the light of the lantern. In other respects such an instrument may be varied as desired; so long as the directions necessary for exact and easy observation are kept to. For other things are either for ornament or for showing off the skill of the instrument maker. That which I had made for my observations consists of more than eighty-four parts assembled by brass screws so that it can easily be taken apart and put together again.

It is obvious from his account that this microscope was in fact actually constructed and made to work, unlike some of the designs which can be found in seventeenth-century books!

As a result of the researches of Bedini it now seems possible to summarize the contribution of the early Italian instrument makers to the development of the microscope. Divini appeared to be responsible for the use of two separate plano-convex lenses as a doublet, united in one mount with their convexities facing each other, and designed to serve as the eyepiece. He also used a combination of draw tubes for focusing and the system of sliding the whole body-tube up or down in its sliding collar in order to vary the distance between the specimen and the microscope objective lens. In some of his later models Divini used a coarse screw thread on the outer part of the lowest body-tube in order to provide more control over the focusing movements.

Campani's developments on the other hand seem to include the invention and the perfection of the screw-barrel device as a means of achieving accurate focusing. This device, which was to survive for many years especially in the simple microscope (see Chapter 3), has often been attributed to another Italian, Tortona, but Campani seems to have the priority. Campani also was responsible for the reduction in size of the microscope, which made it more portable and easier to use and included the slide holder as part of the instrument itself, which helped to bring the illumination system more under control and also allowed the use of a greater variety of illumination methods, especially the use of transmitted light.

Other important improvements also made by Italian workers towards the end of the seventeenth century were the invention of the multiple slide holder (attributed to Marco Celio) and the spring stage of Bonanni for holding the wooden or ivory specimen sliders. It is thus very clear that many of the most significant advances in the development of the compound microscope took place in Italy at this period.

The emphasis in this chapter has been upon the mechanical features of these early instruments. It is a great pity that most of the authentic examples which have survived have lost their lenses; of the few which are in working order, such as the little instrument mentioned above by Campani (Fig. 1.15), no measurements of optical performance appear to have been made as yet and hence comparison with later instruments cannot satisfactorily be made.

With these instruments the first phase of the development of the compound microscope may be said to be at an end. Subsequent development, especially in England, led to the construction of much larger and more elaborate instruments which will be considered in the next chapter. A tremendous new tool, however, had been placed at the disposal of scientists, especially those studying biology and medicine. Even though these instruments of the seventeenth century, and those which followed for the next hundred years or so, were extremely imperfect optically, they nevertheless stimulated a tremendous interest in the study of minute structure which was to result in remarkable discoveries.

It is not often realized what an important role the microscope has played in the development of biology and medical science and, as we shall see later, the construction of an optically efficient microscope opened the way to the discovery of the causative agents of many diseases and laid the foundations of the study of cellular pathology. These early instruments laid the foundations of these studies in the hands of some of the distinguished scientists of the seventeenth century. Indeed it may be said the latter half of the seventeenth and the early part of the eighteenth centuries constituted the first golden age of microscopy.

Not all the early studies were carried out with the compound microscope because although convenient to use, it suffered from severe optical faults, which led to indistinct images. Some of the really important discoveries were in fact made with the single-lens or simple microscope. It was not until about 1830 that the compound microscope was sufficiently well-developed to surpass in performance the simple microscope once and for all. In the next two chapters we shall first see how the compound microscope developed in England during this early period and consider some of the results which were obtained by means of the new invention, and then consider how the simple microscope developed and attempt to describe the part it played in the rapidly expanding and exciting new field of microscopical discovery.

CHAPTER 2

THE COMPOUND MICROSCOPE
IN ENGLAND: 1650-1750

WE HAVE seen that, although the early development of the microscope was largely taking place on the Continent, examples of the compound microscope were certainly sent to England. The letter of William Boreel, quoted in the first Chapter, tells us that Cornelius Drebbel showed him an instrument (almost certainly one made by the Janssens) when Boreel was in England in 1619 as the Dutch envoy. This new instrument, even in its very rudimentary form, must have impressed the English students of the natural sciences, and very naturally they would demand such aids for themselves. It fell to the instrument makers, the opticians and the spectacle makers to satisfy this need.

Many records of the instrument makers have survived, especially for the eighteenth century; a great deal of our knowledge derives from their practice of printing a "trade card", as well as the more usual catalogue. The trade card not only gave the name and address of the worker, but also his particular symbol or trade-mark and very often it illustrated a representative selection of his products. Such cards naturally provide a very valuable source of information about the instruments, not only microscopes, of the period; one sample trade card, that of one of the best known microscope makers of his day, John Marshall, is shown in Fig. 2.1. The earlier instrument makers of the seventeenth century are not so well represented, but some information is available from contemporary writings. One of them was Richard Reeves, of Long Acre, London. He was predominantly a telescope maker, or in the terminology of the day a "prospect maker", since these instruments were often referred to as "prospect glasses". Reeves was known to Samuel Pepys, the diarist, who mentions him on several occasions:

> August 13th, 1664: There comes also Mr. Reeves, with a microscope and a scotoscope. For the first I did give him £5. 10s., a great price, but a most curious bauble it is, and he says, as good, nay the best he knows in England and he makes the best in the world.

36

August 19th, 1666: (After Reeves had called and both he and Pepys had spent some time looking through the latter's telescope)

But it vexed me to understand no more from Reeves and his glasses touching the nature and reason of the several refractions of the several figured glasses, he understanding the acting part, but not one bit the theory, nor can make any body understand it . . .

It is obvious from this extract that even such an eminent instrument maker as Reeves was working very empirically and remained in the

Fig. 2.1. The trade-card of John Marshall.

dark about the theoretical aspects of optics! Further references in the diary of Pepys indicate that John Browne was active as a supplier of mathematical instruments at this period. Nehemiah Grew, the physician and one of the early Fellows of the Royal Society, mentions Mellen as one of the optical instrument makers of the day. Grew tells us that Mellen made one set of lenses, probably intended for use on a simple microscope, for the Royal Society and another for the use of Malpighi. Contemporary evidence tells us that Mellen's lenses were highly thought of, and indeed were used as a standard by which others were compared.

In the *Lexicon Technicum* of John Harris, published in 1708, he says with reference to simple microscopes:

> These kind of Microscopes, when the Glasses are well made, do magnifie exceedingly: Such are our very Famous Mr. Mellen's Glasses, which, I believe, are the best of any in the World of this kind:

Later, Harris again emphasizes this point when he writes:

> The best Glasses of this kind that ever I saw, are made by the above mentioned Mr. Mellen, who formerly lived in Abchurch Lane.

The microscopes of this period were usually constructed with bodies made of cardboard, which was covered with either ray skin or, in many cases, leather which in turn was finished off by embossing or "tooling" it with gold leaf pressed in by a metal stamp. Formerly it was considered that the patterns of these stamps varied according to the individual instrument maker, and that each worker apparently adhered rigidly to his own stamps, so that to an expert the pattern of the tooling served almost as well as a signature, and helped establish the authenticity of the instrument. Recent work by G. L'E. Turner in Oxford has disproved this. He believes that three basic groups of patterns were used in successive periods, and hence the "tooling" represents a means of dating a microscope, not of identifying a maker.

Hooke, writing in the Cutlerian lectures published in 1679 says, with reference to the simple microscope and his design for a compound microscope:

> Both these Microscopes I have directed Mr. Christopher Cock, in Long-Acre, how to prepare, that such as will not trouble themselves in the making of them, may know where to be accommodated with such as are good.

This passage, together with that from Pepys quoted above, suggest that the design and development of these instruments was carried out by gifted workers such as Robert Hooke, whilst the instrument makers and opticians contented themselves with the construction alone. It is interesting to contrast this situation with that prevailing in the nineteenth century, when most of the instrumental and optical advances came from the microscope makers themselves and not from the scientists.

Robert Hooke was undoubtedly one of the great personalities of English science of the seventeenth century, and certainly he was one of the first to realize the potentialities of the new invention which had been recently brought to England from the Continent. He was born in 1635 in Freshwater, Isle of Wight, and upon the death of his father he was apprenticed to a portrait painter in London. He soon abandoned this, however, and went to Westminster School and subsequently to Oxford; it is perhaps significant that the originator of the superb microscopical illustrations later to appear in the *Micrographia* obviously had not only artistic talent, but also some formal training in a branch of art which required accurate delineation and observation of detail.

Whilst at the University, Hooke carried out the studies in physics which led to his discovery of the ability of a spiral spring to render the vibrations of a balance wheel isochronous. Hooke had a tremendous breadth of interest, devising amongst other things, a double-barrelled air pump, a spirit level and a marine barometer; his discovery that the elongation of a spring is proportional to the force producing it is still referred to as "Hooke's Law". Hooke became associated with the newly formed Royal Society, and acted as its Secretary and Curator of Experiments. It was during this time that he carried out microscopical studies, and the Royal Society recognizing the importance of this new branch of study, encouraged this; in 1663 he was solicited by the Society to prosecute his microscopical observations in order to publish them and a week later he was ordered to

bring in at every meeting one microscopical observation, at least.

Hooke faithfully complied with this directive; he showed them the appearance under the microscope of common moss, of the blue mould on leather, the appearance of the edge of a sharp razor and of a point of a needle. He demonstrated various insects, such as the flea, the louse, the gnat and various types of hairs. All these observations, and many others besides, were published in 1665 under the title "*Micrographia: or some physiological description of minute bodies made by magnifying glasses with observations and enquiries thereon*".

Also included in the book are descriptions of his actual microscope, of a lens-grinding machine and detailed discussions of surface tension, refraction and colour. It was a great success and still ranks high today as one of the great masterpieces of microscopical literature. There is no doubt that the publication of the *Micrographia* stimulated a tremendous interest in the microscope, not only among the scientists or "natural philosophers" of the day, but also among the general public, as we may gather from Pepys' diary:

> January 20th 1665 — To my bookseller's, and there took home Hooke's book of Microscopy, a most excellent piece, and of which I am very proud.

The following day's entry concludes:

> Before I went to bed I sat up till two o'clock in my chamber reading Mr. Hooke's Microscopical Observations, the most ingenious book that I ever read in my life.

The great importance of the work of Robert Hooke in microscopy makes it necessary to look at his microscope in some detail and see how it compares with other instruments available at that time. The action of the lenses in the compound microscope was imperfectly understood in the seventeenth century and it is not therefore very surprising to see that most of the improvements in the microscope at this period and for a century after Hooke's death were largely directed towards the general form and mechanics of the microscope. It is clear that Hooke himself was not happy about the optical performance of his instrument, for in the preface to the *Micrographia* he writes:

> The glasses I used were of our English make, but though very good of the kind, yet far short of what might be expected, could we once find a way of making Glass Elliptical, or of some more true shape; for though both Microscopes and Telescopes, as they now are, will magnifie an object about a thousand times bigger than it appears to the naked eye; yet the Apertures of the Object-glasses are so very small, that very few Rays are admitted, and even of those few there are so many false, that the Object appears dark and indistinct: And indeed these inconveniences are such, as seem inseparable from Spherical Glasses, even when most exactly made; but the way we have hitherto made use of for that purpose is so imperfect, that there may be perhaps ten wrought before one be made tolerably good, and most of these ten perhaps every one differing in goodness one from another, which is an Argument, that the way hitherto used is, at least, very uncertain. So that these Glasses have a double effect; the one that very few of them are exactly true wrought; the other, that even of those that are best among them, none will admit a sufficient number of Rays to magnify the Object beyond a determinate bigness.

Hooke's microscope is shown in Fig. 2.2; this instrument is illustrated in the *Micrographia*, but no specimen of this exact type has survived. The instrument bears a very strong relationship to the telescopes of

FIG. 2.2. Hooke's own drawing of his microscope, published in the *Micrographia* of 1665. The illuminating apparatus is shown on the left. The nosepiece, with its coarse thread is clearly visible, as well as the mechanical stage.

the period, common features being the concave eye-cup which serves to keep the eye at the correct distance from the eyepiece, the separate draw-tubes sliding one within the other, and the method of mounting on the pillar by means of a ball and socket joint. The body of the instrument, probably constructed of cardboard, after the fashion of the time, was about six inches long when the draw tubes were fully closed. There was a single, bi-convex object glass which was fitted at the lower end of the narrow screwed "snout" attached to the broad

Spherical Aberration

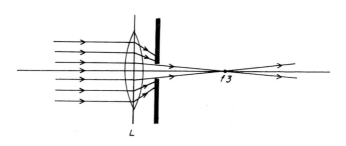

Partial correction of spherical aberration by a stop

Fig. 2.3. The effect of spherical aberration in a convex lens. The peripheral rays are brought to a focus f_1 much closer to the lens than the central rays, which are converged to a focus at f_3. This effect may be minimized by fitting a stop, as shown in the lower part of the figure.

body tube. Such an uncorrected objective lens would produce a very poor image, due to the numerous aberrations which are introduced. Two of these aberrations are particularly troublesome and must have seriously marred the performance of Robert Hooke's instrument. The first of these faults, termed "spherical aberration", is a defect of spherical lenses arising from the fact that the rays of light passing through the peripheral parts of the lens are more strongly bent towards the axis than those which pass through nearer to the optical axis. This phenomenon results in the focus of the peripheral rays being focused at a point nearer to the lens than the more axial rays, and is illustrated in Fig. 2.3 which shows the focusing of monochromatic light rays by a bi-convex lens. It will be seen that the peripheral rays are focused at a point f_1 which is nearer to the lens than the focus f_2 of the intermediate rays; this in turn is nearer to the lens than f_3 which represents the focus of the rays which passed through the lens close to the optical axis.

In Hooke's time the only way in which it was possible to correct this fault was by the use of a diaphragm with a small central aperture placed behind the lens. This served to stop out the more peripheral rays and prevent them taking any part in the formation of the image; this is shown in the lower part of Fig. 2.3. Such a solution did not prove very satisfactory as it did not completely eliminate the spherical aberration. If the stop were made with an aperture which was small enough to achieve this end, then the amount of light passing was so severely restricted that the brightness of the image was extremely low, making it difficult to see when high magnifications were used. The eventual solution of this problem was not found until the end of the eighteenth or the first years of the nineteenth century, when the development of optical knowledge enabled lens combinations to be calculated which brought the peripheral rays to the same focus as the axial rays and at the same time enabled the other troublesome defect, that of chromatic aberration, to be eliminated.

Chromatic aberration is due to the fact that the different wavelengths which make up white light are bent or refracted to different degrees by the material of the lens. The shortest waves are the most strongly refracted, whilst those with the longer wavelengths are affected least. This means that there will be a series of foci from a beam of white light, extending along the optical axis; the focus for blue light would be nearest to the lens, whilst that for red is furthest away as shown in Fig. 2.4. When such an uncorrected lens is used in an instrument like a microscope the result of chromatic aberration is to surround the image with a series of strongly coloured fringes. This is not only distracting to the eye, but markedly affects the definition of the instrument. Although Hooke was well aware of the nature of chromatic aberration, it was not known as that time how to correct such a defect by combining optical lenses of differing dispersive power and the development of achromatic lenses did not come for another hundred and fifty years. It would be possible to eliminate trouble from chromatic aberration by the use of monochromatic light (that is, light of a single colour) but there is no evidence to suggest that this solution was used by these early workers with the microscope. The first record of the use of filters to produce monochromatic light for microscopical illumination appears to be that of Sir David Brewster in 1836. It seems possible that these early lenses of the seventeenth century suffered far more from spherical aberration and that most of the efforts at correction were directed towards this end. With severe restriction of aperture in an effort to mitigate this trouble, chromatic aberration may have been of less importance.

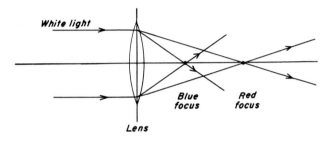

Fig. 2.4. The effect of chromatic aberration in a convex lens. The shorter wavelengths (blue) of the white light are brought to focus closer to the lens than the longer (red) wavelengths.

It must be remembered that if the microscope is a compound one, i.e. one in which the image produced by an objective is examined and further magnified by a second lens acting as an eyepiece, then any aberrations due to the lack of corrections in the objective may well be augmented by the effect of the eyepiece lens. It was this feature, especially, which as we shall see in the next chapter, led many microscopists to persevere with the use of the simple microscope even though the compound microscope possessed some advantages such as a greater working distance and greater comfort in use.

It seems that Hooke's lenses did possess the diaphragm to restrict the aperture, and from the extract already quoted (p. 40) it is obvious that Hooke wished for means of increasing the aperture, not in order to gain more resolution, but to allow more light to pass. He was much troubled by the fact that the object appeared "dark and indistinct" and thought that if the lenses were better made then he could use a larger hole in the diaphragm and hence obtain more light and so be able to use still higher powers. As there seemed no possibility of improving the lenses, he was led in his search for greater magnifications to devise means of concentrating more light on the small area of the object under examination and overcome the lack of light transmission of his lenses in this way.

Hooke was almost entirely concerned with the examination of objects by reflected light, a technique which is still in use today, although the majority of biological microscopy is carried out by transmitted light, i.e. light which has passed through the object. One of the essentials for the study of objects by reflected light is the need for a rather bright source of light; that devised by Hooke is shown in Fig. 2.2 and forms a very simple and effective method, which would be easy to use. A facsimile of this apparatus has recently been constructed by Dr. J. R. Baker at Oxford and has proved very effective in use, when tested with the actual microscope illustrated in Fig. 2.5. The figure shows the device in use with artificial light from the flame of an oil lamp, but he tells us that he also used sunlight. The light was concentrated onto the object by the glass globe and a convex lens. Hooke gives a description of his method of using this type of illumination, which is full of practical detail and is worth quoting as an example of the approach of one of the early microscopists:

> I make a choice of some Room that has only one window open to the South, and at about three or four foot distance from this Window, on a Table, I place my Microscope, and then so place either a round Globe of Water, or a very deep clear plano-convex Glass (whose convex side is turned towards the Window) that there is a great quantity of Rayes collected and thrown upon the object; Or if the Sun shine, I place a small piece of oyly Paper very near the Object, between that and the light; then with a good large Burning-glass I so collect and throw the Rayes upon the Paper, that there may be a very great quantity of light pass through it to the Object; yet I so proportion that light, that it may not singe or burn the Paper. Insted of which Paper there may be made use of a small piece of Looking-glass plate, one of whose sides is made rough by being rubbed on a flat Tool with very fine sand, this will, if the heat be leisurely cast upon it, endure a much greater degree of heat, and consequently very much augment a convenient light. By all which means the light of the Sun, or of a Window, may be so cast on an Object, as to make it twice as light as it would otherwise be without it, and that without any inconvenience of glaring, which the immediate light of the Sun is very apt to create in most Objects; for by this means the light is so equally diffused,

> that all parts are alike inlightened; but when the immediate light of the Sun falls on it, the reflexions from some few parts are so vivid, that they drown the appearance of all the other, and are themselves also, by reason of the equality of light, indistinct, and appear only radiant spots.

Here we have the writings of a man who has actually performed the experiments and discovered for himself the necessity for diffusing the focused light source in order to avoid specular reflections. This contrasts very strongly with the earlier writings, in which there is so much confusion that one strongly suspects that the authors were not speaking from practical experience!

From his experience Hooke found that observations made by natural light were often undesirable, the illumination from the sky and the sun is variable and very often it proved impossible to complete an examination which had begun; again one had to contend with the uncertainties of the climate:

> the Weather is so dark and cloudy, that for many dayes together nothing can be viewed.

Furthermore it is often more convenient to work at night, so Hooke devised the oil lamp and epi-illumination equipment shown attached to his microscope (Fig. 2.2). Here the lamp is shown at K, the globe, filled with brine is labelled G. The plano-convex condensing lens, I, is fastened to the same pillar by a jointed arm, so allowing the lens to be adjusted and fixed in any position. By the use of this equipment

> with the small flame of a Lamp may be cast as great and convenient a light on the Object as it will well endure; and being always constant, and to be had at any time, I found most proper for drawing the representations of those small Objects I had occasion to observe.

One of the optical features of Hooke's microscope was the introduction of a lens at the upper end of the body tube, so that it came between the objectives and the eyepiece lens. This third lens or "field lens" has often been thought to have originated with Robert Hooke, but this does not seem to be the case. Clay and Court (the authors of a standard book on the history of early microscopes) believe the field lens must be attributed to Monconys who described it, and tells us that it was made in 1660 by the "son-in-law of Wiselins", who was said to be Campani, although no documentary evidence of this relationship has survived.

There is evidence, from a letter written by Dr. Henry Power (who included a section of microscopical observations in his *Experimental*

Philosophy published in 1663) to Reeves the instrument maker, that the latter was supplying microscopes fitted with a field lens; this would be between 1660 and 1662 and it seems that Power himself was using a microscope with this device in 1661. The field lens in a modern microscope is part of the eyepiece and serves to correct some of the aberrations remaining in the image formed by the objective, but in these early microscopes it must have added still further to the imperfection of the optical system. The only use known for the field lens was to increase the field of view; when Hooke wished to examine fine detail, he invariably removed it!

The mechanical form of Robert Hooke's microscope was well in advance of the general practice of the time. All the previous instruments had been of the tripod construction, where the body tube was solidly supported by three legs. This arrangement fulfilled one of the first requirements of a microscope stand, namely that of furnishing a stable mount for the lenses, but the tripod form suffers from the great drawback that the positioning of the lens with respect to the object is very limited. This is not of much consequence with the examination of transparent specimens, for which purpose the lens system must be mounted to move at right angles to the stage holding the object and in the same optical axis as the illuminating system. With the type of microscopy which was predominant in the seventeenth century, i.e. the examination of opaque objects by means of reflected light it is often very important to be able to incline the microscope tube with respect to the specimen. This feature is provided by the large pillar type of stand, seen in the microscopes of Hooke and in the later Marshall instruments and those of the other seventeenth- and early eighteenth-century makers and it has persisted in a modified form up to the present day.

For focusing the microscope Hooke relied on the screwing up or down of the whole body by means of the rather coarse thread on the "snout" of the body, which worked in the ring labelled G in his picture (Fig. 2.2). This method would seem to have suffered from the rather poor workmanship, which provided a thread of rather coarse pitch which would have the drawback of rather too rapid movements and also probably to very rapid wear. The ring G was in turn attached to the upright supporting pillar C of the microscope by means of a large ball and socket joint F, which was clamped to the pillar by a wing nut passing through the ring D. The object of this complex fitting was to enable the user to vary the height of the body tube and its angle of

FIG. 2.5. A photograph of a microscope reputed to be made about 1678 for Hooke by Christopher Cock. Note that there are now only two draw tubes, and the nosepiece has a greater diameter and a much finer pitched thread. The workmanship of this instrument is of a very high order.

(*Crown copyright, The Science Museum.*)

inclination in order to suit the particular object under examination. This particular method of achieving the inclination, which was essential as microscopes became larger in order that the user could work in comfort, would not have proved very satisfactory in practice as the ball-and-socket joint would have been difficult to make and would have suffered from wear and soon become slack in use. In other instruments made in the next ten years or so (including one reputed to have been used by Hooke, and now in the museum at South Kensington) this ball-and-socket joint has been replaced by a straight rod fixed firmly into the ring which slides on the pillar; the threaded ring into which the objective screws is now fixed to the rod by a joint secured by a clamp screw, so that inclination of the microscope body may still take place but the body can now be fixed much more securely. This instrument, shown in Fig. 2.5, also shows numerous other small refinements, such as possessing a larger pillar, it has only two draw tubes, the eyepiece cup has been abandoned, and the "snout" has a much greater diameter and a finer thread; these latter features would ensure greater rigidity of the body tube and a much more precise method of focusing. It is interesting, however, to note that in both instruments the means which was used to hold and position the object was the same, suggesting that this proved one of the most successful aspects of the original design.

When an object was simply held under the microscope for examination the results must soon have been considered unsatisfactory; not only would the object be magnified but also every minute tremor which is present even in the steadiest hand, so making accurate observations very tiresome. This problem was overcome by use of a feature designed to hold the object and allow of its movement in any desired plane. Such an accessory (now called a mechanical stage, of which that devised by Robert Hooke is probably the first) is found on almost every large research microscope used today. The device used by Hooke was more complex than a typical mechanical stage, being more closely related to the accessory used at the end of the last century for holding and rotating small opaque objects in any desired plane.

The essential feature of any device of this type is that the object is firmly held so that precise movements may be imparted to it by mechanical means. Leeuwenhoek had achieved the same end in a rather similar way with his simple microscope (see Chapter 3), but the form of mechanical stage adopted by Hooke was of a much more elaborate construction. It may be seen in Fig. 2.2 and in detail in Fig. 2.6.

The object was attached to or impaled upon an iron pin (M in the figures) which could be rotated; the pin was mounted through a small pillar L, which in its turn was carried at the edge of a round plate (I, I in the figures). This plate was free to rotate around the central point K, so that the whole provided a means of orientating the object with respect to the optical axis of the microscope. Further flexibility was provided by attaching the rotating plate to the end of a brass slotted link (H, H in the figures) which was clamped at any position by tightening the wing nut N on the pillar of the microscope. This stage is very carefully designed and evidently proved so successful that a very similar design was adopted by Marshall for use with his

FIG. 2.6. Details of Robert Hooke's mechanical stage. M is the rotatable pin, to which the object may be fixed; the pillar is eccentrically mounted on a disc I, which can rotate about the centre K. This disc in turn is carried by the slotted link H which fits under the microscope pillar. See also Fig. 2.2.

"great double microscope" which came into use somewhere around the year 1693.

It was with the instrument which has been described above, mechanically sound but optically rather crude, that Robert Hooke produced his superb observations of common objects. At this time there was no systematic science of microscopy, everything was new and even the most trivial of everyday objects was a source of great wonder when seen under magnifications of up to hundred diameters. Hooke was a most meticulous observer who was clearly aware that an erroneous impression of structure might be gained when studying an object under the microscope. He says that his constant endeavour was to

> first discover the true appearance, and next to make a plain representation
> of it. This I mention rather, because of these kinds of Objects there is
> much more difficulty to discover the true shape, than of those visible to

FIG. 2.7. Hooke's drawing of the edge of a razor and the point of a
needle. (Figures 2.7 to 2.10 inclusive are taken from the *Micrographia*
of 1665.)

the naked eye, the same Object seeming quite differing, in one position to the Light, from what it really is, and may be discovered in another.

He notes the difficulty which one finds in recognizing whether there is a prominence or a depression and of distinguishing between a reflection and a true whiteness.

When Hooke was carrying out his microscopical studies the subject was new and strange and techniques of preparation of objects were

FIG. 2.8. The surface of a nettle leaf.

rudimentary or non-existent. It is not surprising, therefore, that much of the *Micrographia* is devoted to the obvious way of using the instrument, i.e. looking at the surface detail of an object which was illuminated from above. With this technique the most commonplace objects took on a new form. Figure 2.7 shows his drawing of the edge of a razor and the point of a needle whilst Fig. 2.8 shows the surface of a nettle leaf with the stinging hairs and the outlines of the epidermal cells carefully represented.

The range of observations is very wide; seeds, hair, fabrics, crystals and insects all are faithfully depicted. One of the best known of Hooke's

FIG. 2.9. The famous drawing of a flea. The original is over sixteen inches long.

drawings of an insect is reproduced here as Fig. 2.9. The original plate of this flea is truly superb, folding out of the book, and is over sixteen inches in length. Perhaps the most significant observation in view of subsequent developments in biology is the illustration of the structure of cork, which is presented as "Observation XVIII: Of the Schematism or Texture of Cork, and of the Cells or Pores of some other such

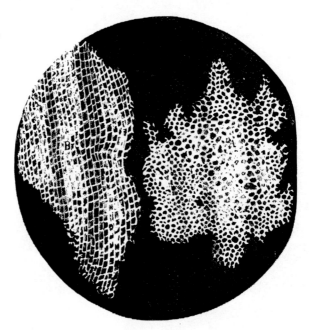

FIG. 2.10 The cut surface of cork.

frothy Bodies". In this Section Hooke faithfully illustrates the appearance of the surface of freshly cut cork (Fig. 2.10) and states

> these pores, or cells, were not very deep, but consisted of a great many little Boxes, separated out of one continued long pore, by certain Dia-phragms.

Hooke goes on to measure them and found that there were rather more than a thousand in the length of an inch and from this he estimated that there would be

> in a Cubick Inch, above twelve hundred Millions, or 1,259,712,000 a thing most incredible, did not our Microscope assure us of it by ocular demonstration.

He realized that these cells contained air and that this was the reason why cork was so light and floated on water, and why it has such a spongy texture and springiness when compressed. This is the first use in biology of the term "cell", a concept which is now of fundamental importance in the definition of the functional units of living organisms. More than a century was to pass, however, before the realization of their unitary nature was enunciated by Schleiden and Schwann. There can be no doubt that Robert Hooke discovered the factual basis of the cell theory; not only did he picture the cell walls of plant cells, but he also saw their contents, the protoplasm. He writes:

> for in several of those Vegetables, whilst green, I have with my micro-
> scope, plainly enough discovered these Cells or Pores filled with juices,
> and by degrees sweating them out.

The time was not ripe for the comprehension of the principles of cellular organization and of the production of new cells by the division of pre-existing cells, so the credit for the cell theory as a biological concept undoubtedly belongs to the later workers. Nevertheless, the genius of Robert Hooke stands revealed by his observations.

Hooke, in addition to preparing superb detailed drawings, also made estimates of the size of the objects which he was examining with his microscope. This may be regarded as perhaps the first example of micrometry or the measurement of the dimensions of minute objects. He did this by the simple expedient of placing a ruler on the base of his microscope, and looking at the divisions on the rule with his unoccupied eye while, at the same time, observing the object down the microscope with the other. The result of this was to create the impression that the magnified image of the object was superimposed upon the ruler so that the *apparent* diameter of the structure as seen with the microscope could be measured; this could then be compared with the actual diameter measured directly. In this way, Hooke was able to estimate the magnification of his instrument.

Hooke was one of the first, and certainly the greatest of the English microscopists, but others were rapidly accepting the challenge posed by the new instrument and were exploiting it, despite its obvious imperfections for biological research. One of Hooke's contemporaries was the Italian Marcello Malpighi; he was born in 1628, near Bologna at which University he graduated as a doctor in 1653. Throughout his life Malpighi was harrassed by professional jealousies and by personal troubles and family squabbles, in spite of which he proved himself to be one of the most original scientists of his time. Much of his work was in the field of physiology, in particular the study of respiration. He published accounts of the lungs and the circulation of the blood through them in the form of letters to Borelli who at the time (1661) was Professor of Science at Pisa. Malpighi described the lungs of frogs which he studied with a small compound microscope of the type shown in Fig. 2.11 from which it is clear that his instrument is very closely akin to those of Campani. He showed that the substance of the lungs consisted of a network of thin-walled alveoli which are

Fig. 2.11. An Italian "vase" microscope of the type used by Malpighi.

connected to all the branches of the trachea or windpipe; he further speculates that the lungs serve to keep the blood flowing and prevent its coagulation. The significant observation is his discovery (by microscopical inspection) of the capillary circulation in the lungs which connects other arteries to the veins and so completes the pulmonary circuit of the blood. Malpighi made the point that this can be seen in the living animal only with difficulty but he managed to confirm it by looking at the dried inflated lungs of an animal in which the coloration of the blood was preserved. Malpighi himself believed this observation to be important, an impression which has been supported by the view of later workers. It is doubly interesting because it seems that this is one of the first applications of the microscope to the study of living tissues, a branch of microscopy which is now of the utmost importance in biological research.

Malpighi made many other observations with the microscope, using among other techniques the method of injection of an opaque substance into the blood vessels of an animal in order to make them more easily visible under the microscope. He established the vascular pattern in the kidney, and in so doing he gave a good description of the microscopic structure of this organ, certain regions of which still bear his name. Further proof of his skill and care as an observer is furnished by his embryological studies, in which he describes the development of the chick. Some of his drawings and descriptions of various organs, such as the heart, could hardly be bettered today. Malpighi also studied insect anatomy, discovering their excretory organs which are now termed "Malpighian tubules" and also he pioneered a new field of vegetable anatomy, in which his microscope showed him the cells or, as he called them "utriculi" and a great deal of the organization of the tissues of the plant. He showed for the first time the stomata or pores on the undersurfaces of the leaves, the vessels with their spiral thickenings in the cell walls and a great many other features which are so familiar to present-day students of plant anatomy.

His compound microscope was more rudimentary than that of his English contemporary, Robert Hooke, but there can be no doubt that as observers they ranked equal.

We have already mentioned the second instrument which was used by Hooke (Fig. 2.5) and shown that it differs from that pictured in the *Micrographia* in several important features. In the five years that elapsed between the *Micrographia* and the development of this modified instrument, which is alluded to in the Cutlerian Lectures of 1678, very rapid progress in microscope design had been taking place. It must be emphasized, however, that such improvements were limited to the mechanical aspects. This pattern of development was to persist until the early years of the nineteenth century; such optical changes as were made appeared to be random and purposeless, owing to the lack of basic theoretical and applied knowledge of optics. On the mechanical side, however, the pattern of the microscope stand, focusing mechanisms and specimen-holding devices became established and carried to a high degree of proficiency.

The tremendous interest in microscopy at the end of the seventeenth and in the early eighteenth centuries was stimulated to a large degree by Hooke's *Micrographia*, but also by the publication by Harvey in 1628 of his discovery of the circulation of the blood. This led to the desire for an instrument which could enable a direct visualization of this interesting process and so most microscopes sold in the eighteenth century were provided with accessories for this specific purpose.

The new instruments stimulated interest, and investigations began to progress rapidly into the techniques for preparing objects for study. They were no longer solely concerned with looking at the surface structure of opaque objects but were beginning to examine biological material by transmitted light, a procedure which often yields much more information. Hooke himself was again in the forefront, for as he says in the Cutlerian lectures with respect to the examination of liquids:

> because the common Pedestal hitherto made use of in Microscopes is generally not so convenient for trials of this nature, I lay those by, and instead thereof I fix into the bottom of the Tube of the Microscope, a cylindrical rod of Brass or Iron. Upon this a little socket is made to slide to and fro; and by means of a pretty stiff spring, will stand fast in any place. This has fastened to it a joynted arm of three or four joynts, and at the end a plate about the bigness of a half-crown, with a hole in the middle of it about three quarters of an inch wide; upon this plate I lay the Muscovy glass, and upon that I spread a very little of the liquor to be examined; then looking against the flame of a Candle or a Lamp, or a small reflection of the Sun from a globular body, all such parts of the liquor as have differing refraction will manifestly appear.

Hooke also realized that in order to see structures in fluids such as milk or blood, they had to be spread as very thin films; he gives detailed directions for preparing films of the right thickness by squeezing drops of liquid between two clear glass plates and even suggests a device with a frame and clamping screws to assist in the spreading. This gadget must surely be the ancestor of the compressorium, which was used so much by the Victorian amateur microscopists in their studies of pond-life! Another of Hooke's very far-sighted comments is that in order to see the structure of muscles and tendons they must be dissociated and examined not in air but

> in a liquor, such as water, or a very clear oyl.

Here is an observation, which forms the basis of modern mounting techniques where the difference in refractive indices between the object and the mounting medium is known and controlled in order to enhance or suppress contrasts and which plays a large part in certain measurement methods which are used today with phase-contrast microscopy (see Chapter 7). Again, Hooke working purely with empirical methods had hit upon one of the basic principles of microscopy. It is clear that this branch of science had made enormous strides in the space of ten years and the foundations of the modern study of histology (the detailed structure of the tissues of the body) had been laid by a few isolated observers, led by Hooke and Malpighi.

Another extensive worker with the microscope around this time was Nehemiah Grew; indeed, it seems probable that he actually used the instrument commissioned by the Royal Society from Christopher Cock and which may have also been used by Hooke. Grew was educated as a physician, in Cambridge and Leyden where he graduated in 1671. He returned to London and applied himself to medical practice and at the same time carried out scientific research. Like Hooke, Grew was elected a Fellow of the Royal Society and in due course became its Secretary. Nehemiah Grew was much more of a specialist in his studies than the other workers we have described, concentrating on the anatomy of plants. His descriptions of the stem, the root, the fruit and the seed all testify very clearly to his tremendous enthusiasm for the subject and to his passion for detail. His researches were published in full in the *Anatomy of Plants* which appeared in 1682 and established him, together with Malpighi, as the founder of the systematic study of plant anatomy. It seems strange to us, looking back on these tremendous discoveries in the field of plant structure, that they were regarded as little more than curiosities of Nature, and no attempt was made to follow up or exploit them. It may be that the chief interests were devoted to animal anatomy, also being revolutionized by the microscope, because of its much greater relevance to the medical sciences.

Hooke, Grew and Malpighi, together with that other genius of the microscope — Antoni van Leeuwenhoek (who worked, however, entirely with the simple microscope) — form the great quartet of workers who established the microscope in the seventeenth century as a tool of scientific investigation; by their prolific writings and observations they stimulated the curiosity of men and excited interest in the study of the minute details of the structure of common objects. At this time when everything revealed by the microscope was new and exciting, the manifest optical imperfections of the instruments did not prove such great drawbacks to microscopical discovery as might be imagined. The aberrations only prove significant when high powers are used and a tremendous field lay open which was well within the limited capabilities of these early instruments. It was only in the following century, when the need for higher and higher powers arose, that the aberrations of the lenses began to cause uncertainty in the interpretation of the images and led to suspicion of discoveries made with the aid of the microscope. This suspicion reached such a pitch that critically-minded people often refused to use or accept as valid any discoveries made with the aid of the microscope. We shall see later (Chapter 5) how such scepticism was only overcome with the introduction of achromatic, corrected lenses, and an understanding in the Victorian era of the scientific principles of microscopical resolution.

Towards the end of the seventeenth century, John Marshall began to make microscopes and working at the sign of "The Archimedes and Two Pairs of Golden Spectacles" he produced around the year 1693 what may be regarded as the natural successor to Hooke's instrument. One of the first figures of Marshall's "Great Double Microscope" (so called because of its size, and to distinguish it from single-lens microscopes) appears in the first volume of John Harris's *Lexicon Technicum* 1704, together with an account of the method of its use. Fortunately at least fifteen of the original instruments are still in existence so that the features of this microscope can easily be studied. A typical example of Marshall's instruments is shown in Fig. 2.12 from which it will be seen that the general form of the microscope very closely resembles that of Hooke. The body of the microscope is carried on a pillar of a square section, about twelve inches long, which is in turn mounted by means of a large ball and socket joint to an octagonal wooden base. In this base, which was very heavily weighted with lead at the end opposite to the pillar, was mounted a drawer which served to carry the spare objectives and the accessories. In this instrument, as in the later Hooke microscope, each of the separate objective lenses was mounted in its own cell which could be screwed onto the nosepiece, whereas in the early Hooke microscope it seems that the various powers of the objective lens were not supplied with separate cells, but that one cell was made to hold any one of the lenses.

The large ball and socket joint, which served to incline the microscope body and allow it to be fixed at any angle up to an inclination of about 45° from the vertical or to allow the body of the instrument

Fig. 2.12. A photograph of John Marshall's "Great Double Micro-scope". Note the substantial construction of the instrument. Five extra objective lenses are displayed on the box foot together with a pair of forceps and the stage forceps, whilst in the foreground on the right are seen the lead "coffin" for holding down a fish in order to see the circulation of the blood, and the attachment for holding the stage forceps.

(*Crown copyright, The Science Museum.*)

to be swivelled right round so as to overhang the box foot, was placed at the bottom of the pillar, an important difference from the Hooke instrument. This meant that, as the specimen stage was carried on the same pillar, the body could be inclined to give a convenient angle for working, without altering the relationship of the objective to the specimen. In this respect, too, Marshall's instrument differed from its predecessors. Most of the contemporary drawings of the Marshall

FIG. 2.13. The Marshall microscope in use for examining the circulation of the blood. From a late eighteenth-century encyclopaedia.

microscope in fact show the body swivelled right round, the weighted box foot keeping the instrument in balance, so that the transparent glass stage could be used for transillumination of a fish's tail with light from a candle placed on a stool or on the floor (Fig. 2.13); a small plano-convex lens fastened on an arm and clamped beneath the object-stage served to concentrate the light onto the object.

The microscope body was again screwed into a nosepiece fixed onto an arm attached to a sliding sleeve which could be moved up and down the pillar. One of the most significant improvements (formerly thought to be an invention of Marshall's but now believed to be due to an earlier Continental worker named Helvelius) is the method which has been used for providing a fine focusing adjustment for the objectives. This, together with other details of the construction of a Marshall instrument is shown in Fig. 2.14; it consists of a second sleeve, above the main sleeve which carries the body, which can be clamped firmly to the pillar by means of a wing nut. The main body sleeve, which is loose on the pillar, is linked to the fixed sleeve by a metal screw thread with a large octagonal nut above the upper sleeve. When this latter is set roughly to one of the marks placed on the column (these were numbered to correspond with the number of the objective in use at the time) and clamped, then the instrument would be roughly in focus. Final adjustments were made with the octagonal nut, the operation of which caused a movement of the lower sleeve (and hence of the whole body of the microscope) when the upper sleeve was locked to the pillar. The rise and fall so obtained was very gradual and the object could thus be focused much more precisely. Some form of fine focusing is almost essential to the successful use of any lens system giving a total magnification of over 50 diameters.

The body of Marshall's microscope was usually about three to four inches in diameter and of the same length. It had a most characteristic shape of eyepiece mounted at the upper end of the inner draw tube; the total length of the eyepiece which was turned from wood, was about eight inches. It carried the large bi-convex lens near the place of junction with the body, and the eye lens was situated in the swelling near the top of the eyepiece, which was surmounted in turn by the usual eyepiece cup to maintain the eye of the observer in the correct place. There was usually provision for some form of screw-on dust cap to protect the eye lens.

Most of these microscopes were supplied with six different objective lenses. Apparently no figures for optical performance are available in the literature but one authority has given the magnifying powers as extending from $4\times$ for the lowest power, $12\times$ with the third, $50\times$ with the fifth to $100\times$ with the sixth lens in use. Some slight increase on these figures could probably be obtained by extending the draw tube. Following the development of corrected lens-systems, the draw tube was used as a means of completing the correction by compensating for such variables as cover-glass thickness and thickness of the mountant. In the seventeenth and eighteenth centuries, however, the sole function of

FIG. 2.14. Some details of the mechanical features of the Marshall microscope. The fine focus screw is shown at the left, together with the stage for opaque objects, the spring stage and the condensing lens for epi-illumination. At the top right of the figure is shown the ball and socket joint for inclining the column, together with the mode of attachment of the stage forks.

the drawtube seemed to be to control the magnification within small limits and also to assist in focusing.

The basic form of specimen holder or stage for the Marshall microscope was very simple, being a brass plate or ring with a turned ledge into which a glass plate or an object carrier, which was black on one side and white on the other, could be inserted. The whole arrangement was carried, as in Hooke's microscope, by means of a pair of forked legs which slipped over the pillar of the instrument (Fig. 2.14). They were clamped in position by means of a nut mounted just above the ball at the lower end of the pillar. As perhaps the greater part of the microscopical work was still the examination of opaque objects, Marshall arranged for the mounting of a plano-convex lens on an arm to serve as a condenser which would concentrate the light upon the surface of the object. Interest in the study of transparent objects was developing rapidly; in particular, users would expect to be able to study the circulation of blood. Marshall expressly catered for this and, indeed, used it as a selling point in his advertisements, pointing out that the microscope was newly invented for this very purpose. The microscope was provided with an accessory for this which was to form an essential part of the equipment of every microscope for the next two hundred years — the fish plate or frog plate. These were designed to hold the living animals so that the capillary circulation could be viewed by transparency through the tail fin of a small fish or through the web of the frog's foot. In Fig. 2.13 this fish plate is shown in use, with a small fish in place on the glass. The animal was covered by a small heavy lid in order, as John Harris puts it:

to hinder it from springing away, and moving his Tail out of the Light.

For this examination the microscope was to be swivelled on its base so that the body tube overhung the edge of the table, and the light from a candle placed on the floor was concentrated onto the fish plate by using the plano-convex lens now mounted underneath the plate. Many eighteenth-century microscopes still have their fishplates and their frog plates, with the original tapes used to hold the frog down, in what seems to be perfect condition; perhaps the vogue for the study of the living circulation soon passed, a fact which was not appreciated by the makers who faithfully continued to provide these accessories.

One of the characteristic features of the modern microscope, namely the mirror used to reflect the light into the substage, has not yet been mentioned as occurring in any of these instruments. It certainly was not yet in general use. Although one or two undoubtedly genuine Marshall microscopes with a mirror are extant it seems likely that this represents a later addition. As signed instruments made by Marshall in the later years of his life do not possess a mirror, all such modifications were probably carried out after Culpeper had brought it into general use. There is no doubt that the Marshall microscope was to some extent inconvenient to use when set up for examining specimens by transmitted light and the Culpeper microscope (which will be described in Chapter 4) was to a large extent adapted to remedy this fault. In addition, the Culpeper instruments would be much easier to manufacture and therefore would be much cheaper than large instruments of the Marshall type.

Contemporary records give us some idea of the price of these early large microscopes. The Royal Society paid Christopher Cock £8. 6s. for the instrument which he supplied to them, whilst Samuel Pepys tells us that what was probably a very similar microscope from Reeves cost him £5. 10s. It is probable that a Marshall instrument would cost about the same, so that in terms of the money values at that time a microscope was not to be considered cheap. In the *Lexicon Technicum* John Harris wrote about Marshall's microscope in these glowing terms

> and I take his Double Microscope here described, in all respects to be the most useful, handy and ready Instrument of this kind. I have had Mellen's Glasses, and seen Leeuwenhoek's and Campani's but I would sooner have the Double Microscope than any of them, and the Price is much easier.

If the purchase of a microscope constituted a very considerable financial outlay in those days then perhaps it is not very surprising that there was no tremendous follow-up of the pioneering studies of the early workers with the compound microscope. All the great microscopists of the seventeenth century were somewhat eccentric in their habits and did not seek to train pupils or found a school of followers.

Also we must remember that many people of that time considered their complex and unusual studies of the microscopical structure of things as almost sacrilegious, in seeking to pry into the secrets which God had obviously not intended to be revealed to the eyes of men. As a consequence there was no great use of the microscope for scientific purposes and the eighteenth century was to a large extent a barren period of microscopy. The instrument which had proved so powerful a tool in the hands of Hooke, Malpighi, Grew and Leeuwenhoek was to a large extent demoted to the status of a toy to entertain the idle rich.

Such work as was carried out was done not with large instruments on the Marshall pattern, but with either a Culpeper type of microscope, which in many ways represented a retrograde step in design, or with a simple microscope. It is to the development of the simple microscope that we must now turn our attention.

CHAPTER 3

SIMPLE OR SINGLE-LENS MICROSCOPES

WE HAVE seen in the previous chapters that much interest was shown in the development of optical devices for assisting the human eye; some of the various types of compound microscope which were devised for this purpose have already been described.

At the same time the property of a single plano- or bi-convex lens to furnish a magnified image in the manner indicated in Fig. 1.3 must

FIG. 3.1. A "flea-glass", as pictured by Kircher 1646. D represents a candle flame, C the object under examination mounted on a plane glass. AB is the tube of the simple microscope, whilst E represents the eye of the observer.

have been noticed. When such lenses were fastened into a mount or cell, so that the eye was forced to look through the axis of the lens, the first "single microscope", as Hooke called it, was born. At first such lenses would have had a low magnifying power, of the order of a few diameters only, and these instruments were in common use for the examination of insects, especially fleas, hence the name often given to such magnifiers of "vitra pulicaria" or "flea-glasses".

One of the earliest pictures of a flea-glass is to be found in Kircher's book *Ars Magnis Lucis et Umbrae*, published in 1646. This instrument is shown here in Fig. 3.1. The lens was a small sphere of glass mounted in the end of the tube AB, which was closed at the end A by a flat piece of glass. The object to be studied was attached to this glass at C

A   **B**

Fig. 3.2.

(a) A simple microscope mounted on a stand. The object is impaled upon the rod carried in the cross arm. After Zahn, *Oculus Artificialis*.

(b) A similar instrument in which the object is carried on a spring arm so that focusing may be easily carried out.

and viewed by pointing the whole at the candle flame, labelled D in the illustration.

At a later period several different types of flea-glass were made, with lenses of different magnifying powers and often they were sold as a set, all being supplied in a small case of leather or wood covered with fish skin. Some of these are still extant and a set in the National Museum of the History of Science at Leyden contains seven different flea-glasses, each of which consists of two cylinders about an inch long and slightly

less in diameter, which fit closely one inside the other. One cylinder
carries the lens plate, the other the object and hence focusing can be
carried out by sliding the inner tube a greater or lesser distance into
the outer cylinder.

Another early form of the simple microscope, little more than a
mounted magnifying glass, is illustrated and described in Zahn's *Oculus
Artificialis* of 1685 (shown here as Fig. 3.2a). The lens was fixed in
an elaborate wooden holder on a stand which was transfixed by a
rod. This in turn carried the arm bearing the specimen. This latter,
often an insect or a part of a flower, was focused by sliding the
rod through the upright pillar, so varying the distance between the
lens and the specimen. This particular example, according to Zahn, had

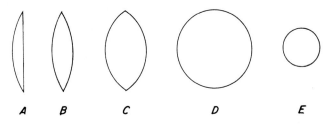

FIG. 3.3. The increase in power of a simple lens; (a) represents a plano-
convex lens. A biconvex lens (b) of the same radius of curvature
would have a greater power. Further increase is possible by increasing
the radius of curvature (c) until the lens is spherical (d). Any further
increase is then only possible by reducing the radius of the sphere, as
shown at (e).

a bi-convex lens with a magnifying power of fourteen diameters.
Several similar instruments have survived in our museums. Some of
them, undoubtedly intended for botanical work in the field, have the
table stand replaced by a turned wooden handle, whilst others instead
of having the specimen mounted upon a rod which was slid through
the stand, had a simple spring device to serve as the object holder
(Fig. 3.2b). This is probably the simplest possible form of controlling
the specimen/lens distance, as the object was moved nearer to or away
from the lens by pressure of the hand. Such a crude device would
only serve for examination at very low powers.

Experience with such simple magnifying lenses no doubt led
serious workers to attempt to increase their power. In practice, in
order to increase the power of a simple lens, its radius of curvature

must be increased. This, as shown in Fig. 3.3, leads from A, a simple plano-convex lens, via B, a bi-convex lens of the same radius, through stage C of increased curvature and power to the condition drawn at D, where the maximum radius of curvature has been reached for that diameter resulting in a spherical lens. Further increase in power can only be obtained by reducing the diameter, as shown at E, a solution which has the drawback of demanding both the eye and the object to be placed even closer to the lens. The construction of such small lenses was not easy in the seventeenth and early eighteenth centuries, as lens making was an art still in its infancy. The great advantage of the simple microscope in providing an image relatively free from chromatic aberration soon led to the use of small lenses produced by melting glass capillary rods in a flame and to greater and greater efforts at grinding and polishing lenses.

Most of the simple microscopes which have survived possess lenses made of melted or "blown" glass, as this type was much easier to construct. Robert Hooke used this form of lens at some time and in his Cutlerian lectures of 1679 he tells us how they were made:

> Take then a small rod of the clearest and cleanest glass you can procure, free if possible from blebbs, sands, or veins; then by melting it in the flame of a Lamp made with Spirit of Wine, or the cleanest and purest Sallet Oyl, draw it out into exceeding fine and small threads; then take a small piece of these threads, and in the same flame of the aforesaid Lamp, melt the end of it, till you perceive it to run into a little ball or globule of the bigness desired; then suffer it to cool, and handling it by the aforesaid thread of glass, which is as it were a handle to it, fix it with a little wax upon the side of a thin plate of Brass, Silver or the like, that the middle of it may lie directly over the middle of a small hole pricked through the said thin plate with a needle: then holding this plate close to the eye, look through the said little hole, and thereby you may also see very clearly through the aforesaid Globule, fixed with wax on the side that is from the eye: if then either by a little joynted arm, or by a little soft wax, and a needle, or a thin plate of Muscovy Glass, you fix the object you would examine; so that it may be at a due distance from the said little Globule, you will perceive the minute parts thereof very distinct.

Hooke, although he preferred to use the compound microscope, described in the last chapter, was well aware that advantages were to be found in the use of the simple microscope:

> in truth they do make the object appear much more clear and distinct, and magnifie as much as double Microscopes: nay, to those whose eyes

can well endure it, 'tis possible with a single Microscope to make discoveries much better than with a double one, because the colours which do much disturb the clear Vision in double Microscopes is clearly avoided and prevented in the single.

The other great English microscopist of this period, Nehemiah Grew, writing in 1681 in his *Catalogue of the Rarities belonging to the Royal Society* agreed with this view, and gives us some valuable information about simple microscopes in England at this time. Contrasting the compound with the simple microscope, he says:

> The advantage of one with more Glasses, is that it takes in a bigger Object, or a greater part of it. Of one with a single Glass, that it shows the Object clearer. So that to have a distinct representation of it, 'tis convenient to make use of both. Of the latter kind, I have seen several made by Mr. John Malling in this City, not only with melted, but with Ground-Glasses so very small, that one of these Ground-Glasses being weighed in the Assay-Scales in the Tower, was found not above the fourscorth part of a Grain. The Diametre or Chord 1/25th part of an inch. Another, so small, that those Scales were not nice enough to weigh it. The Chord hereof to that of the former, is as two to three. These are the clearest and best that ever I saw.

The reference here is almost certainly to Mellen, an instrument maker who had a very high reputation at this time for the excellence of his microscopes. It is obvious, too, that although he produced "blown" glasses, Mellen also undertook the grinding of lenses at this time. Blown glasses would be the easier of the two to make, but it must be remembered that in the seventeenth century even the production of simple melted glass spheres would not be the easy, reliable operation that it is today.

Van der Star, in the introduction to his catalogue of simple microscopes in the Leyden Museum, expresses the opinion that the quality of the available glass was poor and uncertain, and it would prove no light task to draw out thin threads of such glass in an oil or spirit flame. Hooke also advised his readers to select their glass carefully. Tests which van der Star recently carried out on the optical performance of glass spheres from a microscope made by Jan Musschenbroek and on glass spheres made by himself, showed that the quality of these lenses produced in the seventeenth century was generally inferior to that of the modern spheres produced very easily and quickly from modern glass by van der Star himself. The poor glass quality and the difficulty of melting it so as to form high quality spherical lenses, was suggested by van der Star as the explanation why the most famous of all the users of the simple microscope — Antoni van Leeuwenhoek — always used ground lenses.

One further advantage of the ground lens over the "blown" spherical lens is that the image produced by the latter is only sharp over a very small portion of the centre of the field, i.e. the usable field of view is very small. In biological work this is often undesirable and the only remedy is to use ground and polished lenses. In order to emphasize this difference van der Star photographed a scale through a Musschen-broek sphere and through a Leeuwenhoek ground lens of nearly comparable resolution and magnification. With the spherical lens the sharp area of the image produced at a distance of ten inches from the lens was about half-an-inch in diameter, whereas with the Leeuwen-hoek lens the area of the field which was acceptable had a diameter of two inches. This lens, with a magnifying power of 275 × proved superior to a Zeiss doublet lens of the second half of the nineteenth century, which had a power of only 155 × and a sharp area of the pro-jected image at ten inches from the lens of only one inch! Leeuwenhoek must certainly be acknowledged as one of the master lens-makers of all time.

Before passing on to a detailed consideration of the microscopes of Leeuwenhoek and some of the results which he achieved with them, it is appropriate at this point to stress that the simple microscope, although possessed of an undoubted optical superiority, was not much used for investigations involving a high degree of magnification. There are several reasons for this. First, the single lens, because of the short focal length needed for high magnifications, has to be brought very close to the eye. Hooke, in particular, found this an insuperable drawback.

> I have found the use of them offensive to my eye, and to have much strained and weakened the sight, which was the reason why I omitted to make use of them.

If the lens is spherical then, as mentioned above, the field of view is rather restricted. This proved a serious drawback to the use of such lenses for serious biological work, especially as the devices for moving the specimen relative to the lens were extremely rudimentary in the seventeenth and eighteenth centuries. Again, one must remember that at this time the greater proportion of the microscopical examinations were carried out by means of incident illumination, that is, light reflected back from the specimen through the lens system of the microscope.

With single lenses of high power, not only did the lens have to be close to the eye but also it had to be equally close to the object; the "working distance", as it is termed by microscopists, was inconveniently short and this interfered with the satisfactory illumination of the specimens. This objection, of course, does not apply to transparent objects or to thin sections of specimens which are viewed by transmitted light, the light actually passing through the specimen before reaching the lens. To quote Robert Hooke once more:

> the object is necessarily brought so near the glass, that none but such as are transparent, and to be viewed by a through light are capable of examination by them.

Finally, we have seen in Fig. 3.3, that once the lens has been made spherical, reduction of its diameter, giving smaller and smaller lenses is the only way of increasing its radius of curvature and hence the power. A very small lens, however, will only transmit a minute pencil of light rays, so that the pupil of the eye, instead of being filled with light, as would be the case with the compound microscope, receives only a very small amount of light and so the image produced by a simple microscope of high power lacks brilliancy.

In spite of these drawbacks, however, the simple microscope survived. Although there was very little original microscopical work in the eighteenth century, such as there was of lasting value proved to be carried out on a single lens microscope. Even today, although compound microscopes have been brought to a high degree of perfection, uses can still be found for the single lens microscope.

In the seventeenth century, microscopes — both simple and compound — were being made and sold by the instrument makers; Hooke tells us not only how one could do it oneself, but also says:

> Both these Microscopes I have directed Mr. Christopher Cock, in Long-Acre, how to prepare, that such as will not trouble themselves in the making of them, may know where to be accommodated with such as are good.

It is evident, however, from the fact that several eighteenth century works on optics include detailed directions for constructing glass spheres for simple microscopes that most workers would expect to construct their own instruments; the most noted maker and user of simple microscopes at this time was no exception to this, although he preferred to grind his lenses rather than use the simple "blown" sphere. Antoni van Leeuwenhoek was born in 1632 at Delft. He was the fifth child of Philip Anthonysz van Leeuwenhoek, a basket maker, and Margriete Bel van der Berch, the daughter of a brewer. When young Antoni was only five years old his father died and his mother married for the second time; he was sent to school in a town a few miles north of Leyden. Later the boy was sent to live with an uncle who held the position of town clerk of Benthuizen, near Delft, and was eventually placed in a linen draper's shop in Amsterdam to serve an apprenticeship to that trade. On completion of his indentures Antoni van Leeuwenhoek remained in Amsterdam as a cashier and book-keeper for several years, before returning to Delft in 1654, where he remained until his death as a famous microscopist and scientist in 1723.

Leeuwenhoek apparently had his own draper's business in Delft and although we have little evidence on this point, he probably carried on this business for many years. He was eventually appointed to the position of Chamberlain to the Sheriffs of the town, a position which he retained until his death; evidently he was held in high regard by his fellow citizens for in 1679 he received the further appointment of "wine-gauger", an office entailing the assay of all wines and spirits entering the town and the checking of the vessels in which they were contained. Leeuwenhoek presents the figure of a prosperous business-man, active in civic service but in 1673 he began to come into prominence in the world of scholarship as a result of the publication of a letter from him in the *Philosophical Transactions* of the Royal Society. This letter dealt with some observations on the sting, mouth parts, and the eye of the bee and of the louse.

A few years previously, in 1678, the *Philosophical Transactions* had published an account (which had been translated from the Italian *Giornale dei Letterati*) of Divini's new microscope. This has already been quoted in Chapter 1, and it will be remembered that the claim was made that by the use of this instrument, "an animal lesser than any of those seen hitherto" had been discovered. In 1673, Reinier van der Graf, a fellow countryman of Leeuwenhoek, wrote to the Secretary of the Royal Society, Henry Oldenburg, and told him of Leeuwenhoek's achievements:

> A certain most ingenious person here, named Leeuwenhoek, has devised microscopes which far surpass those which we have hitherto seen, manufactured by Eustachio Divini and others.

Van der Graf enclosed Leeuwenhoek's letter which Oldenburg translated and published in the *Philosophical Transactions*. The observations contained in this letter obviously pleased the Fellows of the Royal Society and Oldenburg was instructed to write to Leeuwenhoek asking for any more observations which he might make; as a result numerous letters, containing many remarkable microscopical discoveries, were sent by Leeuwenhoek to the Royal Society throughout the next fifty years.

Leeuwenhoek became accepted as an international authority on microscopical matters, but he remained in Delft working away on his own. In 1680 he was accorded the honour of Fellowship of the Royal Society, which he esteemed very highly. All his research and studies were reported by him in his native Dutch (for Leeuwenhoek did not know Latin, in which most of the scientific communication was carried on at that time) in letters to the Royal Society and to fellow scientists all over Europe. As Leeuwenhoek's fame increased he was plagued with numerous visits from people, including Royalty, who wished to see at first hand the marvels which he was describing with the aid of his microscopes. He regarded these visits as a regrettable interruption in his work, in which he remained active until very shortly before his death in 1723 at the age of 91.

Leeuwenhoek was a scientific amateur, totally lacking in formal training; this is emphasized in his letters (he wrote no books or scientific papers as such) where he writes down his observations as they were accomplished, intersperses them with personal details and then as often as not continues with a completely different topic. He made no attempt to arrange his facts or classify his ideas. He must, on the other hand, be given credit for his integrity and clarity; any one reading his letters is never in any doubt as to when he is describing a microscopical observation, i.e. stating facts, and when he begins to speculate on the explanation of these observations. This clarity of expression is rare in the formal scientific writings of the day.

Leeuwenhoek studied well over two hundred different animal types which, unfortunately, he seldom bothered to describe adequately, so that it is often difficult today to be sure which species he is referring to. He made many discoveries of lasting scientific value and may be regarded as the founder of the sciences of protozoology and bacteriology. Such was his stature among his contemporaries that in 1692 Robert Hooke was driven to comment that they

> were now reduced almost to a single Votary, which is Mr. Leeuwenhoek; besides whom, I hear of none that make any other Use of that Instrument, but for Diversion and Pastime.

Later he added that the microscope

> is become almost out of Use and Repute: So that Mr. Leeuwenhoek seems to be the principal Person left that cultivates those Enquiries. Which is not for Want of considerable materials to be discovered, but for Want of the inquisitive Genius of the Present Age.

Leeuwenhoek himself was largely reticent as to his methods of microscopy and the nature of his instruments. Contemporary writings, such as letters from people who were fortunate in obtaining an interview with Leeuwenhoek, often stress this point. It seems that he had one type of microscope which served as a demonstration model for display to his visitors, but he never showed off his best instruments. There are several references in Leeuwenhoek's letters to this subject; he says that his "best microscopes" he kept for himself alone and in a well-known letter written in 1678 he says:

> My method for seeing the very smallest animalcules and little eels I do not impart to others, nor yet that for seeing many animalcules at once, but I keep that for myself alone.

Apparently Leeuwenhoek used to make all his own equipment and lenses; as it seems that he used each microscope he made for only one or possibly two objects, it follows that he must have made a very large number during the course of his long researches in microscopy. One estimate places the number of his microscopes at over five hundred at the time of his death. Of these, twenty-six were bequeathed to the Royal Society and the rest were sold by auction after the death of his daughter Maria. Unfortunately, of all this number only nine authentic examples are known to have survived, six of which are now still in Holland. The Royal Society bequest was preserved for many years and the instruments were described in some detail by Martin Folkes who was Vice-President of the Royal Society in the year of Leeuwenhoek's death. Later still, in 1740, Henry Baker re-examined them and provided us with a list of their focal lengths, magnifications and the objects mounted for examination in each microscope. These instruments remained in the possession of the Royal Society until about a hundred years ago, when they apparently vanished without trace from the Society's collection.

From examination of the surviving instruments and from the early descriptions it has proved possible to assess the optical performance of some of his microscopes and to study their mechanical construction.

The lenses were always ground and polished to the bi-convex form, an operation at which Leeuwenhoek became extremely skilful. One example, measured by van Cittert, has a thickness of just over one millimetre and a radius of curvature of 0·75 millimetre. The finished lenses were mounted between two plates of metal each containing a small hole; the plates were riveted together to hold the lens firmly in

Fig. 3.4. A drawing of both front and back views of a typical microscope constructed by Leeuwenhoek. The pin which carries the object can be clearly seen, as well as the screw threads which serve to adjust its position. The whole microscope was about two inches in length.

position between the two holes. The objects were fixed upon a point which was then moved into the focus of the lens by a system of screws which can be seen in Fig. 3.4. This anticipated by many years the moveable stage focusing which reappeared in the eighteenth century and is used today on many research microscopes. All Leeuwenhoek's microscopes are small, the total length of the metal plate, which served as a handle as well as a lens mount, being usually under two inches and the width usually about one inch.

One is immediately struck by the mechanical crudity and imperfections of these microscopes, the metal plates being poorly finished and the screw threads ill-made. The objects were mounted on the pin and when this was rotated by means of the small knob attached to it some variation both in placing of the specimen and in its height with relation to the optical axis of the lens would be introduced. The height of the specimen was roughly set by means of the long vertical screw which passed through the right-angled bracket attached to the lower end of the metal lens plate. There was a short thumb screw which passed horizontally through one end of the object support block and which came to bear upon the lens plate. By manipulation of this screw the object pin would have been brought closer to the lens or carried away from it, so effecting the focusing movement.

Leeuwenhoek's lenses were of surprisingly good quality. Van der Star has measured the resolving power and the magnification of several examples. Two of these, now in the Leyden Museum, magnified $79\times$ and $126\times$ respectively and had a resolving power of $3\cdot5$ microns. They were characterized, as previously noted, by possessing very large fields of view over which the image was in sharp focus. The instrument in the possession of the Utrecht museum seems to be exceptional. It has a very high magnifying power ($275\times$) and even though the lens is very badly scratched it has an excellent resolution which very closely approaches the theoretical maximum (one micron) for this type of lens. When this lens was new it must have been a magnificent tribute to Leeuwenhoek's skill as a lens maker. It is a characteristic of all his ground lenses — he probably never used "blown" spheres on account of the difficulty of getting satisfactory glass and because of the small field of a spherical lens — that they all have exceptionally large fields of view. The resolution of the Utrecht lens is so good that it is possible that the lens could have been used for the famous observations on bacteria, although some authorities, notably Schierbeek, believe that Leeuwenhoek must have used a lens with a magnification of nearly five hundred times.

This type of microscope, as constructed by Leeuwenhoek, must have been very difficult to use. The working distance is very short, that of the Utrecht instrument measured above has been found to be $0\cdot5$ millimetre. The observer's eye would have to be placed so close to the lens that they must have been very uncomfortable to use. Although mechanically primitive and difficult to use, these instruments were optically superior to the lenses made by many of the leading opticians of the day. Furthermore, these microscopes had a rudimentary form of control over the movements of the specimen and, perhaps most important of all, they could be used to study a specimen by transmitted light. This type of illumination which is often the most valuable for microscopy of biological material was effected with the specimen mounted in a short length of capillary glass tubing or spread on a thin piece of blown glass or talc. What does not appear clear is the nature of the illumination, for there does not seem to have been any device for concentrating the light onto the specimen. Leeuwenhoek may have used bright daylight or the flame of a candle as light sources; certainly use of the former is suggested by a passage in a letter written in 1674 where he says:

> I would venture to recommend that, when one of these sections has been brought upon the pin of a microscope, you then hold the microscope towards the open sky, within doors, and out of the sunshine, as though you had a telescope and were trying to look at the stars in the sky through it.

In using such a microscope, in addition to any problems caused by the lack of resolution in the lens, or by insufficient illumination, we must remember that great difficulties in seeing the specimen would be caused by the lack of contrast, due to the transparent nature of living material. There is some evidence that Leeuwenhoek was aware of this particular problem, for Henry Baker says in 1740 that Leeuwenhoek's skill was also shown

> in the contrivance of the Apertures of his Glasses, which, when the Object was transparent, he made exceeding small, since much Light in that Case would be prejudicial; But, when the Object itself was dark, he inlarged the Aperture, to give it all possible Advantage of the Light.

This would certainly help to improve visibility, for reducing the aperture would enhance the diffraction effects around the edges of a transparent object and so contribute to its visibility.

Another possibility has been suggested by Dobell, who believes that Leeuwenhoek's particular method, which he kept so secret, was the use of some form of dark-ground illumination. This is used in microscopy today and takes the form of illumination of the specimen by light rays which are so oblique to the optical axis of the microscope that none of the direct light can enter the lens. The image is then formed by rays of light diffracted from the object; these can pass into the lens and give the effect of a brilliantly illuminated object on a black background

This greatly enhances the contrast and so enables objects of low inherent contrast to be studied with ease.

Although it is intriguing to think that Leeuwenhoek might have discovered the principle of dark-ground illumination, it must be mentioned that Kingma Boltjes conducted experiments with "blown" glasses, i.e. spherical glass globules, in 1941. He found that he was able to observe the fine details of the cilia of various Protozoa quite well by direct observation; in fact he found that any obliquity of the illumination actually tended to cause the structures to appear distorted. This may perhaps have been because the organisms were mounted as described by Leeuwenhoek, in a drop of water taken up in a capillary tube. Probably too, the aperture of the lens was so small that the diffraction effects already mentioned would prove a much more valuable source of increased contrast.

If, as seems probable from his later writings, Leeuwenhoek eventually abandoned the use of the capillary tube and adopted the technique of spreading a drop of liquid between thin glass plates by capillary attraction then some rudimentary form of dark-ground illumination might have proved valuable, but the question must remain open. Even though considerable obscurity still surrounds Leeuwenhoek's techniques of microscopy there can be no doubt of the value of his observations, particularly in the fields of bacteriology and protozoology which he initiated. The first account of the free-living, or as Leeuwenhoek describes them "the very little animalcules" is to be found in a letter of September 7th, 1674; the study was continued and the famous letter to the Royal Society in which they are described at length is dated October 9th, 1676. It is a very long letter and is not possible to quote here, but the interested reader is referred to Clifford Dobell's translation in his biography of Leeuwenhoek which makes interesting reading.

In addition to studying and describing free-living protozoa and bacteria, Leeuwenhoek also described the vorticellids, the rotifers and the fresh-water polyp (now called *Hydra*) upon the roots of the duckweed; with his description of *Hydra* he stimulated interest in this organism which lasted throughout the eighteenth century and indirectly influenced the future design of microscopes, as the requirements of workers studying the free-living fresh water coelenterates led to the development in the mid-eighteenth century of the so-called "aquatic" microscope.

Leeuwenhoek's interests did not stop at the inhabitants of water; following Malpighi, he studied the circulation of the blood, and the structure of many of the organs of the body, such as the striated muscle. To this latter end he proved well in advance of his time in the field of preparative techniques, attempting to improve the contrast of some of his material by staining it in a solution infused from saffron. He also investigated very thoroughly the life cycle of ants, aphids and mussels, and with his rather primitive microscopical apparatus provided a tremendous mass of information on these topics; Leeuwenhoek also studied plant structure and other botanical topics. Unfortunately, lack of formal training often resulted in his observations being set down completely without order or apparent purpose, but this does not in any way detract from his achievements. It might well be thought remarkable that all these different spheres of observation could be attempted with such simple home-made equipment, but as van Cittert remarks "these discoveries were made, not in spite of, but thanks to, the simple microscope".

One of Leeuwenhoek's best known contemporaries was also a fellow countryman and a microscopist. Jan Swammerdam had a short career as a naturalist, from 1663 to about 1675 but during these few years he worked with frenzied activity. Unlike Leeuwenhoek he had a formal education in science but his great work in this field, the *Biblia Naturae*, was not published during his lifetime. During the period of his life in which he was a microscopist, Swammerdam carried out a great deal of microdissection of insects, especially the honey bee; he pioneered techniques of dissecting the parts under water and of injecting minute vessels with wax or mercury to assist him in following out their course. Swammerdam's observations were carried out with a simple type of dissecting microscope which was probably made for him by Samuel Musschenbroek of Leyden.

Later, Samuel's young brother Johann also entered upon the business of an instrument maker and achieved great fame as a maker of microscopes and also of air-pumps. Several of Johann Musschenbroek's instruments have survived and they can be readily identified by his trade mark of an oriental lamp and crossed keys (taken from the Leyden coat-of-arms), which he placed on all his products. Johann Musschenbroek devised two types of simple microscopes, one for high-power and one for low-power work such as dissecting. The general form of the construction of the high-power instrument can be seen from Fig. 3.5; these instruments were probably intended to use glass spheres as lenses but the lenses have not been preserved in those microscopes which have been studied and documented.

Fig. 3.5. An exploded view of the high-power microscope of Musschenbroek. The handle and specimen carrier together with the focusing screw and object adjusting screw are at the lower left. The lens (mounted in a rectangular metal plate) slides in a wooden holder which fits onto the horizontal bar attached to the handle. A metal cover, which also clips onto the holder is shown at the top of the diagram. This cover serves to exclude unwanted light from falling on the object, and carries a quadrant with different sizes of aperture which can be seen in the front view (upper right of the illustration).

The objects for study were intended to be fixed onto one or other of a number of rods of differing form, terminating in a single or a double spike, a ring, and so on. These specimen holders are themselves held in a hollow rod which fits into the stem of the instrument. Two screws serve to move the rod around and so position the specimen in front of the lens. The actual mount for the lens is a metal plate, which slides into a holder attached to the handle of the microscope by means of a U-shaped rod. As the lens holder has a crude form of dovetail slideway for the lens plate it is to be supposed that several lenses of different powers were provided, each in its own little metal plate. Some instruments, although not by Musschenbroek himself, have survived with their lenses mounted in this manner.

Over the lens mount was fitted a hollow box which served to exclude light from the sides. A hole was drilled in it exactly opposite the lens position and in front of this, as can be seen in Fig. 3.5, a sector diaphragm was placed. This latter contained a series of holes of different sizes, any one of which could be brought in front of the fixed hole. This device seems to be the first instance of a diaphragm being used to control the amount of incident light falling on the specimen. A similar device is found in modern microscopes although today it serves to regulate the aperture of the illuminating cone of light and not as a means of regulating the intensity of the light or as a means of increasing contrast. As mentioned before, it seems likely that in these early single-lens microscopes restriction of aperture, either by carefully choosing the size of the lens aperture as Leeuwenhoek did, or by the use of a crude diaphragm by Musschenbroek served as a valuable means of obtaining more contrast in transparent or semi-transparent specimens which were viewed by transmitted light.

Focusing in Musschenbroek's high-power microscope was carried out by the action of one of the wing nuts which served to move the plate carrying the lens either towards or away from the specimen holder.

The low-power microscope designed by Musschenbroek was of a completely different pattern, but again there was provision for interchange of the lenses to vary the power. Each lens was mounted in a circular cell which could be attached to the end of an arm. This, shown in Fig. 3.6, served as a handle and hinged to this by a ball and socket joint was a second arm which carried the specimen support by mean of further ball and socket joints. Several lenses were provided, six usually forming a set, with powers ranging from about $8 \times$ to $70 \times$

Measurements of the optical performance of several of these lenses in the Leyden museum show that they are of good quality, the higher power ones especially.

Ball and socket joints to allow for the adjustment of the position of the specimen or the lens came to be widely used and the device was referred to as "Musschenbroek's nuts".

FIG. 3.6. Musschenbroek's low-power microscope. The lens is mounted at the base of the recessed eye-cup shown at the top left of the illustration. The object is impaled upon the pin which is carried on an arm. This in turn is adjustable by means of three ball and socket joints or "Musschenbroek nuts", so that the position and focus of the object may be changed.

Lyonet, in particular, used them to carry the lens in the dissecting microscope which he designed around 1740 (Fig. 3.7).

The movement of the lens over the glass table was made easy by the use of Musschenbroek's nuts but this very mobility made focusing difficult, especially with the higher power lenses. In order to get round this difficulty, Lyonet used to bend the arm carrying the lens a little too close to the object and then insert a tapering wooden wedge underneath the arm to elevate it very gradually until the point of correct focus was reached. At about the same time Musschenbroek nuts were used to provide a flexible mounting for accessory lenses used with compound microscopes and intended to serve for concentrating light upon the upper surface of an object. This arrangement was to be found, for example, in some of the microscopes of George Adams the Elder (see Chapter 4). Often other accessories such as stage forceps were also provided with this type of flexible mount.

In the high-power design of Musschenbroek we have the focusing arrangement in which the lens holder and the object holder are pivoted and can be separated or brought nearer together to effect the

Fig. 3.7. Lyonet's dissecting microscope. The lens is carried on an arm composed of several "Musschenbroek nuts", so allowing its positioning with respect to the specimen.

focusing. This movement resembles that which takes place between the two legs of a pair of compasses and hence simple microscope built on this plan have come to be known by historians of science a "compass microscopes". One form was sold by Wilson with the firs model of his screw-barrel microscope; it was intended to accept the same lenses as the screw barrel but to serve as an auxiliary microscop for the study of opaque objects. All the compass microscopes wer intended to be held in the hand and by the middle of the eighteenth century they proved to be very popular instruments as they require very little skill to use.

Fig. 3.8 shows the typical form of a later type of compass microscope in which the lenses are inserted in the centre of a silvered reflector which acted as an illuminator for opaque objects; the analogy to a pair of compasses is clear from this illustration. One drawback of this type of instrument is that the object and the lens will move in an arc in relationship to each other as the focusing is carried out and hence their relative heights will vary. This was usually overcome by the device, already described in connection with the high power Musschenbroek microscope, by which the object-holder rod is made to slide within a sleeve and so can be brought into the correct viewing position. The addition of the silvered reflector for the illumination of

Fig. 3.8. A compass microscope probably made by George Adams about 1745. This instrument has a brass frame with an ivory handle and possesses interchangeable lenses, each of which is surrounded by a reflector or "Lieberkühn". The specimen was held in the forceps, or attached to the opaque stage (shown at the bottom right) which fitted onto the other end of the specimen rod.

opaque objects was made in 1738 by a German named Lieberkühn and such a means of illustration of an opaque object is still known by his name today. The device was not new, however, having been first described by Descartes in his *Dioptrique* in 1637 (see Chapter 1, p. 18) and by others since his time. The silvered reflector has the lens mounted in its centre and the focus and figure of the mirror are so adjusted that when any object is sharply focused by the lens, then it also lies at the focus of the mirror and so will appear brightly illuminated by the light reflected on to it.

The majority of the early compass microscopes had a simple friction joint between the legs, so that precise focusing was not easy. As, in general, the lenses were of low power this did not prove too great a disadvantage in practice. Wilson's first form of compass microscope

(Fig. 3.9) had a crude form of screw thread focusing which must have been an improvement on the friction joint, but even this did not prove entirely satisfactory for it is criticized in the Philosophical Transactions of 1703 by an anonymous writer in letters addressed to "Sir C. H." (probably Christopher Holt). This writer is full of praise for the lenses of Wilson's microscopes but would have the screw thread replaced by one of much finer pitch in order to give a smoother focusing motion.

It is interesting to note, in passing, that the writer praises Wilson's lenses highly, rating them better than those of Mellen who, as we have seen, was much esteemed by Nehemiah Grew:

> As for the glasses themselves, I think them very good and well wrought and (tho' not so neatly set) to go far beyond any I have seen of Mellins.

He did not, however, place these lenses of Wilson's in the same class as those of Leeuwenhoek:

> But the best of ours must needs fall short in power and goodness of Mr. Leeuwenhoek's Glasses, whose skill both in making and using them I fear we shall not easily reach.

Later forms of compass microscopes such as that sold by John Cuff and the one made by George Adams, illustrated in Fig. 3.8, had a much improved form of screw focusing and were of a much higher standard of manufacture but still were not of much value for any serious study and they remained in use probably more for their simplicity in operation, serving to provide an easy way of observing some of the marvels of the minute world of Nature which were being revealed so rapidly in the seventeenth and early eighteenth centuries.

Before considering what is perhaps the most important of all the various forms of simple microscope, namely the screw-barrel type, it is worth digressing briefly to describe a type of microscope which was never more than a curiosity and was invented about 1696 by one Stephen Gray. He was experimenting with "blown" glass spheres and he observed that some of the irregular particles which remained in the glass after the globule had solidified appeared greatly magnified when the globule was held close to the eye for use as a simple microscope lens. This gave him the idea that if there were any objects or organisms in a drop of water they might be seen distinctly in the same way, using the drop of water itself as the lens. He tried the experiment by applying a drop of water to the end of a piece of wire and found that he was able to see the minute organisms in the water very clearly magnified

From this Gray developed the so-called "water microscope" which simply consisted of a brass plate with holes of differing sizes drilled in it. These holes were then filled with the water which contained the organisms to be examined; because of the thickness of the brass plate, the water drops assumed a cylindrical form with hemispherical ends and acted as lenses of differing powers, according to their diameters. It was then possible to use the one which provided the most suitable image to study the organisms.

Later, Gray developed the principle still further by providing a crude object holder and focusing device and using a drop of pure water solely as a lens, acting exactly in the same way as the spherical "blown" glasses in use at that time. The water microscope did not prove practicable although Nelson in 1911 discovered another account of a still more refined form dating from around 1750. This had a plate provided with no less than thirteen holes of different sizes to provide as much variation in power as possible for the water droplet lenses. It had a refined compass type of action and was provided with an elegant turned handle. Such instruments, however, were probably never more than curiosities; it may well be that any further development was abandoned because of the introduction of the screw-barrel microscope. This instrument provided a cheap, portable microscope which above all was much simpler and easier to use than any of its predecessors; it had for the first time a reliable method of varying the power by means of interchangeable lenses and was provided with an accurate system of focusing the object.

The original idea for the screw-barrel system of focusing was taken from earlier continental developments, involving compound microscopes. As far as can be determined the credit for the original idea must go to an Italian inventor named Tortona, who described microscopes embodying this system to the meeting of the Physics Mathematical Roman Academy held in 1685. Tortona, however, was reticent as to the methods of construction of these microscopes. The designs of Tortona were probably copied very closely by workers such as Campani and Bonanni, who have already been mentioned in Chapter 1. The latter figures (in his *Micrographia Curiosa* of 1691) a compound microscope with screw-barrel focusing to which his own spring stage had been added.

The application to a simple microscope seems to be due to Nicolaas Hartsoeker, about 1694. His drawing shows that in all essential features the microscope which gained such popularity in Wilson's name is that

Fig. II.

Fig. IV.

FIG. 3.9. Wilson's first model of the screw-barrel microscope of 1702. The screw-barrel microscope is shown in the centre of the illustration at the bottom. The focusing screw D is clearly shown, the specimen being placed between the plates EE and FG. The lens is mounted in the centre of the bottom plate labelled B. The compass attachment is shown at the right of the illustration with the arm AB, upon which were fixed the lens plates; the specimen rod and forceps are on the jointed arm at the left. In the upper right hand corner of the illustration one of the lenses is shown in position on the arm AB, whilst the lowest power lens is at the upper left. Also shown in the figure are an ivory slider with mounted objects and a tube containing a small fish ready for the examination of the circulation of the blood.

designed by Hartsoeker eight years previously. In fairness to Wilson, who has been accused of direct plagiarization, it should be stated that in his first article in the *Philosophical Transactions* for 1702 he makes no claim to be the inventor. James Wilson, who was in business "At the Willow Tree in Cross Street, Hatton Garden" was a typical practising optician of the time.

> He makes all sorts of Dioptric and Catoptric Glasses and Tellescopes, Prospects, Camera Obscuras, Magic Lanterns and Selleth the best of Spectacles and Reading Glasses.

His article in the *Philosophical Transactions* makes it clear from the title that he lays no claim to originality, reading,

> The description and manner of using a late invented set of small pocket-Microscopes, made by James Wilson; which with great ease are apply'd in viewing Opake, Transparent and liquid Objects; as the Farina of the Flowers of Plants, etc. The Circulation of the Blood in living creatures etc. The Animalcula in Semine, etc.

The screw-barrel type of instrument (Fig. 3.9) has the lens mounted in a circular disc which screws into one end of the barrel which forms the main body of the instrument. Within the body two thin brass plates are mounted so that they can slide up or down. Each plate has a central hole in it and they are pressed towards each other by the action of a strong spiral spring inserted into the body between one plate and the lens holder. The ivory sliders containing the objects to be studied or a small tube containing a living animal may be inserted between these two brass slides, when the pressure of the spring keeps the object firmly held. The two stage plates, as we may call them, together with the included object, are firmly pressed into contact with the "screwed barrel" (from which the name of this type of microscope is derived); this in turn is screwed into the main body of the instrument from the end opposite to the lens mounting. The amount to which this barrel is screwed in regulates the focus by pushing the stage plates and the object between them nearer to the lens, acting against the pressure of the strong spring. The basic features of this type of construction may be seen in Fig. 3.9 at the bottom centre.

In Hartsoeker's original version, a condensing lens was fitted into a separate mount which screwed within the focusing barrel. In later Wilson instruments, however, this condensing lens was often made integral with the focusing barrel and its cell served as a hand grip for screwing the whole in or out to obtain the position of correct focus.

This lens may be seen labelled C in Fig. 3.9. Hartsoeker's original design is superior to that adopted by Wilson as it allowed the position of the condensing lens to be regulated independently of the focusing movement. Hartsoeker's microscope was devised solely for the study of objects by transmitted light, and from the title of Wilson's first paper it may be seen that he extended the versatility of the instrument to deal with opaque objects also.

In the first paper in 1702, Wilson in fact described two instruments, the actual screw-barrel microscope, which served for the examination of transparent objects, and a crude compass microscope for the study of objects by reflected light. In the latter the specimens were either held in the forceps or by swinging the rod around on the joint P the disc H, which was black on one side and white on the other, was brought into use. The lens mounts, generally of ivory, were fixed on the arm B by inserting the spike labelled A into a small hole drilled into the mount.

In the illustration (Fig. 3.9) the rather crude form of the compass focusing can be seen. As mentioned above, this came in for some criticism by a writer in a later number of the *Philosophical Transactions*. In the same figure at the bottom is shown the screw-barrel microscope. The objects were mounted dry in the ivory slides, shown at the bottom left-hand side. The condensing lens of the screw-barrel instrument is at C in the figure, mounted integral with the focusing barrel D. It is obvious how, when this was screwed up and down in the body AA, the plates GF and EE would be pushed against the pressure of the spiral spring. In this original form the indentation cut into the plate FG is designed to hold the fish tube, which is drawn, together with its occupant, at the bottom right of the figure. The lens, together with its mount, is visible at B. The cylindrical object shown at H in the top left-hand corner is a very low-power lens designed for use only with the compass microscope or as a separate hand magnifier.

In later years Wilson made several minor modifications to his design. In a pamphlet published in 1706 he mentions a turned brass handle which screwed onto a threaded fitting attached to the body of the screw-barrel microscope; it is clear that he altered some of the constructional details such as substituting leather for cork in the plate FG which pushed the brass stage plates together and by making the spiral spring of steel. The compass microscope was of better construction, stimulated perhaps by the adverse criticism, and the lenses were now attached to it by screwing them into a ring. This pamphlet, together with its plate, were reproduced by Harris in the second volume of his *Lexicon*

Technicum published in 1710 and furnished the basis for most descriptions of the Wilson microscope.

Some time between 1706 and 1710 Wilson published a further pamphlet which used the letterpress of the 1706 edition (and hence bears its date) but had a picture of his new opaque holder substituted on the plate. This rendered the compass attachment obsolete and hence it was no longer provided. The other minor point of difference was that the handle had a male screw thread instead of a female one and was now turned from ivory.

FIG. 3.10. A later model of Wilson's screw-barrel microscope, probably made by George Adams around 1746. At the extreme right of the picture is the lens holder for use when examining opaque objects; extra lenses and ivory sliders are shown in front of the actual microscope.

In this latter form, the screw-barrel microscope entered on its long career; such an instrument is seen in Fig. 3.10, with the handle attached to the screw barrel and an ivory slider in position. Extra lenses in their mounts, together with spare sliders are seen surrounding the instrument and on the right of the illustration is shown the opaque holder. This fitted to the barrel and the lenses were screwed into it, so that they were in effect outside the instrument. Culpeper about 1720 introduced the forceps plate which inserted between the stage and served to hold opaque objects for examination. A further innovation of Culpeper was the mounting of the body on a tripod stand to convert it from a hand-held instrument into a small table model.

Six lenses were usually supplied with a screw-barrel microscope and as many examples are extant it has proved possible to obtain some idea of the quality of the lenses and of their resolving power. Most of the instruments which have been studied probably date from the second half of the eighteenth century, and are from such makers as George Adams and Ed. Culpeper. The average range of magnifications was from $15\times$ to $150\times$, one example (No. M7a2 in the Leyden collection, made by Culpeper) having lenses with the powers of $19\times$, $25\times$, $35\times$, $44\times$, $137\times$ and $160\times$. Some examples have been found in which the highest power lens magnified over $290\times$. In the Culpeper instrument mentioned above, the resolution was $10\,\mu$ for the lowest power and $1\cdot6\,\mu$ for the highest, although as the lenses suffered from severe chromatic aberration, the quality of this image left much to be desired.

The lenses of screw-barrel microscopes show great variation in performance and a considerable difference in quality can be found between the products of one maker and another, and even between the various lenses of any given microscope so that the image quality might have varied widely over the range of powers.

There is no doubt that the development of the Wilson type of screw-barrel microscope contributed largely to the popularity of the simple microscope among the eighteenth-century amateurs. In addition to the superiority conferred on it by the very fact that it was a single lens microscope (and so did not suffer as much as the compound microscope from chromatic aberration), the screw-barrel microscope was of small size and therefore very portable. This presents a marked contrast to the microscopes of makers such as Marshall which have already been described in Chapter 2 and the Culpeper microscope which succeeded the latter. In addition, the screw-barrel microscope was very easy to use, almost the only precautions necessary in its use being succinctly summarized by Wilson himself:

> In the viewing of Objects, one ought to be careful not to hinder the Light from falling on Them, by the Hat, Perruke, or any other thing, especially when they are to look upon Opake Objects: for nothing can be seen with the best of Glasses, unless the Object be in a due distance, with a sufficient Light.

Harris in the preface to the second volume of the *Lexicon Technicum* praises Wilson's microscope very highly:

> of all the Microscopes I have ever seen for Commodiousness, various Uses, Portability, and Cheapness, I never met with anything like Mr. Wilson's glasses.

This opinion was evidently endorsed by the public and the screw-barrel microscope was produced by all the instrument makers of the eighteenth century, and often at a very low price. A catalogue of Henry Pyefinch, dated 1775, shows that although he was producing his best compound microscope with a jointed pillar for 7 guineas, a Wilson screw-barrel could be bought for only 2 guineas, or £2. 10s. 0d. if the adaptor for opaque objects was included.

Many modifications of the screw-barrel microscope appeared during the eighteenth century, most of them in the form of stands or accessories designed to make the instrument adaptable for all fields of study. One of the most obvious, to leave both hands free for writing or drawing, was to mount the microscope on a pillar or table stand. Both Culpeper and Scarlett, who produced large numbers of screw-barrel microscopes, sold table stands. The base of that devised by Culpeper, who was also a mathematical instrument maker, was developed from the sector to which a third arm had been added at the hinge, so forming a folding tripod foot. Some microscopes had a condensing lens added onto an arm of Musschenbroek nuts, in order to throw more light onto opaque specimens; others again were provided with a universal joint at the top of their table pillar in order to allow them to be mounted at any angle. Again a mirror was often fitted to the pillar in order to throw light up into the microscope.

Although these early table stands undoubtedly served their purpose, they were not satisfactory as they were lacking in rigidity. This would be a decided disadvantage if the higher powers were in use. By the middle of the eighteenth century, however, various makers, among them John Cuff, James Mann and George Adams, started mounting screw-barrel instruments onto a rigid ornamental scroll stand; in many cases the scroll was hinged at its base in order to enable it to fold into the box and make the whole apparatus more portable. The basic form of a scroll microscope is shown in Fig. 3.11, taken from Henry Baker's book on the microscope. In addition, the screw-barrel was made attachable to a solar fitting (see Chapter 5) so that the basic microscope could then either be used on the handle, as a portable field microscope, on the scroll stand for leisurely examinations in the home, or, mounted on the solar fitting, for projecting an image onto a screen using sunlight as the illuminant.

The screw-barrel microscope was probably more intended for the interested gentleman who wished to see the minute structures which were being described than for the serious researcher. Henry Baker thought otherwise, for speaking of the screw-barrel mounted upon a scroll stand he writes:

The Pocket Microscope thus fixt, is if I may presume to judge, as easy and pleasant in its use and as fit for the most curious Examination of the Animal-cules and Salts in Fluids, of the Farinae in Vegetables, of the Circulations

Fig. 3.11. A "scroll" microscope from the middle of the eighteenth century. This consisted of a screw-barrel microscope mounted upon an arm, labelled A. Light was reflected into the instrument by means of the mirror E fixed on the base.

in small creatures: in short, it is as likely to make considerable Discoveries in Objects that have some Degree of Transparency, as any Microscope I have ever seen or heard of.

At this time the single-lens microscope was proving of great value in the study of the fresh-water coelenterate animal *Hydra* first described by Leeuwenhoek. During the eighteenth century this creature was usually referred to as the fresh water polype, and in 1739 Abraham Trembley published some account of his discoveries relating to this animal. This was followed in 1744 by his famous book *Memoires pour servir à l'histoire d'un Genre de Polypes d'eau douce, à bras en formes des cornes* in which he pointed out the remarkable regenerative power of *Hydra* and proved experimentally that they could produce a complete individual from either portion of an animal which had been cut in two. Working with the simplest of equipment (a glass jar full of water and weed containing the polyps which were examined by a simple lens mounted on an arm of Musschenbroek nuts so that it could be moved to examine any part of the front surface of the glass jar) Trembley also discovered their methods of feeding and reproduction. Such work stimulated others, particularly Henry Baker in this country, to observe these animals.

Baker produced *An Attempt towards a Natural History of the Polype* in 1743 and in 1755 Ellis published his essay on the natural history of the corallines which was to become justly famous. This particular type of microscopical work imposed certain demands upon the instrument and led to certain innovations. As the slightest jar or vibration could cause the *Hydra* to contract and withdraw its tentacles, the tank in which they were kept had to remain quite still. Hence the lens had to be moved over the tank rather than the specimen under a fixed lens as had been the custom.

Again, as the tanks were often of considerable size, the lens traverse had to be of a considerable extent. Such requirements led to the development of a microscope which had a large stage on which the tank could be placed and a lens attached to an arm. The arm was fixed at right angle to the pillar of the microscope and could be moved not only to bring the lens nearer to or further away from the optical axis of the microscope, but also to pivot and so enable the lens to be traversed over any part of the tank. Such microscopes with this type of movement for the lens became known as "aquatic" microscopes (Fig. 3.12) in distinction to those in which the lens could only move up and down with respect to the stage. From their chief use these latter were generally termed "botanical" movements.

In both types the base was usually of heavy construction to give additional stability and, as low powers were almost exclusively used, the screw-barrel for focusing tended to be omitted and the lens was carried in a simple sliding mount. Some instruments did have a simple rackwork focusing mechanism for the lens but in practice it was found that the sliding mount was adequate for focusing at these low powers.

The original form of Ellis's microscope was probably constructed by Cuff; Ellis tells us:

> I have used a very commodious microscope of Mr. Cuff's, the Optician in Fleet Street, which I had altered for that purpose.

This instrument is shown in Fig. 3.12, from which the general construction may be seen. The large stage, focusing method, and device for obtaining the aquatic movement and the large mirror are all obvious.

M. Ellis's Aquatic Microſcope

FIG. 3.12. "Mr. Ellis's aquatic microscope". The aquatic motion was provided by sliding the arm E in the socket X, and by swivelling the rod D in the mount attached to the main pillar labelled A. The stage (C) and the mirror are also shown. The lenses, one of which is drawn separately, are provided with Lieberkühn reflectors.

The method of mounting the pillar in a bush screwed onto the lid of the box was a very common adaptation for portability and occurred frequently in instruments built at this period and for the next century

FIG. 3.13. A modern simple dissecting microscope, with rackwork focusing and glass stage plate.

or so. Ellis's aquatic microscope may be regarded as the direct ancestor of the standard low-power dissecting monocular in use today in schools; this has now the advantage, however, of an achromatic doublet or triplet magnifier. Such an instrument (Fig. 3.13) provides a very adequate means of obtaining magnification of a few diameters for dissection and biological preparation work in general.

The majority of the eighteenth-century users of the simple micro-scope, like Ellis, were content to use rather low-power lenses for their studies, although there were notable exceptions, such as the botanist Robert Brown in the first half of the nineteenth century. In general, however, following the death of Leeuwenhoek there was a lapse in interest in single lenses of high power. This was probably due to difficulties of construction of such lenses and to the discomfort of working with a magnifier which requires a close working distance and has a very small diameter.

Distrust of the images produced by the compound microscope persisted throughout the eighteenth and the early years of the nine-teenth century, so efforts were devoted to improving the single-lens microscope.

Wollaston, in 1812, devised a system whereby two plano-convex lenses were fixed with their plane surfaces together, separated by a small diaphragm. This arrangement, indicated in Fig. 3.14, Wollaston considered would largely mitigate the spherical aberration present in high-power single lenses. Other systems, such as the Stanhope lens and the Coddington lens followed in succeeding years (see Fig. 3.14), but none of them could be considered entirely successful. In order to reduce the spherical aberration to an acceptable figure the diaphragm had to reduce the working aperture of the lens system very considerably.

A new approach came in 1811, when Brewster suggested that it might prove possible to grind lenses from substances which possessed a higher refractive index than glass and so would have a greater radius of curvature for any given power than a lens constructed of glass. This in turn would result in lower spherical errors. Precious stones were suggested, and ruby, garnet and diamond were all tried, although there were many practical difficulties involved in the working of such substances, apart from the great expense of the raw material. Andrew Pritchard (who was at that time assistant to Cornelius Varley) succeeded in constructing a diamond lens in 1824 at the instigation of Dr. C. R. Goring. Goring wrote to Pritchard on January 3rd, 1825, with respect to this first lens:

> It has shown the most difficult transparent object I have submitted to it.

This initial success led Pritchard to attempt the construction of further diamond lenses. The project seemed very attractive at that time because the curvature of a diamond lens would be much less that that of a glass one of a comparable power. The focus would be longer and, as the curvature was less, there would be less spherical aberration than with glass and so the diameter or "aperture" could be accordingly increased. Pritchard calculated that the spherical aberration of a diamond lens would be only one-ninth that of an equivalent glass element. Allied to the high refractive index of these precious stones was their very low dispersion, hence the chromatic aberration, which is anyway not very significant in a single lens, was still further minimized. It proved possible to work diamond lenses to very short focal lengths and therefore to obtain much higher magnifications than could have been attained with a glass lens.

Fig. 3.14. Diagrams of the lens arrangement in various magnifiers of the nineteenth century.

Pritchard, egged on by Goring, proceeded with his experiments but some difficulty was encountered, owing to the fact that very often flaws were found in gems which, when they were opened in the grinding process, filled with oil and grinding materials and formed black inclusions. In addition, some of the lenses proved to give multiple images, which fact made them useless as magnifiers. In order to overcome such phenomena the gem had to be cut in a very special orientation; Pritchard tells us that he became quite skilled at selecting suitable gems and deciding on the correct orientation for grinding into a plano-convex lens. He persevered with his experiments and succeeded in producing two lenses of very short focal lengths, $\frac{1}{20}$ inch and $\frac{1}{30}$ inch respectively, which proved to be satisfactory. This latter lens Pritchard stated to have "amplification enough for most practical purposes". Lenses were also ground from other gems, such as sapphire, ruby and garnet, but diamonds, although harder to work, proved to give the most satisfactory lenses.

Jewelled lenses were not a great success for various practical reasons such as the expense and difficulty of working and polishing the stones; at the same time, however, rapid strides were being made in the development of achromatic glass lenses, which resulted in a revival of interest in the compound microscope as a tool of scientific research.

The single-lens microscope was then to some extent relegated to the role of a low-power naturalist's microscope and to that of a dissecting instrument which served to prepare material for study with the compound microscope. Even though the new achromatic lenses which were coming into fashion in the late 1820's had a better resolving power than single lenses of equivalent power, some workers carried on using the old simple microscope for some time. Coddington in 1829 had developed a form of magnifier, known as the "Birdeye object glass" in which the use of an opaque diaphragm, as shown in Fig. 3.14, reduces the aberrations; about the same time Wollaston produced a fresh design for a doublet which mitigated still further the inconveniences of small field and great degree of spherical aberration which beset the simple lens. This design was taken up and further improved by Chevalier and still later by Zeiss who, in the early part of his career, specialized in this type of lens. In Chevalier's doublet the use of a diaphragm between the lenses (Fig. 3.14) sharpened up the image and later the lower lens of Wollaston's doublet was replaced by a combination which enabled the aberrations to be still further corrected. Van Cittert, who has measured several Wollaston doublets, quotes one made in 1835 by Dollond of London which had a magnifying power of $200 \times$ and a resolution of about 6 microns and another with a power of $300 \times$ and a resolution of 5μ.

In the 1830's these achromatic triplets were far superior to the early simple microscope and they set a standard which has been continued and improved upon to the present day. Achromatic lenses were being applied to the compound microscope, but good work was still being produced by single-lens microscopes; von Baer in 1827 described and discovered the mammalian ovum, and Robert Brown carried out his remarkable botanical studies with such an instrument. He is better remembered today as the discoverer of the movement of small particles in a colloidal solution as the result of molecular bombardment, but he studied many families of plants in great detail. In 1833 he published "Observations on the organs and mode of Fecundation in Orchidaceae and Asclepidaceae" in the *Transactions of the Linnean Society*, a paper which, despite its name, contains observations of profound significance. With the aid of a simple microscope he had been able to see and describe what we know as the nucleus of the cells. Although the cell concept had not been clearly enunciated in 1833, Brown was able to recognize that here he was dealing with a structure of great importance in the life of the plant, a structure which proved so important that it is still a vital object of study to microscopists in the middle of the twentieth century.

Although high magnifications can be obtained from a single lens, the resolution and light gathering power of such lenses are far surpassed by those of a modern objective of similar magnification.

At the present time the use of the simple microscope is largely confined to very low-power work, magnifications ranging from 5–20 diameters. For this purpose the combination of lenses invented by Steinheil in 1864 is largely used. By the use of glasses of different dispersions and differing curvatures it has proved possible to produce an image which is aplanatic, achromatic and free from astigmatism. In addition the whole combination has a reasonable working distance and a large field of view. For dissection work involving powers of from 20–100×, the compound binocular microscope built according to the design of Greenhough, i.e. having two completely separate microscope systems, one for each eye, is now largely used.

The developments of the microscope during the eighteenth century took place mainly in England, and were largely concerned with the mechanical part of the microscope. During this time England was accepted as the centre of microscope progress, a role which she maintained until the latter part of the nineteenth century, when as a result of the work of Ernst Abbe, Germany took the lead in the design of microscope lenses. The changes which occurred during the eighteenth century, and which resulted in the compound microscope acquiring its modern form, will form the subject of the next chapter.

CHAPTER 4

THE EIGHTEENTH CENTURY — A PERIOD OF MECHANICAL DEVELOPMENT

THERE can be little doubt that the writings and researches of the pioneer microscopists, such as Hooke, Grew and Leeuwenhoek, stimulated a tremendous interest in the minute world which lay all around. The new tool caught the imagination not only of the natural philosophers, but also of the layman; towards the beginning of the eighteenth century it was a status symbol to possess a microscope and be able to demonstrate with it the structure of insects, flowers and other natural objects. This development was of profound significance for the future of the microscope, for it resulted in the development of new types of instrument and may well have been the major stimulus for microscopical specimen preparation. We have seen how the early microscopists, with their diverse interests, were skilled in the art of preparing the objects in which they were interested for study with the microscope.

With the spread of a more general interest the number of micro-scopes increased, both the compound instruments of the Marshall type and more particularly the cheaper Culpeper model which we shall consider shortly. Large numbers of simple microscopes of the Wilson screw-barrel pattern were also in circulation and it became the practice to supply ivory or wooden sliders containing the objects for study at the time that the instrument was purchased. These early preparations were either mounted dry on small paper discs if the objects were opaque or mounted dry between two thin circles of talc or mica if the speci-mens were transparent and intended for study by transmitted light. Most microscope outfits also included a pair of stage forceps and spare discs for holding and mounting objects as the occasion arose; extra talcs and their brass retaining rings were also supplied, often in a box which served to screw onto the top of the microscope eyepiece and so act as a dust cap.

In order to display the circulation of the blood each microscope had a frog or fish plate provided with the accessories, but from the number which have survived to the present day in what appears to be a brand new condition, one might conjecture that they were seldom used, and that the amateur microscopist generally confined his attentions to the specimens thoughtfully provided by the supplier of the microscope. From the sheet of instructions provided in 1730 by Edmund Culpeper with one of his microscopes, now preserved in the collection of the Royal Microscopical Society, we learn that four ivory sliders were supplied with the instrument. The contents of each are carefully listed:

No. 1.   Some hairs or down of the Mouse. The Down of a Moth's Wing. The Dust of the Sun Flower. The Dust of Mallows.

No. 2.   The Scales of a Soal-fish. A bit of Sponge, the Pith of Elder, a bit of Cork, and a bit of the Pith of a Rush. The Leg of a Moth, and a bit of a Feather. The Eye of a Fly, and the Wing of a Fly.

No. 3.   A Louse. The Down of a Thistle. A bit of Human Skin. Hairs of the Head.

and so on. In addition, two spare sliders were supplied, "like the above, for Liquids, or to put any other Objects on". The popularity of the microscope among the educated gentlemen of the eighteenth century proved to be a very valuable influence in stimulating some progress and development of the instrument and its techniques.

The professional scientists tended to view the results of investigations carried out with the microscope with some scepticism, probably justified; the poor optical corrections of the lenses and the very low apertures then in use resulted in images which were indistinct and often surrounded by colour fringes. This in its turn probably caused many structures to be described which were in fact false, resulting solely as optical effects produced by the instrument. A good example of this may be found in the microscopical study of the spermatozoa which throughout the eighteenth century were often pictured as containing a minute "homunculus" or fully-formed miniature of the human form. This faulty interpretation was very often due to the mistaken ideas of the observers. Such errors of interpretation and faulty specimen preparation, together with those due to the instrument itself, were responsible for the view that the microscope was only of value for the lowest power work; in the eighteenth and early nineteenth centuries the term "microscopical deception" was much used to signify the suspicion and mistrust which was often felt for results of microscopical research.

The amateur tradition, however, became well established in England and from this in the nineteenth century was to spring a tremendous fount of inspiration and enthusiasm which led to notable technical advances in the optics of the microscope. These amateur users of the instrument, by their very great skill (often far exceeding that of the professional scientist) in using the microscope at its limits of resolution contributed very greatly to the development of the modern instrument and to our present techniques.

The large popularity of the microscope in the eighteenth century was to a great extent catered for by the Wilson screw-barrel instrument, which was cheap and easy to use. Many people, however, wanted a much larger microscope. At first this would undoubtedly have been a Marshall type, as in the case of Samuel Pepys (quoted in Chapter 2). This was large and cumbersome but very versatile in skilled hands. Between the years 1725 to 1730 a new microscope appeared on the market, of a type which was to sweep away the larger, older model and which was to persist in one form or another for the next hundred years.

This new microscope was designed by Edmund Culpeper and it departed from the single pillar type of construction favoured by Hooke and Marshall in favour of a modified form of the tripod used earlier by Campani in Italy. This basic similarity is obvious if Campani's instrument (Fig. 1.15) is compared with a typical Culpeper microscope shown in Fig. 4.1. Edmund Culpeper had been apprenticed to the instrument maker Walter Hayes who traded from the sign of the "Cross Daggers" in Moorfield until his death in 1685.

At this time Culpeper probably took over the business and used the same trade mark. Records of his career are scarce, but it is certain that he was advertising several types of microscope in 1706 and he used Hayes's trade mark of the Cross Daggers on his own trade card together with the usual representation of a selection of his products. As far as we can ascertain, Culpeper was in business until at least 1738, although he moved his premises to the "Black and White House" in Moorfields around the year 1725. Culpeper, it will be remembered, was also responsible for the design of a table stand for the Wilson microscope, based on the sector to which he had added a third arm (see Chapter 3, p. 95.)

A great number of Culpeper microscopes have survived, possibly because they became so popular that they were made by almost every instrument maker and so came onto the market in large numbers. In

FIG. 4.1. A typical Culpeper microscope. Note the relative positions of the tripod legs supporting the stage and the body tube. The instrument is fitted with a Bonanni spring-stage.

consequence it has proved possible for the specialist to trace the various steps in the evolution of this particular model with some certainty, unlike the developmental stages of other, later, instruments which are often uncertain. At this point it must be stressed again that all the changes in the microscope which occurred in the eighteenth century were purely changes of detailed design in the mechanical features; optical design as such was non-existent and changes in the lenses were quite arbitrary and random.

In its basic form, the Culpeper microscope consists of a round base or stand of wood, from which three turned legs rise to support the stage. From this in turn three further legs arise to terminate in a brass ring supporting a sleeve. In early models this tube or sleeve was constructed in the typical fashion of the period, i.e. a cardboard tube covered with leather or ray-skin. This tube acts as a support in which the actual microscope body slides in order to provide a focusing movement. Later a draw tube was often provided. From the illustration (Fig. 4.1) the general appearance may be gauged. The most obvious feature is the eyepiece portion of turned wood which bears a very strong resemblance to those of the Marshall type instruments. The eyepiece would have contained a bi-convex eye lens, together with a larger field lens situated at the lower end of the turned wood portion. Another very striking feature is the disposition of the legs supporting the sleeve which are arranged to come at intermediate positions between the lower legs supporting the stage itself. Early forms of the Culpeper microscope usually had a box cap, designed to hold the spare objectives, which screwed onto the eyepiece and served as a dust excluder.

One very important innovation can be seen from Fig. 4.1; in the centre of the wooden base is fixed a concave mirror in gimbal mountings so arranged that it can be set to reflect light up through any object placed upon the stage of the microscope. It seems probable that earlier workers had in fact used a mirror; the inconvenience of the Campani microscope in which the whole tripod had to be held up to the light, or that of the Marshall where the stage and the body had to be swung over the edge of the table in order to bring the optical axis over a candle placed on the floor, would certainly have resulted in some attempt to use the principle of reflection from a mirror to alter the direction of the illumination.

Any such experiment, however, would have used a plane mirror. Culpeper's idea was to use a concave mirror which not only acts as a reflector but also concentrates the light and so acts to some extent as a condenser. This eliminated the extra bi-convex lens which was used for this purpose in the Marshall instruments. The placing of the mirror in the centre of the base of the Culpeper microscope directly underneath the optical axis was a most important development and this probably resulted in the perpetuation of the upright, non-inclinable form of microscope for many years. In the sheet of instructions which Culpeper supplied with his microscope he made the specific point:

> remember the Concave Looking-Glass at the Bottom is to reflect the Light up to the Object either by Day or Candle-Light (a bright white Cloud gives the best Reflection by Day)

This seems to suggest that the concave mirror was in fact an innovation, otherwise it would not have been necessary to stress in detail what very soon was accepted as an obvious function.

Like the earlier Marshall microscopes, the Culpeper instruments were provided with different powers, usually five in number, each mounted in a cell or "button" made to screw onto the small tube at the lower end of the main microscope body. Van Cittert has measured the optical performance of the instrument when fitted with each of these objectives in turn and he found that the magnifying power varied from about $30\times$ with the objective number five, $60\times$ with number four, through $80\times$, $100\times$ to $275\times$ with the highest power. All these lenses, of course, were uncorrected for chromatic aberration and were provided with diaphragms behind the lens which had only a small opening in order to minimize spherical aberration. In consequence, the aperture was low and the resolution was poor. Measurements with test plates suggest that the highest power lens had a resolution of the order of 5 microns (1 micron or $\mu = 1/1000$ mm) whereas a modern objective lens combination which would be used to produce the same magnification would be expected to resolve about $0\cdot5\ \mu$.

The Culpeper form of microscope stand would undoubtedly have been easy to construct, and this would have helped towards the production of a comparatively cheap instrument. At first the stage was constructed of wood, but very soon Culpeper turned to the use of brass and all his later models have their stages made of this metal. The final modification of this item was the addition of a type of bayonet joint to the aperture in the centre of the stage so that a Bonanni spring stage could be added to hold the prepared ivory sliders firmly. Most of the instruments were provided with a fish plate, either made entirely of glass as in the earlier microscopes, in which case the fish plate was often elaborately engraved with the purpose of the accessory,

> this Glass is to lay ye Fish on.

In the latter models the fish plate was of glass edged with brass or again constructed entirely of metal. In this case the plate had a curved shape, something resembling a shoehorn, with a slot cut at one end over which the tail of the fish was to be laid.

Although the Culpeper microscope was easy to make, was relatively cheap and had the advanced concave mirror design, it nevertheless represented a definite regression in microscope design. This is particularly so when one considers some features of detail, such as the fact that the access to the stage was severely limited by the arrangement of the tripod legs supporting the microscope body. This limited the use of the instrument almost entirely to the study of objects by transmitted light, although the maker was reluctant to admit this and even provided a place for mounting a bi-convex lens on the edge of the stage for illuminating opaque specimens. Again it must be noted that the inclining limb of the Hooke and Marshall microscopes has disappeared, so that the Culpeper microscope can only be used in the upright position. Finally, the fine focusing adjustment to be found on the Marshall instruments has been abandoned and the instrument is focused solely by sliding the draw tube in the sleeve.

This instrument as sold by Edmund Culpeper obviously became a commercial success and pointed the way to many imitators. Culpeper himself was aware of the danger from his rivals and at the bottom of one of his pamphlets describing the microscope he adds the following plaintive appeal:

> It is desired of the Gentlemen who purchase these Microscopes to keep them secret from Persons of the same Trade with the Inventor, lest they should steal his Invention, as they have too often done, imposing upon the World by their awkward Imitations, and bereaving him of the Fruits of his own Industry, which 'tis hoped therefore all lovers of Art will endeavour to prevent.

The rival instrument makers were soon in the field, however, one of the first being Edward Scarlett. Indeed his name is often linked so closely with Culpeper's that it has been suggested that they were in partnership, although what evidence there is seems to be against this idea. Scarlett's instruments were figured for the first time in Smith's *Opticks* published in 1738. Fig. 4.2 shows one of Scarlett's microscopes and it can be seen how closely they resemble those of Culpeper. The most important change is the extension of the three legs of turned brass up through the stage to support the body tube; this device has the effect of improving the access to the stage very considerably. In addition Scarlett built the whole instrument on a wooden base which served to contain a drawer for the accessories and extra lenses. Culpeper was in the habit of making this drawer a part of the pyramidal wooden case of the microscope.

Fig. 4.2. One of Scarlett's microscopes. Note that although there is a general similarity to Culpeper's model, the tripod legs supporting the body are now continuous with those for the stage. There is a disc, containing mounted objects, attached to the stage.

(*Crown copyright, The Science Museum*)

One innovation which assists the optical performance of the instrument is to be found in later microscopes, both of Culpeper himself and of other makers, and is known as a "cone diaphragm". This accessory is simply an inverted hollow cone which was fixed to the underside of the stage and served to exclude some of the more oblique rays of light and so improve to a slight extent the contrast in the image of a transparent object.

Instruments of the same basic pattern were made by the majority of the instrument makers of the period; particularly fine examples were produced by Matthew Loft who was active between 1720–1747. His microscopes are notable for their fine workmanship and for their decoration. The legs of his microscopes differ from those of Scarlett's in that they are all of one piece and they are made of a diamond cross-section and are slightly bowed outwards. It is typical of the period, when the beauties of design in furniture and the other arts were really appreciated, that the microscope should also receive its share of decoration and become an object of beauty as well as use. Certainly the bodies covered with the prepared ray-skin and the polished brass and mahogany of microscopes of the Culpeper pattern result in an extremely attractive instrument, although one which was not very practical to use. As the tubes were made of cardboard, the fit of one within another would be constantly changing, and to a large extent dependent upon the weather conditions; the only real solution to this problem was to construct the whole instrument of brass, which was eventually achieved by John Cuff.

Cuff, who was an inventor in his own right, as we shall shortly see, made several experimental versions of the Culpeper microscope. About 1744 he introduced a screw thread inside the brass ring which formed the base of the outer body tube and by then cutting a similar thread onto the brass nosepiece he was able to obtain some measure of fine focusing. Later he introduced an eyepiece of brass which he substituted for the turned wooden mounts then in use. Another instrument had a long brass snout fitted to the bottom of the instrument to carry the objective. On this snout was arranged an outer tube which carried a "concave silver speculum" or "Lieberkühn", as it soon became known. This speculum could be slid up and down on the snout and used for the illumination of opaque objects by light passing up through the stage and being reflected downwards onto the specimen which was placed at its focus. Later still Cuff abandoned the cardboard tubes entirely and substituted an all-brass body which allowed the use of rackwork focusing and represented an undoubted step forwards in the construction of the microscope.

With the exception of the Culpeper type microscopes made by the toy makers of Nuremberg for the next century or more, and with the exception of the lucernal microscope designed by Adams in the latter part of the century (see p. 160) no more microscopes were made with tubes of anything other than metal. Culpeper microscopes with brass bodies and rackwork focusing were produced for over a hundred years. Illustrations of this type appear regularly in almost every book on microscopes published in this time and Adams in fact refers to this form of instrument as the "Common Three-pillared Microscope". Peter Dollond was making this pattern of microscope in 1780 and it is likely that examples were in production until well into the nineteenth century.

Although there were many mechanical improvements in the design of the microscope in the early part of the eighteenth century, it is a pity that the basic principles of microscope design which involved the mounting of the body and the stage on an inclinable pillar, so ensuring their constant alignment, were abandoned for the inconvenient tripod form. This latter form persisted as a negative influence on instrument design for far too long, and the real break-through did not come until the emergence of Benjamin Martin and George Adams the Elder as the two great figures in microscope design and manufacture in the second half of the eighteenth century. Before we turn to consider their contributions to the evolution of the microscope, the instrument which John Cuff himself designed must be mentioned. It was probably due to the instigation of Henry Baker (1698–1774), a most interesting figure in the scientific life of the period. A memorandum book, preserved in the archives of the Royal Microscopical Society, gives us some picture of Baker as a man and of his work. Headed "Memoranda, principally relating to pecuniary affairs: Interspersed with Anecdotes of himself and family. Henry Baker 1720–1758", it tells us that Baker earned a very substantial living by teaching deaf and dumb children to speak and by curing speech impediments. All his pupils are listed and full accounts of his fees are provided for such matters as

> teaching Master Garbrand to speak plain.

It is evident that Baker's methods were often attended with success; with reference to a Mr. Bryan who was under treatment for stammering, Baker closes the account with the words

> excessive stammering, of which he was made easy!

Perhaps the most interesting portion of the book is the autobiographical details contained in a short note headed "Memorandum of my own Family". As this does not seem to have been published before, it is

worth quoting in full in view of the interesting information which i
gives us about one of the eighteenth-century microscopists.

> My father William Baker had a seat in the six clerks office and wa
> one of the clerks in Chancery, but attending not much to Business h
> sold his seat some years before his death. He was the son of W^m. Baker
> the son of John Baker of Shrewsbury in the county of Salop gentleman
> About the year 1694 he married Mary, daughter of Aaron Pengry wh
> was then Comptroller of the Petty Bag Office, and I was born 8th May
> 1698. From about 4 years old, I was brought up by my Father's Mothe
> and was put to school first at Richmond and afterwards at Hammersmitl
> both in the county of Mddx. Feb. 17 1713 I was placed as an apprentic
> with M. John Parker Bookseller in Pall Mall: an honest, good-natured
> man who treated me with the utmost kindness and made the seven years
> continued with him as agreeable a part of my life as any I have ever known
>
> 26 April 1720. I took leave of good Mr. Parker and went to Enfield
> on an invitation from Mr. Forster who was my relation by marriage. My
> visit here was intended only as an amusement for about a month, afte
> a confinement of seven years; but providence so ordered that I continued
> in this family till my marriage in 1729. For this gentleman having a
> daughter born deaf and consequently dumb, who was then about 8 year
> old, Heaven put into my thoughts a method of instructing her to write
> read, understand and speak the English language, which communicating
> to her Father, he intreated me to make a Trial and from that time would
> never part with me till I had perfected her in the Language and taught he
> not only to write, read and speak it readily, but likewise to understand th
> Speech of others by Sight and be able to hold a regular Conversation witl
> them upon any Subject.

In this fashion Baker began his life's work of speech therapy and
he proved most successful at it, building up a very sizeable fortune ir
the course of time. In 1729 he married Sophia, the youngest daughter o
the writer Daniel Defoe. Baker found time for literary and scientifi
pursuits in addition to his teaching, and he was so esteemed that in 174(
he was elected a Fellow of the Royal Society. From his account book
we learn the interesting fact that Baker became a friend and patron o
John Cuff the instrument maker, lending him money on more thar
one occasion. It was Cuff who made the simple "Aquatic" microscop
used by Baker in his famous investigations on the fresh water coel
enterates which were published in 1743 as *An Attempt towards*
Natural History of the Polype. Later the microscope which he used ir
this work provided the model for the aquatic microscope designe
by Ellis.

Baker also carried out experiments on the crystallization of salts under the microscope, for which work he was awarded the Copley medal of the Royal Society in 1744; at first he used a Culpeper type of microscope but he found that the legs were a great nuisance for this type of experiment. In his book *Employment of the Microscope* (1753) Baker tells us that

> The cumbersome and inconvenient Double Microscope of Dr. Hook and Mr. Marshall were many Years ago reduced to a manageable Size, improved in their Structure, supplied with an easy Way of enlightening Objects by a Speculum underneath, and in many other Respects rendered agreeable to the Curious, by Mr. Culpepper, and Mr. Scarlett. Some farther Alterations were however wanted to make this Instrument of more general Use, as I fully experienced in the Year 1743, when examining daily the Configurations of Saline Substances, the Legs were continual Impediments to my turning about the Slips of Glass; and indeed I had found them frequently so on other Occasions. Pulling the Body of the Instrument up and down was likewise subject to Jerks which caused a Difficulty in fixing it exactly at the Focus: there was also no good Contrivance for viewing opake Objects. Complaining of these Inconveniences, Mr. Cuff, the Optician, applyed his Thoughts to fashion a Microscope in another Manner, leaving the stage intirely free and open by taking away the Legs, applying a fine threaded Screw to regulate and adjust its Motions, and adding a concave Speculum for Objects that are opake.

Baker goes on to give a drawing and a description of the resulting instrument which he refers to as "Mr. Cuff's new-constructed Double Microscope". From a pamphlet by Cuff, dated 1744, we learn that although he had attempted to achieve his purpose by modification of the traditional Culpeper stand he was not able to claim success in this way. Cuff continues:

> But the legs I could not get rid of, nor was it possible in that form to make the whole fully answer the desires of the curious. In order, therefore, to remove all complaints the present microscope is contrived on a new construction whose motion is easy and regular and steady; whose application for opaque and all other objects will be found convenient; whose stage is quite free for any object to be applied on; and whose general figure cannot, it is hoped, be thought unhandsome; but this is all humbly submitted to the opinion of the best judges on whose favour I rely and whose obedient and most devoted servant I am, John Cuff, Fleet Street, 20th September, 1744.

There is no doubt that this new microscope of John Cuff represents a decided step forwards in the evolution of the microscope stand,

FIG. 4.3. A Cuff-type microscope in the Wellcome collection. This instrument is fitted with a Lieberkühn reflector mounted at the end of a tube, which slides upon the parallel nosepiece, and with a condensing lens providing incident illumination. The fine-focus screw is visible at the rear of the pillar of the instrument.

although of course optically it was no different from what had gone before. The general form of the instrument may be seen in Fig. 4.3 and some of the details are shown in Fig. 4.4. The whole is constructed around a strong rectangular-section brass pillar, about ten inches high, which is fixed to a stout rectangular box-foot. Immediately

Hole for mounting condensing lens

Slot for fish plate

A

Body tube

Focusing screw and milled head

B

Sliding pillar

Clamp screw

Fixed pillar

Box base

FIG. 4.4. A. The typical stage which was fitted to the Cuff-type of microscope.
B. Diagram to show the mechanical focusing arrangements of the Cuff microscope.

behind the fixed pillar is fitted a second, sliding pillar of similar size and section to the former; fixed to the top of the sliding pillar is the cross arm which carries the body of the microscope and in so doing surrounds the fixed pillar (see Fig. 4.4). Below the microscope arm a second sliding block is fitted over both of the upright pillars. This has a clamp screw which can be tightened onto the fixed pillar and is connected to the upper microscope arm by a long rod with a fine screw which passes in turn through the microscope arm, in which it is free to revolve, and is screwed into the lower block. In order to focus the instrument, the rear pillar with the microscope arm and body is slid to approximately the correct position. This is marked by numbers engraved on the fixed pillar corresponding to the numbers marked on each lens. The lower sliding block is then clamped firmly to the front pillar by the screw. Fine focusing can now be effected by turning the hand knob fitted to the top of the rear link-rod which, because of its screw thread fitting into the fixed lower block, will now elevate or depress the rear sliding pillar and with it the microscope arm and body by a small amount. This mechanism is shown in Fig. 4.4, from which it is possible to see the parts referred to in the above description. The focusing mechanism is very reminiscent of the Marshall microscope and is probably derived from it.

The body of the instrument is fitted into the arm so that its optical axis is parallel to that of the two pillars; it is secured by means of a cone joint which provides a positive location and at the same time allows easy dismantling of the body when necessary. The stage is firmly fixed to the non-movable brass pillar and has a strange shape, rather reminiscent of that of a Maltese cross. There is a large central hole, often adapted to carry a Bonanni-type spring stage or a live box to contain and restrict the movements of small live animals. At the opposite arm from the pillar was a small hole which enables the user to mount the condensing lens for epi-illumination of opaque objects or a pair of stage forceps; one of the side arms has a long keyhole-shaped slot for the attachment of the fish plate. The mirror was mounted onto the box foot, immediately beneath the optical axis of the microscope, just as in the Culpeper model. The objective lenses were mounted in small "buttons" which screwed onto the end of the long nosepiece. This latter is marked with a series of numbers which served to denote the correct position of the Lieberkühn or silver speculum used for the illumination of objects from above. This idea was first used by Cuff on one of his modifications of the Culpeper instrument (see p. 112), but here he used only a single speculum for all the lenses, sliding it up or down on the parallel nosepiece in order to suit it to the focus of the different lenses.

In some cases Cuff supplied the conical diaphragm which was inserted beneath the stage in order to improve the optical performance, but in at least one example which he made, the attachment intended to hold small fish and newts for examining the circulation of the blood was designed to fit in this position underneath the stage so that the cone diaphragm could not be used. Cuff got round this difficulty by inventing a set of flat diaphragms with a central hole of various different diameters which could be placed on the mirror and served to restrict the angle of the illuminating beam of light.

The lenses of one of Cuff's microscopes were measured by van Cittert, who found that magnifications of about 45 × and 100 × could be obtained, in each case with a resolution of somewhere around 10 microns. Van Cittert comments that the lenses gave a very chromatic image. Many examples of Cuff instruments are extant, complete with lenses, and it is to be hoped that some attempt will be made in the near future to measure the resolution and magnifications of more of his microscopes. Much attention has been given to the mechanical construction of these early microscopes but their most important part — the optics — has been unjustly neglected.

Cuff's microscope was a sound design and it achieved a great success. Most of the instrument makers of that time paid it the compliment of using it as a model for their own copies, and it was produced in essentially the same form up to about 1800. The Cuff microscope had a neat appearance, it had a reasonable degree of rigidity and the focusing mechanism and access to the stage was good. It may well be that the immediate and sweeping success of the Cuff microscope was responsible for the rapid change in the design of the microscopes offered for sale by some of his contemporaries, especially George Adams the Elder, leading to the rapid replacement of their own models by instruments which owed a great deal to Cuff's microscope.

A very close copy was produced by Mann and Ayscough, instrument makers who were in partnership until about 1749. Their microscope differed in that it was mounted on the top of a box into which it could be packed by sliding the pillars out of a dovetail mounting screwed onto the lid. The focusing was of the moving-stage type with a fixed body tube; the mirror too had been transferred from the base to the pillar and arranged to plug in at one of two places. Later, the mirror was mounted on a sliding sleeve so that it could be placed in any position below the stage.

A further point of minor difference was that Mann and Ayscough omitted the front projection of Cuff's stage, so that their instrument

FIG. 4.5. A Nairne "chest" microscope. The pillar is hinged so that it will fold into the box to allow the instrument to be packed away easily for transportation.

only had the lateral points, one arm of which accepted the bull's eye and the stage forceps whilst the other had the standard keyhole slot for the fish plate.

One of the trends initiated about this period and which continued through well into the nineteenth century was the portable microscope.

which could be packed away and carried around very easily. Many special models were designed for this purpose but most of the current instruments were adapted as portables by some maker or other. Nairne achieved this with his version of the Cuff microscope by mounting the pillars on a hinge fixed to one end of the box so that they could swing down, taking the microscope stage and body with them into the box (see Fig. 4.5). This particular development of the Cuff model is often referred to as a "chest" microscope, and it not only has the virtue of making the microscope easily portable, but also allows more convenience in use by permitting the angle of the limb to be altered so as to bring the body and eyepiece to a convenient height for the observer.

As microscopes began to increase in size during the eighteenth century, some means of inclining the tube became an essential feature of the design. All the leading instrument makers produced their version of the Cuff microscope each with their own variations and to attempt to list them all would be of interest only to the specialist. Perhaps it is worth just mentioning that Benjamin Martin produced a copy of this microscope which was almost identical with Cuff's own, but George Adams the Elder was rather more original as he supplied this form of microscope with a sliding device for changing the objectives and with interchangeable eyepieces. This feature was retained in most microscopes subsequent to this and has persisted to the present time. Adams also added a substage condenser to his version of the Cuff microscope, together with Mann and Ayscough's two-arm stage, stage focusing and a double-sided mirror, plane on one side and concave on the other.

In the fourth edition of the *Micrographia Illustrata* published in 1771, Adams includes a catalogue at the back. Here the "double constructed microscope", i.e. one of the Cuff type, is listed at £6. 6s. 0d., or £8. 8s. 0d. if supplied with a triangular foot. At the same time Adams was still supplying Culpeper microscopes at 3 guineas each, together with Wilson screw-barrel and Ellis's aquatic microscope both costing 2 guineas.

The development of the microscope throughout the remainder of the eighteenth century revolves very largely around the inventions of Benjamin Martin and the two Adams, father and son. George Adams senior was an optician and instrument maker by trade; his early life remains shrouded in obscurity but we know from one of his advertisements that he was established in business as a mathematical instrument maker at the sign of "Tycho Brahe's Head" in Fleet Street by 1735. He continued constructing instruments until his death in 1773 when the business passed to his elder son, also called George, who continued it in his turn. George Adams the Younger died in 1795, upon which his brother Dudley assumed the direction of the firm.

George Adams the Elder was very skilled, both as a designer of microscopes and as a craftsman; it is obvious that his instruments were designed with the user in mind, to fill a definite demand felt by his customers. He was also a prolific writer on microscopy, his first book entitled *Micrographia Illustrata* was published in 1747 and proved so popular that it reappeared in several editions throughout the next thirty years or so.

Benjamin Martin was almost exactly contemporary with George Adams the Elder, but started off in a very different manner. He was certainly well educated and probably had a formal mathematical and scientific training. Early in his life he was a schoolmaster and wrote extensively on mathematical, philosophical and astronomical subjects. In a book of his devoted to trigonometry he dates the preface "From my school in Chichester, April 8th 1734". Later in the same work he advertises himself as "Teacher in writing in all the common and useful hands, arithmetic, etc., etc., down to the use and construction of the most useful mathematical instruments". This suggests that he started making instruments and microscopes as a hobby, but by 1736 he had begun to offer them for sale to the public. It is obvious that he had already achieved some considerable reputation for instrument making at this time, for in his *Description of the Globes* he comments in an advertisement:

> N.B. Whereas the Jews, pedlars, etc. in all parts of England sell visual glasses with the initials of my name (B.M.) upon them, and pretend on that account that they are of my make and were bought of me, I thought it necessary to undeceive the public by assuring them that I never sold any to those who hawk goods about the country, they dealing in a sort of glass too bad for any but themselves to recommend, or for anyone to buy who knows anything of optical glass, or has more regard to the safety of his eyes and the preservation of his sight than the saving of his money.

From the catalogue and price list appended, we find that at this time Martin was selling a "large parlour compound microscope" for £3. 12s. 6d. and the same in brass for £5. 5s. 0d. A Wilson microscope and apparatus cost £2. 12s. 6d. as did "Dr. Lieberkühn's opake microscope". Martin also advertised his pocket compound microscope at 2 guineas and a "Universal compound microscope" for 5 guineas, thus suggesting that these instruments were in production some years earlier than has previously been supposed. There is another advertisement in *The New and Compendious System of Optics* of 1740 for the "New Pocket Reflecting Microscopes, with Micrometers, made and sold by Benjamin Martin in Chichester."

At this point it should be mentioned that the word "reflecting" as applied to a microscope of this period only signified that a mirror was used to reflect light upon the object placed upon the stage of the instrument, and not as in the early nineteenth century and at the present time, to indicate that the image itself was formed by reflection.

Martin was well launched upon his second career as an instrument maker while he was still a schoolmaster, selling his instruments either direct by post or through his agents in London. His first pamphlet on the microscope appeared (if we accept the evidence of the date upon the plate which illustrates it) in 1738; in it Martin describes in detail the "Universal" microscope and the "Pocket Reflecting Microscope" although these may have been available for some time previous to his publication. Martin is here using the word "universal" in a different sense from that adopted by Adams in the *Micrographia Illustrata*. To Martin it merely signified that the instrument was mounted upon a ball and socket joint in order to allow easy adjustment of the instrument; to Adams "universal" meant an instrument which could be adapted for all types of observation on all possible objects.

In this pamphlet, Martin sets out his approach to the construction of microscopes:

> The microscope is doubtless a noble invention, and great improvements have been made therein at sundry times: But as almost all human contrivances, or works of art arrive to their perfection by very slow advances, so I conceive the Microscope according to its present forms or methods of using it, is capable of much farther improvement.

Benjamin Martin proved to be a very fine craftsman and a skilled user of the microscopes which he made; he was, moreover, an original thinker. All these attributes contributed to establishing him as one of the notable figures in the development of the microscope during the eighteenth century.

The pocket microscope of 1738 was almost certainly made, as its predecessors had been, of cardboard tubes and wooden mounts. No example of this instrument is known but from the description we gather that the instrument would have been about six inches long when the draw tube was closed, with a diameter of about one and a half inches. The general form of the instrument is shown in Fig. 4.6, which is redrawn from Martin's pamphlet. The concave mirror which reflected light onto the specimen could be opened out for use and one further feature of interest is that the eyepiece was provided with a slider to act as a dust excluder, just as in the majority of telescope eyepieces of

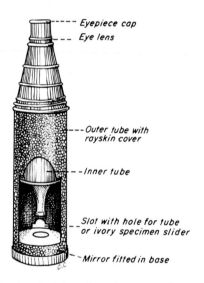

Fig. 4.6. Benjamin Martin's pocket microscope of 1738. This instrument was the forerunner of the famous drum microscopes.

the time. This particular type of instrument may be regarded as the ancestor of the "drum microscope" which proved so popular and which was made by Martin for many years. This type of instrument was widely imitated, both in England and on the Continent, and Martin must be given the credit for this highly successful design, although there is some evidence that he was preceded by a German, Nicolai Bion, around the year 1717.

Martin provided two objectives with the pocket microscope, one of focal length which he stated as $\frac{3.7}{100}$ inch and the other $\frac{6.6}{100}$ inch. The eyepiece lacked a field lens, consisting solely of a single biconvex lens. The microscope was obtainable either with or without Martin's new screw micrometer. This latter was simply a pointed wire which projected from one side into the plane of the primary image. The wire had a screw thread with a pitch of fifty turns to the inch and was attached on the outside of the microscope to a pointer which moved around a circular dial divided into ten parts, each of which was further subdivided into two. By screwing the pointer round, the image of the point of the needle could be made to span the diameter of an object in the field of view and by noting the number of whole turns and parts of a turn as indicated on the dial, and as the optical power was known, the dimensions of the object could be found quite easily. Martin obviously believed that the great merit of this microscope was its portability, and he describes in some detail how it may be adapted to screw into the hollow handle of a walking stick or rigid whip. The price of this new instrument was stated to be 12s. 6d. in its simple form or 1 guinea if the micrometer was fitted.

The "Universal" microscope (Fig. 4.7) was also intended to be used in the field:

> The unusual construction of the Microscope and its Frame is such as confines it to the view of one sort of objects only, and to only one position of them, which is that below the microscope. But as there is frequent occasion for one, who would observe nature in all her operations and effects, to view every part of her workmanship great and small, and in every position or situation whatsoever without constraint or encumberance, so it is necessary to have a new way of mounting this machine that shall permit its use to be with perfect freedom and liberty; and such I shall propose the mounting of it on a BALL and SOCKET . . . .

The pillar of this microscope was provided with what appears from the plate to be a rather coarse pitch screw thread. On this was threaded a nut bearing an arm which carried the stage. The top of the pillar was provided with the ball and socket joint bearing the body of the microscope, again on a short arm. In the normal position this brought the body tube of the instrument over the stage, as the arm was dropped into a slot cut in the housing of the socket, so that the optical axis of the microscope came to lie parallel to the axis of the pillar, and the stage could be screwed up underneath to bring the object into focus. In addition to acting as the focusing mechanism, the rotation of the stage on the pillar screw thread would also allow examination of the various parts of the specimen which lay on that arc of movement of the stage. In order to reflect light up through the object a plane mirror was fixed onto the pillar beneath the stage. By manipulation of the ball and socket joint the optical axis of the instrument could be altered at will and the objectives brought to bear upon any convenient surface, so fulfilling Martin's definition of a universal microscope.

This instrument was fitted with an improved version of his micrometer with a movable index in addition to the actual measuring screw. There was a field lens in the eyepiece of this instrument and the micrometer was fixed between this lens and the eye lens. Later, Martin

Fig. 4.7. Martin's first and second "Universal" microscopes of 1738 and 1742 respectively. The first "Universal" model is on the left. The coarse thread which served to move the stage in order to effect focusing, and the ball and socket joint attaching the arm to the pillar may be seen. In the second "Universal" model the stage is now slid up and down the pillar and fixed by the action of a clamp screw. The whole is attached to a box foot.

introduced a "Glass micrometer" in the form of a transparent graticule or disc of glass with lines scribed parallel upon it at a distance of 1/40th of an inch; this was placed in the focal plane of the eyepiece so that it appeared in sharp focus at the same time as the object and in fact appeared superimposed upon the latter. Although Martin gave very precise directions for using his microscopes, it seems that many people were still uncertain how to proceed and so only succeeded in obtaining indifferent results which they blamed not upon their lack of skill, but upon the faults of the microscope. In an appendix to his pamphlet Martin comments rather sourly:

> I could never have thought that the nature and use of the microscope (so exceeding curious and useful an instrument) had been so little understood at this time of day, in a land of so much Knowledge as England, that any difficulties could arise concerning the use of the Pocket Microscope, whose nature, construction and use are and must be allowed the most obvious, simple and easy of all others yet invented.

He then proceeds to explain the method of use yet again and stresses the importance of paying attention to the suitability of the illumination, adding:

> A very cloudy, dark air, or gloomy room, will always defeat your purpose, and make you have an ill opinion of the instrument without cause.

Four years later, in 1742, Benjamin Martin published his *Micrographia Nova* which contained an account of the second version of his Universal microscope (Fig. 4.7). The large fold-out plate, which illustrates this, shows the instrument to resemble its predecessor very closely, but the pillar now lacks the screw thread and the stage takes the form of a sector of a circle with an opening also in the form of an arc. The ball and socket joint was still in evidence at the top of the pillar which was now mounted on an octagonal wooden box foot. The only apparent method of focusing appears to have been by sliding the stage up and down the pillar and fixing it by clamping a sliding sleeve, which was below it, on the pillar and then allowing the stage to rest on this by its own weight. In the *Micrographia Nova* Martin repeats his description of the pocket reflecting microscope and then sets about his main task as detailed in the Preface:

> I have often times been requested by Gentlemen to give a Catalogue of Microscopic Objects, which I have here done, and I presume so compleat, that scarce any extraordinary Phaenomenon, which requires the Use of the Instrument, and with the Reach of a Person in Private life, will be found wanting in it.

This is typical of the microscopical writing of the time; such books served to introduce to readers (who used the microscope purely as a diversion) objects which would entertain and amuse them. Henry Baker's *The Microscope Made Easy* which appeared in the same year also fulfils the same function.

Shortly after these early instruments of Benjamin Martin had appeared, George Adams announced in his *Micrographia Illustrata* of 1746 the "New Universal Single Microscope" and the "New Universal Double Microscope". George Adams considered the microscopist's needs to be rather different from those envisaged by Martin. Adams says:

> It hath long been the Desire of the Curious and Inquisitive part of Mankind, to have a Microscope which would be Portable and Universal, that is to say, ONE ONLY instrument, by which all sorts of minute Objects might be observed.

The two microscopes described in the book were designed to fill all the possible roles of a microscope; they could be used as a simple microscope, as a compound instrument or even be adapted to serve as a solar microscope in which the image is projected onto a screen (see Chapter 5).

The "Universal Single" microscope is illustrated in Fig. 4.8; it was made, as Adams tells us, "either of Brass or Silver, and is composed of six double Convex Lens's of different Foci". These lenses were mounted on arms which projected from a disc. This disc was capable of rotation around the axis of the pillar on which it was mounted, so that each lens in turn could be brought under the eye shield (labelled N in the illustration, which is taken from Adams's book). One of the lenses carried a Lieberkühn or as it was then termed "a reflecting Speculum of Silver or other Metal, highly polished, which when an Opake Object is to be viewed must be placed under the eyepiece N."

Focusing of the object is effected by moving the stage up or down the pillar by means of the action of a threaded rod which passes up inside the pillar and is actuated by turning the nut P at the base, at the centre of the tripod foot. The numbers engraved on the pillar serve to indicate the approximate position of the stage to focus the object with each of the appropriate lenses. When the mark on the sliding piece (indicated by the finger of the engraved hand) was brought to the number corresponding to the lens in use, then the focus would be nearly right and would only require minor adjustments. Adams was pleased with the convenience of the focusing screw:

> I must here observe that the Screw P is to be turned as your Hands and Arms are resting upon the Table, which is a Convenience to be met in no other Microscope. All others require the Observer to raise his Body and Arms in adjusting the Object to fit his sight; which is not only very

THE
NEW UNIVERSAL
SINGLE MICROSCOPE,
Invented, Made and Sold by
GEORGE ADAMS
at Tycho Brahe's Head in Fleet Street,
LONDON.

Fɪɢ. 4.8. George Adams's "New Universal Single" microscope of 1747. The fine focus control is at the base of the pillar and the wheel of lenses can be clearly seen.

FIG. 4.9. Adams's "New Universal double microscope". Note the similarity of this in construction to the microscope illustrated in Fig. 4.8. The circular fitment above the specimen stage is an adjustable Lieberkühn mirror.

troublesome but tiresome too; especially if it requires considerable Attention. Whereas in this new Universal Microscope a leaning Posture is sufficient, and consequently the easiest of all others for Microscopical Observation.

This device is also found in the "Universal Double" microscope (Fig. 4.9) and although it did not become standard practice in the eighteenth or nineteenth centuries, it has reappeared as a feature of most research microscopes which are manufactured today, so that the arms may rest upon the table during operation of the instrument.

The Single microscope suffers from the drawback that owing to the diameter of the disc-shaped lens carrier (which is about four inches) it is rather difficult to place one's eye close to the eye shield without an awkward bending of the neck. Another fault in the design is its lightness; such flimsy construction makes it impossible to operate the focusing screw unless the microscope stand is firmly held down onto the table with one hand.

The "Universal Double Microscope" is of very similar construction. That shown in the *Micrographia Illustrata* carries the compound body in a ring attached to a short arm which slides up and down the pillar with the ring of lenses. The coarse focus was obtained by sliding this complex up and down, the rough position being indicated by numbers as in the single microscope. On clamping the socket the fine focusing mechanism was provided by an internal screw which acted upon the stage, in exactly the same manner as in the other instrument. This model of the Double Microscope must have been abandoned very quickly, for the examples which exist in our collections today represent a slightly modified version (Fig. 4.10) in which the compound body screws into the socket in place of the eye shield and the separate supporting arm is no longer provided. The Lieberkühn is now mounted on an independent slider working on the back face of the block which supports the stage. This allows focusing of the Lieberkühn quite independently of the lens.

Both of these instruments reintroduced the sector folding foot, which Culpeper had used for his table stand for the Wilson microscope, but in these new microscopes of Adams the sector foot forms an integral part of the whole assembly and not just an optional extra. The main drawback of these microscopes must undoubtedly have been their lack of solidity. This same fault is also apparent in microscopes of a very similar pattern made at about the same time by the optician and enthusiastic microscopist François Watkins. The instruments of this particular maker do, however, have some advantage in

FIG. 4.10. The "Prince of Wales" microscope made by George Adams. The compound body is fitted above the typical "wheel of lenses". The stage fitted to the instrument was intended for holding a frog for the examination of the circulation of the blood. The micrometer stage is illustrated at the left of the microscope.

(*Crown copyright, The Science Museum.*)

that the diameter of the disc carrying the lenses was much reduced in order to facilitate the mounting of the body upon the limb. More important, the limb itself was constructed with a hinge joint so that the whole limb, bearing the mirror, stage and body could be inclined with respect to the pillar and the foot. Although Watkins' stands were well made, often of silver, and tastefully engraved, they suffered from the same grave functional disadvantage of the early stands of George Adams, in that they were very light and therefore necessarily lacking in stability. The introduction of Cuff's microscope in 1744 almost certainly resulted in the failure of this small, light type of microscope.

Probably one of the best ways of increasing the rigidity of the microscope stand, whilst still retaining the flexibility and ease of operation conferred by the ability to incline the limb, is by supporting the whole limb at its centre of gravity between trunnions. This type of construction was in fact adopted by both Adams and on the continent by a famous French instrument maker named Magny. It does not seem possible to say which of the two makers had the priority, or whether they both independently came to the same decision, but in 1754 Magny was constructing stands of this pattern. He arranged for the whole limb to swing between trunnions, not with a fore and aft inclination as one might expect but laterally. Adams, on the other hand, when he adopted this type of construction for the microscope which he made for King George III whilst he was still Prince of Wales, used the more conventional idea of having the pivots on either side of the stand so that the inclination resulted in the body being brought nearer to the observer who is normally sitting behind the microscope.

Adams's "Prince of Wales" microscope is now in the Science Museum at South Kensington and it may be dated between the years 1751 and 1760, when the Prince of Wales ascended the throne. The stand, which is shown in Fig. 4.10, has a Cuff-type focusing mechanism with a wheel of objectives which vary from $\frac{1}{20}$ inch to $\frac{3}{4}$ inch focus, much as in the second version of the "New Universal Double Microscope". There are three stages, any one of which may be mounted onto the stand; the one shown attached in the photograph is formed of a lattice work of wires and is intended for holding a frog or similar animal by tying it down whilst the circulation of the blood is studied. The second stage is a single ring stage, but the third (which may be seen close to the box foot in the figure) is a beautifully made mechanical stage with micrometers registering the movements in the two directions at right angles to each other. In addition to the micrometer screws two other slides are provided for rapid movements; it is notable that all four movements are provided with dovetail slides in order to promote easy action.

This particular microscope may well be regarded as the peak of George Adams's achievements, certainly as far as a practical instrument is concerned, although for sheer craftsmanship and beauty the later microscope in silver (shown in Fig. 4.12) ranks very highly. As will be seen this latter instrument cannot be regarded as a useful scientific instrument, intended for serious observational work.

In the meantime Benjamin Martin was continuing his highly successful activities as an instrument maker. He had moved from Chichester and set up in business as an instrument maker in Fleet Street, London, where he traded from the sign of the "Globe and Visual Glasses". This move to London probably occurred around the year 1750; soon Martin was doing very good business and continuing with his extensive literary activities. He produced a new version of his "Universal" microscope of 1742, but unfortunately the plate illustrating this instrument was omitted from the second edition of the *Philosophia Britannica* published in 1752, so that we have no certain knowledge of the form of this third "Universal" instrument. Around this period Martin produced many so-called "optical cabinets" which consisted of a drum microscope (developed from his earlier pocket reflecting microscope), a solar microscope and sometimes a telescope, all fitted into a single case. There was obviously a demand for this outfit and Martin, together with other makers, continued to supply ever more and more elaborate versions at least until the 1770's.

In 1759, however, Martin introduced yet another "Universal" microscope. This particular model may be regarded as one of the milestones in the development of the microscope as it was with this instrument that Martin introduced what was to become known as the "between lens". This represented the first advance in optical design since the field lens had been added to the eyepiece in Hooke's day. The between lens was not Martin's invention, for as he himself pointed out, he found it included in a microscope built at least thirty years before he introduced it into his own instruments. The lens is situated at the lower end of the body, just above the long narrow snout which in those days carried the objective. The extra lens acted to some extent as a compound lens, working with the objective so as to correct some of the spherical aberration of the latter. This allowed the use of larger apertures than had hitherto been possible. As this development was so important, it is worth quoting Martin's own account taken from his *New Elements of Optics*, 1759. In this passage the "between lens" is referred to as "GH" in consequence of the lettering on the plate to be found in the original.

> and therefore a third lens GH added to the former two, will contribute to make the Image more distinct, and consequently the Instrument more compleat.
>
> At the same time the Field of View is amplified, and the Use of the Microscope render'd more agreeably by the Addition of the Glass GH, and that very sensibly above what is to be found in the common Construction of a Three-Glass Microscope.
>
> Since the Distinctness of Vision is thus promoted by the Glass GH, we may allow a somewhat larger Aperture to the Objects Lens KI; and thereby encreate the Brightness of Objects, and greatly heighten the Pleasure of viewing them.
>
> And tho' each of these Particulars is easily confirm'd by Experiments, as well as demonstrable from Theory, yet are all the Optic Writers totally silent with respect to a Four-Glass Microscope. And as there is no mention of such a Thing, there is no Iconism of it of Course; and therefore this which I have here given, will prove at least a Novelty to the Reader in Print.
>
> For I do not pretend to say no Microscope with four Glasses has been made, I know they have, and it is more than 30 Years since I bought one of the same Construction nearly with what I have here given; and it excell'd by much any Three-Glass Microscope I ever saw; but could not learn who the Maker was, it being an old Instrument when I first had it. It had its Origin therefore from Experience, and not from Theory, as in all Probability it was made before Augenius's Dioptrics was publish'd, which is the first Book that contains the Theory of the Aberration from the Figure of Glasses that I have heard of.
>
> As to the best Manner in which these four Glasses are to be placed in the Microscope, there can be no Difficulty to those who understand the Theory; and those who do not, it does not at all concern.

It has been suggested by Clay and Court that the old microscope referred to in the above passage could well have been constructed by Yarwell, since his "Double Microscope" which resembles a small version of Marshall's instrument contained an extra lens at the bottom of the body.

From 1759 onwards, all Martin's instruments were furnished with the "between lens", and were further characterized by the long parallel metal tube fitted to the lower end of the microscope body. This long

E.M.—K

tube carried the extra lens at its upper end and the objectives were screwed into the lower end. This feature can be seen clearly in Fig. 4.11 (which represents a later development — the "New Universal" model of 1770); it soon became known as "Martin's pipe" and served to carry

FIG. 4.11. Martin's "New Universal" microscope of 1770. Note the coarse focus rackwork cut into the pillar of the microscope and "Martin's Pipe".

the Lieberkühn. It is also interesting in that the screw thread which he used to attach it to the body, and to fit the objective to it, was later to become the model from which the Royal Microscopical Society's standard thread was derived. The "Universal" microscope of 1759 signified an extension of Martin's use of the term "universal", as now for the first time he used it in the accepted sense of an instrument which was capable of use as a single or a compound microscope and which possessed the "aquatic" movement. For the remainder of the century any universal microscope had to fulfil all these requirements and Martin's previous application of the term dropped out of use.

Shortly after Martin's Universal model of 1759 had appeared, George Adams, now instrument maker to King George III, produced his celebrated large silver microscope which he intended for presentation to the King. This instrument (shown in Fig. 4.12) is now preserved in the Museum of the History of Science in Oxford. Adams mentions this microscope in the *Micrographia Illustrata* and tells us that:

> It was made for His Majesty in the year 1761, and with it was presented ι manuscript of its use.

This microscope was obviously intended by Adams to represent the height of achievement of the microscope makers of the time, and although the resulting instrument may be considered as aesthetically very satisfactory, it does not compare favourably with the earlier microscope which he gave the King when the latter was Prince of Wales. It is quite apparent that in the silver microscope use has been sacrificed to ornament. The stand is constructed of brass and steel cased in beaten silver; there is a large central pillar fluted in the Corinthian style arising from a base which is decorated with cherubs. The microscope actually contains two instruments on the one stand, a simple microscope with its own stage and mirror on one side and on the other a completely separate stage and mirror and the compound body. This latter, as can be seen from Fig. 4.12, is beautifully ornamented and is supported by two female figures. There are eight lenses mounted in a disc, as in the earlier "Universal" microscopes by this maker. The disc can be revolved to change the power in use and so the objectives (which are common to both microscopes) can be brought under either the eye shield of the simple microscope or under the compound body in turn. Provision is made for a substage condenser and also for the mounting of a separate lens to act as a superstage illuminator. All the usual accessories including stage forceps and frog plate are provided.

A careful examination of the actual instrument shows that no really serious observations could be attempted with it on account of the general inconvenience of the construction. If the simple microscope is in use, then the body of the compound microscope is so near that it gets in the way of the observer's head, whilst if the compound body is in use

FIG. 4.12. The silver microscope made for George III by Adams. The extremely ornate construction is very obvious, especially at the base and in the compound body which is supported by two sculpted figures.

(Photo: Studio Edmark.)

then one has to bend right over the simple microscope. Alternatively, it is possible to move around to the other side of the instrument to avoid this trouble, but then the illumination must be arranged to come from the side. Again there is no provision for the inclination of the instrument so that if it were placed on a table of normal height then the eyepieces are too high for comfortable observation.

At this time, however, microscopes were tending to increase in size and in some of Martin's later models the microscopes were designed to be used on top of their cases which thus served as microscope tables. It is possible that the silver microscope may have been intended for use in this manner, or more likely, it may just have been intended to display objects for the diversion of the King and his guests and used while people were standing around.

This large and imposing microscope does illustrate the importance of the patronage which King George III gave to the rapidly developing sciences. His collection of scientific instruments originally started by Dr. Demainbray, who became tutor to the Royal Family about 1744, was added to for many years, and was one of the most extensive of its time. Much of the Royal collection may still be seen in the Science Museum in London, and many of the items, especially this particular silver microscope, illustrate very well the fact that in the latter part of the eighteenth century any piece of "philosophical apparatus" had to be aesthetically pleasing as well as functional. The degree of ornamentation and the high finish on microscopes of this period forms a very striking contrast to the much more severe and functional microscopes of the following century, although the quality of the mechanical parts of the stands produced by the best British makers of the nineteenth century has never been surpassed even today.

Both Martin and Adams continued to produce new models, continuing experimenting with the mechanical parts, for in all essential optical features there was little to choose between any of these instruments of the latter half of the eighteenth century. Martin's next design, usually known as the "New Universal" model, was illustrated in the second edition of the "Encyclopaedia Britannica", which was published about 1770. The microscope must, therefore, be ascribed to the later 1760's.

The microscope follows the usual pattern of being workable as either a simple or a compound instrument, but there is not a full aquatic movement. This is overcome, however, by making the stage hinged close to its attachment to the pillar so that it may be swung in an arc in order to bring the various parts of the specimen into the field of view. It can be seen from the illustration of this microscope (Fig. 4.11) that the body is fixed and the focusing is by a rack and pinion motion working on the stage. The rackwork is inside a slot cut into the vertical pillar, in which the block carrying both the stage and the pinion slides. Fine focusing is provided by a variant of the method used on the Cuff instruments. One feature of interest in the stage mechanism was the provision of a superstage arrangement consisting of three cells which may be swung into the optic axis of the instrument and which serve to carry the object. One of the cells was furnished with a plain glass disc, the second with a reversible black and white disc, whilst the third had a concave glass well to contain fluids.

As the size of this microscope would have made comfortable working difficult whilst seated at a table, Martin provided a compass joint at the top of the limb carrying the body; this allowed the body to be inclined from the vertical. When the body was inclined to the horizontal position provision was made for the attachment of an accessory stage as the main stage remained in the normal position and would not be usable. Martin was obviously a great experimenter and was constantly trying out new ideas on his microscopes, so it is very seldom that any two of his instruments are exactly alike. Numerous variations in points of detail can be seen, many of them probably copied from the productions of his contemporaries. It has already been stressed that all these variations only affected the stand, the lenses (with the exception of Martin's introduction of the "between lens") remaining as imperfect as ever.

In 1770, John Hill published a book entitled *The Construction of Timber, from its early growth; explained by the microscope and proved from experiments in a great variety of kinds*. In the introduction to this book he tells us that

> it were vain to lead men into an attempt of the following experiments, without first acquainting them with the machine by which the pieces were cut; and the Microscope thro' which they have been viewed.

The microscope to which he refers was in fact designed by John Hill's patron (Sir John Stuart, the Earl of Bute, who acted as a patron of scientists and amassed a large collection of scientific instruments of his own), and it was built by George Adams; it served to enable Hill to produce remarkably fine drawings of the comparative morphology of various types of wood. This piece of research conceived and executed with the aid of the microscope is one of the few studies carried out in the eighteenth century in which the compound microscope played any serious role.

Hill's book contains a full description of this microscope together with a plate, both of which were reprinted in the fourth edition of Adams's *Micrographia Illustrata* which appeared in the following year. In this latter book, the description is very similar to that in Hill's book, with only odd words here and there changed, whilst the plate is identical. A further engraving, however, appears as the frontispiece of the *Micrographia*, in which the microscope is shown inclined, together with its oil lamp, and with a micrometer in the eyepiece, whereas the plate used in the body of the text shows no lamp, no micrometer, and the body in the upright position; all the usual accessories are included in this latter plate.

This latest model, described as the "New Variable Microscope", is introduced in the following words:

> By this microscope we are enabled to examine the structure, and discover the various and surprising contrivances, in the exact and uniform proportion of the minute parts of the creation; either in animals, insects, fossils, or vegetables, etc.
>
> We owe the construction of the variable microscope to the ingenuity and generosity of a noble person. The apparatus belonging to it is more convenient, more certain, and more extensive than that of any other at present extant; consequently the advantage and pleasure attending the observations in viewing objects through it, must be as extensive in proportion.

This microscope, shown in Fig. 4.13, has a very striking appearance. The most obvious feature is that the limb of the microscope is pivoted near its upper end, and not low down as in earlier models. The angle of inclination is controlled by means of a pinion working on the very large, rather coarse-toothed gear wheel to which the microscope limb was attached. This feature may well have been adapted from the inclination mechanism sometimes used in telescopes. Adams did introduce one new feature into the optics of this instrument. This was the "compounding" of the objective lenses to increase their power. Each lens was mounted in a brass cell or "button", as he termed it, which were so constructed that any two could screw together to form a unit. This device was intended to increase the magnification, but with the uncorrected lenses of this period the spherical aberration of such randomly combined lenses must have been very great. The body tube

FIG. 4.13. The Variable microscope constructed by George Adams, 1770. The limb carrying the microscope body was attached to a large sector wheel which is clearly seen in the illustration.

of the "Variable" microscope was removable and by means of an adaptor single lenses could be fitted to enable it to be operated as a simple microscope. From the illustration it is apparent that the body tube and the fine adjustment owe a debt to Cuff's microscope.

In the same edition of the *Micrographia Illustrata*, Adams introduces a small version of the Variable microscope. This lacked the distinctive large pinion for inclining the limb, reverting instead to the compass joint method. This may well have been a concession to the special function intended for this microscope. Adams wrote:

> This instrument being an abridgement of the variable microscope, is contrived for the pocket, that it may be ready when gentlemen and ladies are amusing themselves in their gardens, parks, etc., to inspect, and collect such objects as may be proper to preserve for a future examination, to be viewed in the variable microscope . . . either in the sunshine or in the long winter evenings.

Although the "Variable" microscope clearly pointed the way by which much greater control of the various movements could be achieved by more use of the rack and pinion, it did not prove a success. George Adams the Younger, when he assumed control of the business on his father's death in 1773, soon abandoned this instrument in favour of another developed along the lines set out by Benjamin Martin. It seems strange that Adams never developed the very stable trunnion type of mounting that he had used in his "Prince of Wales" model. This may well have been due to his dependence upon a wealthy patron and the necessity to conform to some extent to the latter's ideas of microscope engineering!

The "Variable" microscope proved to be the last production of George Adams the Elder, but Martin continued by producing yet another "Universal" microscope, the sixth in line of descent from his first production of 1736. This "Universal" microscope, described in a pamphlet of 1776, is illustrated in Fig. 4.14 which represents an example preserved in the collections of the Royal Microscopical Society. The most striking difference from its predecessors is that the whole limb is now made inclinable from the base, where a stout compass joint was fixed, and that the pillar of the instrument is now constructed of a tubular form. Two further tubes were arranged to slide inside the outer one, the larger of them being extended by rackwork, whilst the innermost one was simply extended by sliding. When it was in the correct position it was clamped by means of a locking collar at the top of the lower tube. This elaborate device allowed a very extensive focusing range and was designed to permit the employment of very low power lenses with long working distances upon the stand. The body tube of the microscope was carried on an arm which moved through the

Fig. 4.14. Benjamin Martin's "New Universal" model of 1776. Note the tubular pillar with the compass joint at its foot; the sleeve was intended to hold a substage condenser. The lenses were carried in a small wheel which was mounted at the bottom of the microscope body.

slot in the cap, which together with a rotation about the optical axis which was possible at this joint, allowed the full aquatic movement. The stage was provided with the superstage fitting, which has been described previously, and in addition there was a Bonanni spring fitting for holding prepared sliders in the usual way. The Lieberkühn wa no longer mounted upon the nosepiece but was carried separately on a ring which plugged into a hole in the stage. This idea probably was taken by Martin from the Adams microscope of 1746.

The reversion to this device was certainly due to the fact that Martin had now abandoned his long "pipe", probably in response to the need for a more rapid method of changing the power of the objective. Martin accomplished this by using an idea which we have seen was found in the microscopes of François Watkins in the early part of the century. The objectives were mounted all together in a small wheel, located just below the body, in such a way that any one of them could be brought into the optic axis in turn by simply turning the wheel. When the lens was in position, the wheel was located by a small spring catch, very much as the nosepiece of a modern microscope.

This microscope of 1776 proved to be the inspiration for Martin's largest and most ambitious instrument which appeared around 1780; today it is usually referred to as the "Grand Universal" model and is shown in Fig. 4.15. One of these instruments, formerly in the possession of a famous microscopist of the nineteenth century, Professor Quekett, is now preserved in the Royal Microscopical Society. It must surely be one of the most imposing optical microscopes ever produced, if only from the point of view of sheer size as it stands over two feet high! The general ornate form of the construction can be gathered from the illustration. The limb was of a triangular construction rather reminiscent of that adopted today for optical benches and was inclined from the base by means of a worm and pinion drive. The stage and mirror were both adjustable in position by means of rack and pinions, working on a common rack let into the back of the triangular limb. Full aquatic motion is provided to the body tube (which is now over three inches in diameter) by further rackwork and by a worm wheel. The former controls the distance of the body from the axis of the limb, whilst the latter moves the arm carrying the body in a radial arc over the stage. The instrument contains Martin's "between lens" and in the eyepiece there are two plano-convex eye lenses, whose distance apart may be varied by means of another rack and pinion. The draw tube is furnished with rackwork, another feature well in advance of its time, for this did not become a regular addition to the microscope stand until 1887 when E. M. Nelson had it fitted to the draw tube of his large Powell and Lealand No. 1 stand.

The stage of the Grand Universal microscope is a most complex affair, as there are, in fact, two stages mounted upon the single main

FIG. 4.15. Martin's "Grand Universal Model", now in the collection of the Royal Microscopical Society. Note the triangular pillar, and the various control knobs for the movements. No objective lens is mounted on the body in this illustration.

fitting which has the form of a U-shaped bar pivoting about its centre. By a simple rotation of this fitting either of the two stages can be brought uppermost into the working position. One of these stages carries a tube which serves as a mount for a compound substage condenser, yet another feature in which this instrument is in front of its time. A very large range of objective lenses was provided, one series ranging in focal length from four inches to $\frac{1}{10}$ inch, whilst three lenses of shorter focal length ($\frac{1}{15}$, $\frac{1}{20}$ and $\frac{1}{30}$ inch) appear to be later additions. In addition four lenses intended to serve as magnifiers for the simple microscope are provided. One of the pieces of accessory equipment which is of great interest is a tube which fitted onto the body in place of the snout with the objective. The extra tube contained a concave speculum at its lower end and had an opening in the side through which a pair of stage forceps holding a specimen could be introduced. The object could be brought into focus by varying its distance from the mirror and when illuminated through the hole in the side of the tube a magnified image of the object was reflected to the upper part of the tube where it was viewed by the eyepiece. When this attachment was fitted to the microscope it was in effect converted into a reflecting microscope or "Katadioptric" microscope which is mentioned in Martin's optical writings. Unfortunately, the speculum of the instrument in the Royal Microscopical Society's collection has lost its polish so that at the present time the performance of this accessory cannot be evaluated. Quekett, describing this instrument in his *Treatise on the Use of The Microscope* stated that this microscope

> in point of workmanship, and the extent and variety of its accessory instruments, can probably not be surpassed even in the present day; it is perhaps one of the most complete instruments ever manufactured in this or any other country and serves to show to what perfection the microscope had been brought prior to the year 1780.

This seems a somewhat sweeping statement, for the microscopes which were in production in the middle of the nineteenth century, when Quekett was writing, were superior not only in optical design, but also in the workmanship. The large "Grand Universal" model of Martin, however, must be acknowledged as placing its maker in the first rank of eighteenth-century instrument makers and it provides a fitting tribute to his skill as a craftsman. In addition to its fine construction this microscope is worth noting for the introduction of the triangular limb, a sound engineering feature which was taken up in the next century by such makers as Hugh Powell in his famous instrument made for the Council of the Royal Microscopical Society in 1841 (see Chapter 6). Similarly, the reintroduction of the compound substage condenser, which had not been used since Bonanni showed it in his horizontal microscope of 1691 (Chapter 1, Fig. 1.16), and the rackwork on the draw tube are very significant features which were incorporated generally in later years.

This last large instrument of Martin was studied in some detail by J. Williams in 1862; he concluded that the stand suffered from unsteadiness as a result of the fact that the only support for the long triangular bar was at its lower end. Furthermore, Williams was of the opinion that the rack and pinion used for the focusing was on the coarse side, so that it was difficult to focus the higher power lenses provided with the instrument. By 1862 when Williams studied the instrument, the use of natural objects as tests for the definition of microscope lenses was well established and he applied such tests to the lenses of the Martin instrument. He used the three lenses with the short focal lengths which have already been mentioned and found that on looking at the scales of the wing of the butterfly *Morpho menelaus* that with the $\frac{1}{15}$ inch the lines were indistinct, the $\frac{1}{20}$ inch showed the lines distinctly, but the definition was "anything but sharp" whilst with the $\frac{1}{30}$ inch the scale was "lined distinctly but still without good definition". The final verdict was that the "Grand Universal" microscope was far superior both optically and mechanically to the ordinary microscope of its day, and was especially valuable for the varied and versatile means provided for holding and examining a great number of objects of all possible kinds and sizes; in addition the workmanship was held by Williams to be of very high quality indeed.

It was largely due to the genius of these two men, George Adams and Benjamin Martin, that the mechanical aspects of the microscope had improved out of all recognition in the latter half of the eighteenth century. The general improvements in instrument-making technique must also be taken into account, for the impetus provided by the development of the telescope had resulted in the establishment of technical methods which were also applicable to the construction of microscopes. As an example it may be mentioned that the early microscope lenses were merely mounted in a tube by means of wire retaining rings or even left loose in the wooden mount with no efforts to secure the glass. Many different methods of securing the glass elements of lenses were tried in the early years of the century, but all were more or less deficient and the final products suffered from the lack of precise centration to the optical axis. Towards the end of the century, stimulated by the practice of the telescope construction, Adams and Martin were mounting their lenses in accurately turned brass cells which were burnished over to hold the lenses immovably in precise position.

There was no systematic development of the microscope, however, progress was haphazard and slow, although it was during this century that the final form of the microscope as we know it was definitely established. Mayall, writing on the development of the microscope in 1886, attributed this lack of progress to the fact that the instrument was not being used for systematic scientific studies but was largely in the hands of amateurs and dilettanti who were using it as a means of diversion. Again, the number of microscopes constructed was relatively small and Mayall contended that the serious faults in design would not show up rapidly under these conditions. As communications were slow in the eighteenth century improvements made by one optician would have to be spread largely by verbal or printed descriptions, as probably few makers had the opportunity of examining their rival's instruments in detail. Today with rapid transport and excellent lines of communication new technical developments are very soon exploited throughout the world and progress is correspondingly much more rapid. Again, the design of instruments now proceeds from a sound basis of theory, and the hit-and-miss empiricism of the former days has vanished for ever.

It can be said, however, that by the end of the eighteenth century definite progress had been achieved; the methods of moving the specimen in relation to the optical axis had been perfected and both Martin and Adams were manufacturing mechanical stages with very fine movements. The aquatic motion had been perfected in response to the demands of the observers who were studying the new and fascinating world of the aquatic invertebrates, although the aquatic movement was soon to be abandoned owing to the very rapid wear which soon ensued rendering the stand unfitted for work with high-power lenses. As such lenses were developed, of ever shorter and shorter focal length, the need for improved focusing methods appeared. With the development of the rack and pinion the coarse focus was rendered satisfactory and the fine focus system of the Cuff microscope was abandoned until the next development in optics forced the reintroduction of the fine focus, perhaps in a new or much modified form. This process sometimes repeated itself several times. Thus we may regard the second half of this century as a period of intense activity on the part of the instrument makers, although very often the activity and so-called development was haphazard. George Adams the Younger expresses this very well in his *Essays on the Microscope* in which he writes:

> Every optician now excercised his talents in improving (as he called it) the microscope; in other words, in varying its construction and rendering it different from that sold by his neighbour. Their principal object seemed to be, only to subdivide the instrument, and make it lie in as small a compass as possible; by which means they not only rendered it complex, and troublesome in use, but lost sight also of the extensive field, great light, and other excellent properties of the more ancient instruments; and in some measure, shut themselves out from further improvements on the microscope. Every mechanical instrument is susceptible of almost infinite combination and changes, which are attached with their relative advantages and disadvantages; thus, what is gained in power, is lost in time; "he that loves to be confined to a small house, must lose the benefit of air and excercise".

It has already been emphasized that the majority of the microscopy carried out in the eighteenth century was for amusement only. It is true that some serious studies were attempted, largely with the aid of the simple microscope, for did not everyone know that if a clear view was wanted then a single lens must be used, even though it proved difficult and tiresome to manage? The studies of Ellis on the natural history of the hydrocorallines, of Trembley on the *Hydra*, and of Joblot who succeeded in seeing the contractile vacuole of protozoa in 1718, all demonstrate that some enquiring spirits were aware of the potentialities of the microscope. It seems strange, therefore, that after the tremendous surge of enthusiasm in the early part of the development of the microscope there should have been such a lapse in interest. This may be partly accounted for by the fact that the early experts like Hooke and Grew were very definite individualists and did not initiate the development of a school of pupils who, after training in their methods applied them and extended their work.

Much has been written about the imperfections of the compound microscope of this period in explanation of the lapse in interest; to some extent it is true that the optical imperfections resulted in the description of artificial structures under the impression that they were genuine. Such artifacts, due to diffraction effects caused by the minute apertures of the lenses of this period, may well have contributed to the eclipse of the compound microscope among scientists. It is probable that this is not the whole story, however, for as Wolfe has recently pointed out the decline of microscopy may also be attributed to some intellectual opposition to the ideas of a microscopic anatomy. This opposition largely came from the rejection of microscopy by Sydenham and Locke, famous physicians and philosophers, to whom the concepts of microscopy and micro-anatomy did not accord with their philosophy of the disease processes. They had a profound influence throughout the eighteenth century and their thinking conditioned scientific ideas for many years. To them, microscopy was reactionary, unrealistic, dangerous and meaningless; the microscope only served to reveal new images which were as mysterious and uninterpretable as those already discovered without such optical aids to vision. Most important of all, it was held that microscopy was theologically suspect, as they reasoned that God determines the possible knowledge of each link in His chain of beings and that to attempt to supplement our knowledge by the use of the microscope was to attempt to break the barrier which God had erected and therefore was intellectually sinful and a rebellion against one's duty. Such views received very widespread acceptance and it may well be to such philosophies, as much as to technical imperfections, that the eighteenth century was such a dark age for microscopy.

CHAPTER 5

THE DEVELOPMENT OF
THE ACHROMATIC MICROSCOPE

GREAT interest had been aroused among the leisured classes of the eighteenth century by the microscope and we have already commented upon their eagerness to display to each other the wonders revealed by this instrument. This interest is reflected in most of the contemporary books on microscopy, which devote a large amount of space to descriptions of insects, plants and minerals as they appear under the microscope. With the ordinary compound microscope there is great difficulty in displaying an object to more than one person at a time; even today this problem is relevant to the use of the microscope for teaching, and various accessories have been devised to overcome this drawback. One solution is to have more than one body tube with a prism at the base to direct the light up each tube in turn. This was very popular towards the end of the nineteenth century; one instrument on the market at that time had no fewer than five body tubes each with its ocular, all radiating from a central box containing the prism. The observers sat around a small table and the light from the objective could be directed into each tube in turn so that everyone was able to study the object without too much inconvenience.

The alternative way of arranging for more than one person to view at one time is to use the microscope objective to project a real image upon a screen. This principle is still used in the "conference" type of microscope, although the screen is now usually translucent and the image is projected on it from behind in order to make the accessory as compact as possible. The origins of the projection microscope however, may be traced back to the sixteenth century "camera obscura", which was used to project an image of the view outside a darkened room upon a paper or screen placed within. This device was much used as an aid to drawing or painting of landscapes. By an extension of this principle the image produced by a simple or compound microscope could be thrown upon a screen, so allowing the object under the microscope to be studied by several people at the same time, and to be drawn accurately, if desired. For all such devices the essential feature is a very strong light source to illuminate the object; in the eighteenth century this effectively meant the use of sunlight and so the use of these projection instruments was restricted to the hours of daylight, and they came to be known as "solar" microscopes.

Their invention has been attributed by Henry Baker (in the third edition of his book *The Microscope Made Easy* of 1744) to Lieberkühn, who as we have already seen, had succeeded in attaching his name to the reflector designed for the illumination of opaque objects. The date of the invention of the solar microscope was usually quoted as 1738. George Adams the Younger, in his *Essays on the Microscope* comments with respect to the solar microscope:

> the vast magnifying power which was obtained by this instrument, the colossal grandeur with which it exhibited the minima of nature, the pleasure which arose from being able to display the same object to a number of observers at the same time, by affording a new source of rational amusement, increased the number of microscopic observers . . . .

A Dutch translation of Henry Baker's book appeared in 1744 and it is interesting to note that the translator comments that the credit for the solar microscope should go to Fahrenheit, who had constructed such an instrument some years before his death in 1736, and that Lieberkühn among others had seen the instrument. Lieberkühn himself never claimed to be the inventor and it is probably true to say that he was responsible for the introduction of the solar microscope to England.

The first solar microscopes were intended to be mounted so that the sun could shine directly into the instrument, but the inconvenience of this soon became apparent and modifications were made to the basic form of the instrument. One of these was to add to it a device, which was known as a "scioptric ball", intended for the projection of sunspots onto a card in a darkened room. A turned mahogany ball with a hole bored through one diameter was mounted in a wooden frame so that it could swivel easily. A long-focus convex lens was fitted into the hole in the ball and the whole device inserted into an aperture cut in a shutter; by moving the ball within its mounting the sun could be followed to some extent and its image projected onto a card placed at the correct distance from the lens. By screwing a tube into the hole in the scioptric ball and fixing a Wilson screw-barrel microscope to the other end of the tube, the apparent movement of the sun could be more easily followed and the microscopic image projected into the room.

Benjamin Martin had experimented with the scioptric ball and found that it had the obvious disadvantage that when the sun was high in the middle of the day, the light which passed into the room through the scioptric ball was a long way from the horizontal and not really suitable for use with a microscope attached to the ball. If the screen was placed flat upon the floor or on a table, then the image would be extremely distorted. In his *System of Optics* of 1740 he announced a mirror attachment for fixing to a scioptric ball in order to provide a nearly horizontal beam of light inside the room. Adjustment was still by moving the ball itself which enabled the sun's motion to be followed.

John Cuff also applied himself to this problem of the solar microscope. Writing in 1743, he commented:

> I added the mirror on an ingenious suggestion of a friend who had introduced me to Dr. Lieberkühn, and with the assistance of several gentlemen of the greatest understanding and ability, I had been able to alter and improve it from time to time.

Cuff devised the very effective idea of fixing the tube, (which had, of course, previously been moved with the ball in order to follow the sun's apparent motion) to a square wooden piece which was inserted into the shutter. The light was then directed into the microscope by means of a movable mirror operated by a system of levers and cords from inside the room. The wooden plate which fitted into the shutter was about eight inches square in the original form of Cuff's solar microscope and the mirror was mounted on a circular disc which could be rotated in a hole cut in the wooden plate by means of a cord which was passed around its rim and around a rod which passed through the plate. This device enabled the whole disc with the mirror to be moved from inside the room. The angle of inclination of the mirror was also adjustable, being controlled by means of a thick brass rod which passed through a cork gland let into the disc and was linked by a jointed arm to the mirror. By a combination of these two movements the sunlight could be directed onto the condensing lens which was fitted in the end of the tube which screws into the centre of the revolving disc. The specimen was mounted in a typical Wilson screw-barrel type of microscope and the image formed by direct projection from the single lens of this instrument.

An example of such an early solar microscope is shown in Fig. 5.1, which is taken from an eighteenth-century woodcut. In this picture the mirror and its hinge are clearly shown as well as the cord drive for the

FIG. 5.1. An early wooden solar attachment. The cord and the lever controlling the mirror can be seen to the right of the attachment board (which is labelled A). A simple microscope, probably a screw-barrel instrument, would have been fitted to the tube at E.

revolving disc. The inclination of the mirror is controlled by the rod H which is linked to the mirror by the joint 7 and the bar numbered 6. The condensing lens is shown at 5 and the tube EDC was for the attachment of the screw-barrel microscope which is not illustrated.

Henry Baker states that a similar arrangement would project the image of a louse to a size of six feet, "but it is indeed more distinct when not enlarged to above half that Size". Baker was very enthusiastic about the potentialities of this type of microscope:

> This Microscope is the most entertaining of any; and perhaps, the most capable of making Discoveries, in Objects that are not too opake: as it shews them much larger than can be done any other way. There are also several Conveniences attending it, which no other Microscope can have: for the weakest Eyes may use it without the least straining or fatigue: Numbers of People may view any Object, together, at the same Time, and, by pointing to the particular parts thereof, and discoursing on what lies before them, may be better able to understand one another, and more likely find out the Truth, than when, in other Microscopes, they must peep one after another, and perhaps see the Object neither in the same Light, nor the same Position. Such too, as have no Skill in Drawing, may by this Contrivance, easily sketch out the exact Figure of any Object they have a mind to preserve a Picture of; since they need only fasten a Paper upon the Screen, and trace it out thereon either with a Pen or Pencil, as it appears before them.

These solar microscopes were often supplied with a scroll stand (see Chapter 3, p. 95) or a handle so that the screw-barrel microscope could be detached from the solar mirror and would then serve either as a portable microscope or it could be mounted on the stand for desk use. The later solar microscopes of Cuff and of the other later eighteenth-century instrument makers such as Martin, Adams, W. and S. Jones and Dollond, were constructed entirely of brass, and showed a very high standard of workmanship. Figure 5.2 shows one such instrument by W. and S. Jones, in which the disc carrying the mirror was revolved by means of a rack and pinion, and the angle of the mirror was controlled by the action of an endless screw on a toothed sector. This arrangement (which proved to be much more robust and practical) became universal to all solar microscopes and in this form they continued in production until the middle of the nineteenth century by all the leading British and Continental makers.

This form of solar microscope would, of course, only operate satisfactorily with transparent objects, and as much interest centred on the study of opaque objects, great efforts were made to adapt the solar microscope for this purpose. This was first accomplished in a practical form by Benjamin Martin, who described his invention in a pamphlet, which he published in 1774, entitled *The Description and Use of an Opake Solar Microscope*. The object was mounted inside a light-tight box attached to the tube of the solar attachment and the

FIG. 5.2. A later brass solar microscope intended for use with transmitted light.

sunlight was reflected onto it by means of an inclined mirror. This is seen in the diagram of Martin's instrument which is given as Fig. 5.3. The angle of this mirror could be altered by means of a small screw in order to vary the angle of incidence of the light upon the object. The object-holder was attached to a plate which was maintained in position by means of a strong spring. This slid within a tube and allowed the plate to be withdrawn so that the specimen could be changed. The projection lens system faced the object; in the case of Martin's microscope it consisted of a single bi-convex lens mounted at the end of a

Fig. 5.3. A diagram of Benjamin Martin's "Opake solar" microscope. The solar mirror is not shown. AB is the condensing lens; the object is represented by an arrow and the objective and projector lenses are shown at X and Y respectively. The latter lens is an achromatized triplet.

tube, together with a large triple achromatic combination at the other end of the tube. Martin said of this instrument:

> With this instrument all opake objects, whether of the animal, vegetable, or mineral kingdom, may be exhibited in great perfection, in all their native beauty; the lights and shades, the prominences and cavities, and all the varieties of different hues, teints, and colours, heightened by the reflection of the solar rays condensed upon them.

Many of these microscopes were provided with attachments to allow them to be used for transparent objects and the fitting was known as the "tooth and pinion" microscope. This could also be used as a hand microscope, for which purpose a handle was usually provided. Here again, we have a nice illustration of the tendency of the eighteenth-century opticians, led by Martin, to provide a microscope which was truly universal and could be adapted to the study of all types of objects

ith all the available forms of illumination. Such instruments, known
s "universal solar microscopes" were also provided by Adams and W.
nd S. Jones when they inherited his business. From their catalogue
e learn that this instrument was sold, complete with all its accessories
1 a box, for ten guineas, or if fitted with an additional lens designed
> enable it to be used for the study of large objects and the projection
f an image at low magnifications for 12 to 16 guineas. In this latter
orm the microscope was termed the "megaloscope" by Martin, and
epresented the highest development of the solar; on the other hand,
small brass instrument designed for the examination of transparent
bjects only would have retailed for $5\frac{1}{2}$ guineas.

Under favourable circumstances the solar microscope was capable
f providing a most impressive picture upon the screen; according to
Adams:

> The effect by this sort of microscope is stupendous, and never fails to
> excite wonder in an observer at his first view, in seeing a flea, etc., aug-
> mented in appearance to SEVEN, EIGHT, or even TEN FEET in length,
> with all its colours, motions, and animal functions, distinctly and beauti-
> fully exhibited.

Later writers, such as Dr. Goring, were sceptical as to the value
f the solar microscope. In 1827, Goring wrote:

> We may as well expect to gather figs from brambles, as to get a fine
> picture from an uncorrected convex lens. The image of a common solar
> microscope may be considered a mere shadow, fit only to amuse women
> and children, more especially if we attempt to exhibit brilliant opaque
> objects, which either become indistinguishable with a limited aperture,
> or enveloped in a glorious mass of aberration, with an enlarged one. The
> utmost it can do is to give us the *shadow* of a flea, or a louse as big as a goose or
> a jackass . . . The swinish vulgar will always be gratified by such spectacles,
> because they have no idea that a microscope of any kind is to do more than
> exhibit objects very much dilated in point of bulk; if any optician could
> contrive an instrument, which would at one swoop take in the whole of
> a horse, ass, or elephant, and exhibit it (no matter how) with a power of
> about 240, to this class of observer, I am sure it would delight them
> infinitely more than the effects of the most beautiful achromatic lenses
> which Mr. Tulley, or M. Chevalier can make.

rom these quotations it seems that in its early days the solar micro-
cope was developed primarily for the display of natural history
pecimens to several people at one time and that the spectacle was of
nore importance than the fine detail which was shown. With the

development of the achromatic microscope lens the solar microscope soon passed into disuse, helped no doubt by the scathing comments of microscopists such as Goring! One claim to fame does remain to the solar microscope, however, which will ensure that it has a permanent place in the history of the microscope. Throughout the eighteenth century all attempts to recover the microscope image had to be made by some process of drawing from the picture, either freehand or by some form of projection. In the early years of the nineteenth century, however, attempts were being made to utilize the effect of light itself to record the image and these developments led to the photographic process. In this connection the solar microscope was used by J. B. Reade and others around the year 1836 to obtain not only what must be regarded as the first photomicrographs, but pictures which may have a very strong claim to be regarded as the first photographs.

No major discoveries can be claimed for the solar microscope and it remained very much a recreational instrument, depending also for its operation upon the vagaries of the weather. It may well have been for this reason that George Adams the Elder invented an alternative form of instrument which was taken up and improved still further by his son who described it in detail in his *Essays on the Microscope* of 1787. He says:

> This microscope was originally thought of, and in part executed by my father; I have, however, so improved and altered it, both in construction and form, as to render it altogether a different instrument.

The construction of this type of microscope differs radically from the conventional microscope of the time, reverting to the horizontal design first used by Bonanni (see Chapter 1). The lucernal microscope as it was known, is shown in Fig. 5.4 (redrawn from Adams's book) and in Fig. 5.5 which is of a specimen in the Science Museum in London. This latter instrument has survived with all its extensive accessories intact. From the illustrations it may be seen that the essential construction is that of a large optical bench supported by a pillar and tripod feet; this ensures that all the components are in the same optical axis.

The main body of the microscope is formed by a large pyramidal shaped box, usually made out of mahogany. This box is about fourteen inches long and six inches square at the larger end. The lenses are screwed onto the smaller end, one of them being shown in position in each of the figures, whilst a pair of large convex lenses is fixed into the larger end of the wooden body. These serve to concentrate the light into the eye of the observer, which has to be placed in a very special position with respect to these two large lenses. In order to achieve this, a "viewing guide" formed from a simple brass ring was placed at the end of the bar which forms the optical bench. When the observer places his eye in this position and looks at the large convex lenses their whole area appears illuminated and contains a very brilliant image of any object placed upon the stage of the microscope. Again this device

Fig. 5.4. Adams's illustration of his "Lucernal" microscope of 1787. The eye-guide is at the left, and to the right of the mahogany body can be seen mounted the stage for opaque objects. An Argand lamp is shown at the right of the illustration.

was claimed to be of value in assisting the preparation of a drawing; Adams stressed this especially when he wrote:

> by it the outlines of every object may be taken, even by those who are not accustomed to draw; while those who can draw well, will receive great assistance, and execute their work with more accuracy, and in less time than they would otherwise have been able to have performed it in.

In order to use the lucernal microscope for drawings, the large convex lenses at the end of the body were removed and replaced by a ground glass screen, upon which the objective lens threw a real image of the object. If a piece of paper was then placed in contact with the ground glass, the real image could be traced.

FIG. 5.5. A lucernal microscope similar to the instrument shown in Fig. 5.4. This specimen is probably of later date and has the lamp mounted on a swinging arm attached to the microscope itself. Seven extra objectives are seen in front of the microscope.

(*Crown copyright, The Science Museum.*)

Focusing of this type of microscope was effected by moving the stage relative to the objective by means of a rack and pinion mechanism. So that this could be done whilst actually observing the image in the convex lenses a large handle was usually provided to work the rack and pinion. This may be seen on the left of Fig. 5.4. In this particular figure the stage which is mounted upon the microscope is one which Adams designed for the study of opaque objects. In this form the light passed through the hole in the lower part of the stage, being concentrated by a lens onto a concave mirror which then reflected the light obliquely upwards onto the object. An additional stage was provided for the accommodation of transparent objects and this is seen below the microscope in Fig. 5.4. In this particular instrument this stage was also intended for use on its own as a simple microscope, in which case the lenses were intended to be screwed into the brass ring which is mounted at the left-hand end of the attachment.

In this original version of the lucernal microscope it will be noticed that the lamp was mounted upon a completely separate stand. Adams recommended the Argand lamp, which was an oil lamp furnished with a circular wick and which was noted for providing a very intense and steady source of light. Many modifications were made to the basic plan of the instrument by various people, many of them friends of the inventor. Of them we may mention the suggestion of Mr. John Hill of Wells in Norfolk, that the lamp should be permanently mounted onto the microscope in order to reduce the space which it occupied and to simplify the setting up and adjustment of the illuminating system. In his version, seen in the photograph Fig. 5.5, the pillar supporting the stage was made to carry the lamp bracket which could swivel on the pillar. The lamp and its condensing lenses, which were carried on the same bar, could then be used to provide oblique illumination of a transparent object, or could be swung round to the front of the microscope to illuminate an opaque specimen. Provision was made for fitting a cylindrical shield with a small hole in it over the lamp chimney so that the glare was reduced and the observation of very transparent objects assisted. As a further means of reducing the glare, it was frequently recommended that transparent specimens should be studied, not by observing the aerial image in the plane of the large convex lenses, but by using the "rough glass" or ground glass to receive a real image. This procedure also allowed several people to view the image at the same time, as when the microscope was used in this fashion there was no need to use the "viewing guide".

All these lucernal microscopes were of course still provided with lenses which lacked correction for spherical and chromatic aberrations. Adams himself was well aware of this failing, for he writes concerning the observation of the aerial image of a transparent object:

> You will then see the object in a blaze of light almost too great for the eye, a circumstance that will be found useful in the examination of particular objects; the edges of the object in this will be somewhat coloured, but as it is only used in this full light for occasional purposes, it has been thought better to leave this small imperfection, than by remedying it to sacrifice greater advantages; the more so, as this fault is easily corrected, and a new and interesting view of the object is obtained, by turning the instrument out of the direct rays of light and permitting them to pass through only in an oblique direction . . . .

Although the lucernal microscope was extremely expensive — it cost £21 — large numbers of them were produced by Adams. He later turned to the use of large cylindrical brass bodies, but W. and S. Jones, who carried on the manufacture of this type of microscope, reverted to the use of the mahogany pyramidal box type of body. With the development of the achromatic microscope the lucernals, like the solar microscopes, dropped out of use.

At this time most microscope manufacturers were well aware of the troubles caused by the lack of chromatic correction in their lenses. Adams regrets that:

> the different refrangibility of the rays of light, which frequently causes such deviation from truth in the appearance of things, that many have imagined themselves to have made surprising discoveries, and have communicated them as such to the world; when, in fact, they have been only so many optical deceptions owing to the unequal refraction of the rays.

He mentions the development of achromatic lenses for the telescope but continues:

> how far this invention is applicable to the improvement of microscopes, has not yet been ascertained; and, indeed, from some few trials made, there is reason for supposing they cannot be successfully applied to microscopes with high powers; so that this improvement is yet a desideratum in the construction of microscopes, and they may be considered as being yet far from their ultimate degree of perfection.

George Adams the Younger inherited his father's business in 1773 when he was twenty-three. He did not prove to be a very original designer; as we have already seen, he adapted the lucernal microscope from his father's designs and in 1787, in the *Essays on the Microscope* he introduced a new microscope which bore a very strong resemblance to Martin's 1776 "Universal" instrument. The last microscope which Adams designed is now usually known as the "Universal Compound" and dates from about 1790. A splendid example of one of these instruments is preserved in the Science Museum at South Kensington. The microscope limb is carried by means of a strong compass joint at the upper end of a strong pillar of circular cross section. Conventional stage focusing is provided by means of a rack and pinion cut into the limb, but two unusual features of this instrument deserve mention. One is the provision of an eyeshade, which was attached to the eyepiece. It consisted of a brass ring, attached to a spiral spring, which was covered with black silk. It was intended that this eyeshade should be compressed by the face until the eye in use was placed at the correct viewing distance from the eyepiece, when the silk shade would exclude all the extraneous light. The second feature of interest is the presence of a single bi-convex lens carried on a hinged arm so that it could be brought into the optical axis at will in order to serve as a substage condenser. Like most instruments of its day, this microscope was intended for use as a simple or a compound microscope and it possessed a full aquatic movement. Recently, Frison has been able to examine one of these instruments in an excellent state of preservation. It was provided with eight lenses, giving magnifications, when they were used as simple microscopes, of from $4\times$ to $142\times$. Frison comments that the optical quality of these lenses was "quite mediocre", as the image was usually rather hazy. Three separate lenses which were provided with Lieberkühn reflectors, however, were classed by him as "quite superior in resolving power and in the quality of the images".

When it was used as a compound microscope, one of two oculars could be used. The first ocular possessed four bi-convex lenses, one of which acted as a field lens, the other three as a compound eye lens. The second ocular had a plano-convex field lens, the flat surface being uppermost, and again a compound eye lens of three bi-convex elements. Both of the eyepieces appear to be of almost exactly the same power so that this appears to be an unnecessary duplication. It is interesting to note that with the highest power lens the magnification was $568\times$, which Frison believes to be the maximum so far recorded for a non-achromatic compound microscope of this period.

Coming from such a reputable maker as Adams, this instrument is surprising in the rather poor quality of the images. The best resolution attainable with this particular example was 5 microns, whereas Frison reports that other lenses by Adams of comparable power had a resolving power of 2 microns and were very well made. This stresses one of the problems inherent in the production of optical systems in the latter part of the eighteenth century, which was that there was no adequate system of controlling the quality of the lens figuring. The whole process was carried out very much by rule-of-thumb methods and such variations in quality as Frison notes must be expected.

One retrograde step in the design of the "Universal Compound" microscope of 1790 was undoubtedly the absence of a fine focusing mechanism. This device had been provided by George Adams the Elder on nearly all his microscopes and it seems strange that his son should have trusted a simple rackwork mechanism with its inevitable backlash to focus a lens with the very high magnifying power that he provided on this stand. There were also other shortcomings in this microscope, such as the fact that the pillar is so high that when the instrument is placed on a normal table the limb has to be inclined almost to the horizontal position in order to bring the eyepiece to the correct height for a seated observer. In this position the stage was then so far above the table top that any manipulation of it required the arms to be held clear of the table, when the lack of support made prolonged use very tiring. At the same time, the mirror is brought so far above the table that any lamp which is used also has to be elevated to such an extent that it shines straight into the eyes of an observer, which does not help accurate microscopical studies! Perhaps the weakest point, however, was the aquatic movement; although the "fore and aft" movement was controlled by rackwork, the lateral swinging motion was only friction tight. This is adequate for small microscopes, but in this example the body tube was extremely heavy and there was a grave risk of the whole tube suddenly swinging violently to one side.

This microscope, although well made, did not have many points of design to recommend it so it seems unfortunate that it was taken by W. and S. Jones as their model when they continued the business after the death of George Adams the Younger in 1795. William and Samuel Jones also bought the copyright of Adams's book and they were responsible for the preparation of the second edition which appeared in 1798. In this the two models of microscope manufactured and sold by the Jones brothers are described and illustrated; known as the

"Improved" and the "Most Improved" models they became popular microscopes of the early years of the nineteenth century.

The "improved" microscope is shown in Fig. 5.6, from which the superficial resemblance to Cuff's microscope is apparent. The instrument was carried on a square section pillar, which was firmly fixed to a square box-foot. Unlike the Cuff microscope, however, the focusing was by rackwork which moved the stage, and the mirror was mounted on a sleeve which could slide upon the main pillar. The body was mounted on the usual arm, designed to provide a full "aquatic" movement, and was furnished with a small wheel at the lower end of the tube. This wheel contained the various lenses and could be rotated to bring them into the optical axis in turn, where they were secured by the action of a small spring catch. This microscope was provided with the full range of accessories current at the time, such as Bonanni spring stage, stage forceps, fish plate, prepared ivory sliders and Lieberkühn reflectors. These were mounted on a ring which was carried upon a straight rod, very much as in some of the instruments designed by Martin, which were discussed in a previous chapter (p. 144). This same rod also served to carry a condensing lens, mounted in a brass tube, which served

> for increasing the density of the light, when it is reflected by the mirror from a candle or lamp.

At this time, Cuff's microscope was still being manufactured, but the "Improved" microscope of the Jones brothers was held to possess several important advantages. It had a larger field of view, the stage and the mirror were both movable, and an "aquatic" motion had been added. This instrument, which was claimed by its makers to be the "second best sort of compound microscope", was sold for £6. 6s. 0d. in 1798. At the same time W. and S. Jones were still advertising Cuff's microscope for £5. 15s. 6d., presumably for the conservative buyer who was distrustful of all the new-fangled developments in the microscope.

According to W. and S. Jones, the best microscope was their other model, usually referred to as the "Most Improved" or, to give it its full description, a "most improved compound microscope, being universal in its uses, and forming the single, compound, opake and aquatic microscopes". In the second edition of Adams on the microscope this instrument is figured and introduced in the following terms:

> A person much accustomed to observations by the microscope, will readily discern the several advantages of this instrument over the preceding

E.M.—M

JONES'S *IMPROVED COMPOUND MICROSCOPE AND APPARATUS.*

FIG. 5.6. The Jones "Improved" compound microscope. Note the similarity in general design to Cuff's microscope, although later features (particularly from Martin) have been incorporated.

one. Besides its containing an additional quantity of useful apparatus, it is more commodious and complete for the management while observing, as it may instantly be placed in a vertical, oblique or horizontal situation, turned laterally at the ease of the observer, and the objects viewed by the primary direct light, or reflected as usual, at pleasure.

The microscope differs chiefly from the "Improved" in that the square-section limb is mounted by a compass joint at the top of a sturdy cylindrical pillar which is supported by tripod feet. As in the other model the actual lenses are mounted in a small wheel which may be rotated under the body tube to change the power in use. The body tube was provided with the full "aquatic" movement; usually the arm holding the body tube slid through a rectangular slot lined with cork at the top of the limb, but occasionally, as in the instrument shown in Fig. 5.7, there was a rackwork added to this movement to increase the control and provide a smoother movement. The mirror and the condenser were again movable on the limb and in the example illustrated the rackwork for the focusing movement of the stage may be clearly seen. It was possible to unscrew the wheel which contained the six lenses and substitute a single brass cell which carried

a very small globule or lens, or an exceedingly great magnifier, usually about the 30th or 40th of an inch focus; . . . . it is for the purpose of viewing extreme minute objects, which may be so small as to elude the power of the magnifiers in the wheel.

By unscrewing the compound body it was possible to use the instrument as a simple microscope, still retaining the full aquatic movement. Although this microscope did not introduce any novel features, nevertheless it represented an important stage in the development of the instrument as it brought together all the basic ideas which had evolved in the latter part of the eighteenth century, largely as a result of the efforts of Martin and George Adams the Elder. The "Most Improved" microscope was well made and was soon copied by other makers. It performed well, within the limitations of an instrument which did not possess achromatic lenses, and continued in production until somewhere around the middle of the nineteenth century. As made by the Jones brothers it was a fairly expensive microscope, being priced at £10. 10s. 0d. in their 1798 list or £12. 12s. 0d. if purchased with "micrometers and vegetable cuttings", i.e. prepared slides of sections of botanical material.

Throughout the eighteenth century the Continental instrument makers, especially those of France, had not been idle, although few original ideas came from these quarters. Brief mention may be made at this point of some of the more prominent, such as Louis Joblot,

Fig. 5.7. Jones' "Most Improved" compound microscope.

who in addition to holding Chairs of mathematics and painting and sculpture at the Royal Academy was active in the early years of the century as a maker of simple microscopes. Magny was another eminent instrument maker who achieved a wide reputation as an "artiste habile et éclaire". He spent over ten years working for a rich amateur named

Bonnier de la Mosson and after the latter's death set up on his own account. All the signed instruments of Magny come from this period and are dated between 1751 and 1754. He achieved such a reputation for superb workmanship that when Louis XV wished to present a fine microscope to Stanislas Leckzinski, he commissioned Magny to undertake the task. We have already seen in the last chapter how Magny invented the trunnion support much at the same time as George Adams used it in his "Prince of Wales" model.

Perhaps the most famous French optician of this period was Dellebarre. He was born in 1726 in Abbeville in France and emigrated to Holland in 1769. He began making microscopes in 1771, whilst he was living in the Hague and soon was persuaded to return to France and set up in business in Paris. Dellebarre proved to be a very successful instrument maker, one of his microscopes being used in the laboratory of Lavoisier, probably the greatest scientist of France at this time. Dellebarre produced many different models of microscopes and when a commission of the French Academy investigated various microscopes in 1777, his instruments received a very good report. Perhaps the most notable feature of his instruments was the large number of separate lenses used in the ocular. It was not uncommon to find four separate bi-convex lenses placed with their surfaces very close together in one of his eyepieces. This may well have been an attempt by Dellebarre to carry out an idea of Euler's that achromatism could be achieved in such a fashion. Mayall, who examined over twenty of Dellebarre's instruments was of the opinion that none of them was achromatic, which is not surprising since the whole concept of Euler's that an achromatic microscope could be developed by using a very complex eyepiece was based on false premises. It was generally held that Dellebarre's instruments were inferior to the best British instruments of this period. Fresnel, a little later when reporting on an early achromatic microscope by Selligue, classified various microscopes by the sharpness or otherwise of their image. He found that Dellebarre's was the worst in this respect, being inferior to the instruments of Adams, Amici and Selligue, whereas in terms of size of field the Adams microscope came out best with Dellebarre's again the worst. It thus seems that at the turn of the eighteenth century the British makers and designers led the world in the production of microscopes, a supremacy which was to be maintained until the later years of the nineteenth century.

Before we pass on to consider the first attempts to develop an achromatic microscope objective, it may be of interest to look at a

small microscope which on the grounds of convenience in use, portability, and workmanship, may well be regarded as the peak of achievement of the non-achromatic microscope. This instrument was designed
in the early years of the nineteenth century by William Cary and it
was intended to be simple but at the same time to incorporate all
the features which he considered essential for a microscope stand.

FIG. 5.8. The Cary type of microscope. This instrument was very
small, the total height being about six inches.

Portability was high on the list, so the stand in this form of microscope
usually consisted of a pillar attached to a round weighted base or to the
lid of the instrument case. The mirror was attached to the pillar as was
the stage which, although small, often incorporated a simple rackwork
movement. This mechanical stage was particularly evident in the later
models, dating from around the 1830's. Figure 5.8 represents a Cary
microscope which is still in the collection of the Royal Microscopical
Society; the small neat construction is especially evident.

There were many variations upon the theme, one of the best known being by C. Gould. Yet another, dating from around 1830, had the optical elements designed by Coddington and they are described and figured in his *Optics* published in that year. From Fig. 5.9 it can be seen that he provided as an objective either a simple plano-convex lens, mounted with the plane side towards the object, and fitted with a diaphragm above the lens to limit the spherical aberration, or for the lower powers a mounted example of one of Coddington's well-known "Bird's-eye" object glasses, which have already been mentioned in Chapter 3. The instrument had a very complex eyepiece, composed

Fig. 5.9. A section of a Cary microscope of about 1830 to show the complex eyepiece and two different types of objective lenses which were used.

of a large field lens mounted at the upper end of the conical portion of the tube and of two eye lenses, one bi-convex, the other plano-convex. This form of microscope was extremely popular in the early years of the nineteenth century and many examples may still be seen in second-hand shops. The active life of this form of microscope was short, however, as the achromatic microscope became a practical instrument and achromatic lenses required a much larger tube. At the same time the use of ivory sliders to mount the object was declining and glass slips were coming into use; this in turn demanded the development of a larger stage, so that the major design features of the Cary microscope were altered by the radical rethinking of microscope design which occurred around the 1830's.

Most Cary microscopes were provided with objectives which could be screwed together to increase the magnifying power. One such instrument measured by van Cittert could provide magnifications from 17–145 ×, according to the various combinations of lenses in use. In no case was the resolution of this microscope better than 5 microns and van Cittert dryly comments:

> Some of the combinations give strongly chromatic images.

There is no reference to the amount of spherical aberration introduced into the image, but the addition of uncorrected lenses would be sure to cause a drastic increase in this fault.

The great authority which was attached to the writings of Newton had led the majority of the opticians and scientists of the eighteenth century to the mistaken view that chromatic aberration could not be corrected in a series of lenses. Newton's experiments with prisms had proved that refraction was always accompanied by dispersion, i.e. the separation of light into its constituent colours. He thought that the dispersion was always proportional to the deviation of the ray (which is not in fact so) and hence concluded incorrectly that it would not be possible to make a satisfactory telescope by the use of lens systems alone. Such views, backed by the weight of his immense authority, led to the development of reflecting systems for telescopes and microscopes as there is no problem of chromatic aberration with a mirror, all the wavelengths of light being brought to the same focal point. Newton himself had suggested the use of a reflecting microscope to the Royal Society in 1672, a short note to this effect appearing in the *Philosophical Transactions* of that year. There is no evidence that this instrument was ever constructed, but in 1736 Barker devised a reflecting microscope based on the reflecting telescope devised by Gregory in 1662. In its essentials the microscope of Barker used the concave mirror to produce an achromatic image of objects placed between nine and twenty-four inches from the instrument. The primary image of the object was reflected into the eyepiece by means of a second small concave speculum and focusing was achieved by varying the distance of this small mirror from the larger one. Eventually the mirrors would be in such a relationship that the point of focus was for distant objects when the instrument was then functioning as a telescope. The plan of the mirrors of this microscope is shown in Fig. 5.10, together with the microscope designed a few years later by Dr. Smith. This reflecting or catadioptric microscope was based on the principle of the Cassegrainian telescope,

with the slight difference that focusing was carried out not by movements of the mirrors but by moving the eyepiece itself. Other workers
experimented with reflecting systems in order to overcome the
tremendous problem of the chromatic aberration but the only real
success was scored by Amici working in Italy, to whom we shall
return shortly.

Around about the year 1733 a significant development occurred in

FIG. 5.10. The optical systems of three different types of reflecting
microscopes.
(a) Barker's microscope of 1736 using the Gregorian principle.
(b) Smith's microscope of 1738 of the Cassegrainian form.
(c) Amici's microscope.

the field of optics. A barrister named Chester More Hall, who was an enthusiastic amateur optician and astronomer, began experiments in this field. He probably worked empirically but succeeded in achieving what the theoreticians believed to be impossible, namely the construction of an achromatic telescope objective. He was aided by the fact that at about this time numerous new types of glass were coming into use, especially the very dense lead-containing glass called "flint" glass. This glass was made in England, but at that time pieces which were large enough to be ground into lenses and were at the same time without flaws were very rare indeed. Chester More Hall evidently stumbled upon the fact that a combination of a convex lens of crown glass allied to a concave one of flint glass would produce the desired result. He appears to have realized the importance of this and the need for secrecy one component of his lens was sent to Scarlett to be figured whilst the other was placed in the hands of James Mann. It seems, however, that both of these opticians subcontracted the work to the same jobbing optician named George Bass. Much later, when John Dollond became interested in this subject, we are told by Ramsden that Bass passed on to Dollond the details of Chester More Hall's experiments and that Dollond then deduced the purpose of the separate components. There can be no doubt, however, that Chester More Hall succeeded in making an achromatic telescope lens in the 1730's and that he did not take out any patent protection for his invention.

Meanwhile, theoretical opticians were not inactive and in 1747 Euler, at the Academy of Berlin, took up Newton's suggestion that spherical aberration could be corrected in a lens system and extended the reasoning to suggest that Newton was incorrect in some of his assumptions concerning chromatic aberration. By carefully calculating the curvatures of the various surfaces of the lens system, Euler believed that the chromatic aberration could be completely eliminated. This work came to the notice of John Dollond who criticized it strongly with the result that a controversy sprang between him and Euler. The latter proved very difficult to convince that his ideas were false and resorted to the device of postulating that elaborate non-spherical surfaces were required to correct the chromatic aberration. A few years later, in 1755, Klingenstiern the mathematician told Dollond that Newton's hypothesis, which had formed the basis of most of Euler's work, was not universally applicable; this stimulated Dollond who immediately repeated Newton's experiments and published his findings three years later. He used two prisms, one of glass and the other hollow shell of glass filled with water. Experiments with this simple apparatus showed that in fact dispersion could occur without refraction and vice versa, so pointing the way to the design of lenses of differing properties which could be combined so that an image could be formed by refraction without the residual dispersion causing colour fringes around the image.

Dollond tried using an idea of Euler's, that two lenses of glass might have water contained between them to form a third lens. This did not prove very satisfactory in practice because although the chromatic aberration could be controlled, the spherical aberration was very high indeed. It was probably at about this stage that he heard from Bass of the differing properties of the lenses which the latter had worked for Chester More Hall. Dollond tried glass lenses made from these two types of glass which had widely differing dispersive powers. By combining a convex lens of the low dispersion crown glass with a diverging lens of the highly dispersive flint glass, a combination can be achieved which will correct both the chromatic and the spherical aberrations at the same time. In 1759, Dollond used such combinations for the objectives of his telescopes and, moreover, he took out a patent to cover this invention.

Thus by the middle of the eighteenth century the main problem of chromatic aberration had been resolved with reference to the construction of the object glasses of telescopes. It seems that Benjamin Martin had independently come to very much the same sort of conclusions. In his *New System of Optics* of 1759 he establishes the principle that achromatism can be achieved by the combination of two crown and one flint glass prisms so that the light emerged "without any dissipation of the Rays, so that the Object or Radiant will now appear without Colours . . . elevated above its true Place". He extended this from prisms to lenses, and in paragraph 261 of the same work he writes:

> Therefore, if we take a Double Convex Lens, ABCG, of *Crown Glass*, a double and equally Concave Lens, CGAFD, of *white Flint*, and a Plano Convex Lens, DGFE, of *Crown Glass*, and in a position similar to that of the three Prisms, they will together make a compound Object-Glass of a telescope, which will form the Image of Objects *without Colours*, and as distinctly as the Nature of such a compound Refraction will admit of.

This contribution of Martin's is often overlooked and it is apparent that he had reached the same conclusions as Dollond who has, however, undoubtedly priority of publication. Martin also considered the possibility of applying this principle to the microscope and actually carried out experiments with instruments or lenses built on this principle. He compared the results with those given by reflecting systems and comes down heavily in favour of the latter:

> Upon the whole, therefore, it appears, both by Theory and Experiments, *that a Combination of Lenses is far from rendering Vision perfect in Refracting Telescopes; and that it is in every respect much inferior to the Effect of a Speculum in a* REFLECTING TELESCOPE, *for exhibiting the best and most pleasing View of Objects.*

John Dollond and his son Peter pressed on with the manufacture of telescopes based on the principle of combined lenses of crown and flint glass and they became extremely successful. So much so that a petition was lodged against Peter Dollond in 1766 by the London opticians who were forced to pay a royalty on each lens made according to this principle. This action was eventually decided in favour of the Dollonds; the summing up of Lord Camden acknowledged Chester More Hall's priority in this matter, but commented that

> It was not the person who locked his invention in his scritoire that ought to profit by a patent for such an invention, but he who brought it forth for the benefit of the public.

It seems that for some time no attempts were made to apply the principles of the achromatic telescope lenses to the microscope although in 1774 Benjamin Martin did use a triple achromatic combination in the projection system of his new "Opake solar" microscope. This lens however, being for projection could be made of a large diameter; the lack of such lenses in the normal optics of the microscope was obviously not due to lack of interest but to the severe technical problems involved in the grinding and polishing of the very small lenses which constitute microscope objectives.

Euler still continued with his theoretical studies of this subject and actually calculated the curvatures of a microscope objective composed of two crown-glass convex lenses and a single concave flint-glass element. This description was extended in 1774 by Fuss, who was one of Euler's pupils and it is possible that such an objective was actually constructed about this time at the Academy of Sciences in Leningrad.

Technical advances in the optical industry were rapid during the last quarter of the eighteenth century and in addition to increased skill in the actual grinding and polishing of lenses, other important developments include the introduction of the cemented lens. In such a lens the various components are stuck together with a transparent cement, usually canada balsam, so that the air film between the various elements of the lens was abolished. This resulted in a great improvement in the performance of the optical combination. One of the first opticians to adopt this new system of lens construction was Chevalier in France,

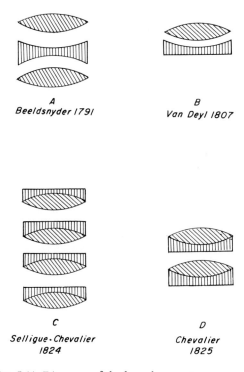

A
Beeldsnyder 1791

B
Van Deyl 1807

C
*Sellique-Chevalier
1824*

D
*Chevalier
1825*

FIG. 5.11. Diagrams of the lens elements in some early achromatic objectives.

but it was not until the early years of the nineteenth century that such lenses were in general manufacture.

One of the first true achromatic microscope objectives must be attributed to François Beeldsnyder (1755–1808). Here again, as so often in this subject, one of the exciting new technical developments was due to the work of an amateur. Beeldsnyder was a colonel in the Amsterdam cavalry and a member of the Amsterdam committee of Justice. He acted as a collector of the burial rates for St. Anthony's church in the same city, so that like Leeuwenhoek, he could be classed as a minor civil servant. He was an enthusiastic experimental physicist and among his interests was optics, which led him to the problem of achromatism in the microscope objective. The lens which he designed may tentatively be dated about 1791 and it is still preserved in the collections of the University of Utrecht. The arrangement of the component elements is shown in Fig. 5.11(a), from which it is clear that the separate lenses were not cemented together and in fact were widely spaced. They were mounted in a short brass tube. Each of the lenses had a diameter of about a quarter of an inch and when they were combined they gave an objective with a focal length of just under one inch (21 mm). Van Cittert tested this objective with a Hartnack eyepiece from the same collection and found that the lens had a magnifying power of about $20 \times$ and a resolution at this power of 10 microns. Mayall, in his Cantor Lectures on the microscope, comments:

> The workmanship is inferior and the definition leaves "much to be desired". If Martin's achromatic objective of 1759 was not better than Beeldsnyder's of 1791, I am not at all surprised that he was not encouraged to throw aside his older constructions in favour of achromatism.

Despite Mayall's disapproval, however, the objective of Beeldsnyder was one of the first practicable achromatic lenses to be constructed on a sound theoretical principle.

Other pioneers in the construction of achromatic microscope lenses were the van Deyls (sometimes spelt van Deijl). Jan van Deyl (1715–1801) and his son Harmanus (1738–1809) were reported to have begun the construction of achromatic microscope objectives long before 1791. It appears that they constructed their first achromatic telescope about 1762 and shortly after this attempted the manufacture of microscope lenses on similar principles. Harmanus van Deyl stated that this early lens, which had a focal length of about three quarters of an inch, was entirely satisfactory, but this early lens does not seem to have survived. In the early years of the nineteenth century, Harmanus van Deyl began to sell microscopes with achromatic objectives, but these were probably only produced in relatively small numbers. Several of these instruments have survived and their performance has been studied by van Cittert. These achromatic objectives were composed of a single flint lens together with one bi-convex element of crown glass. The flint lens was in fact a bi-concave lens, but the curvature of the side which was presented to the object was so shallow that the lens has often been described as plano-concave. This arrangement, apparently hit upon empirically by these workers, would materially assist in the reduction of the spherical aberration in the combination, it anticipates the work of Charles Chevalier (who is usually accredited with the introduction of this disposition of lenses) by about seventeen years. The best resolution which van Cittert could obtain from a lens of van Deyl appears to be 5 microns whilst the focal lengths were either 26 mm or 18 mm. This latter lens, with the highest power of eyepiece which he provided, gave a total magnification of either 92 or 150 ×, according to whether the draw tube of the instrument was fully closed or fully extended.

In the first decade of the nineteenth century several other workers on the continent of Europe realized that the production of achromatic microscope lenses of low power was now a practical possibility. Bernadino Marzoli, an amateur optician in Italy, was making such lenses between 1808 and 1811. When they were exhibited in Milan in the latter year they were received with acclamation by the Royal Institute of Science. Marzoli's lenses were of advanced construction in that they employed cemented doublets. In 1890, a specimen of Marzoli's work was presented to the Royal Microscopical Society and this example of an early achromatic lens was preserved in their collection for a long time. Unfortunately for students of the history of microscopy who wish to investigate the performance of such early achromatic lenses, this unique example now cannot be found. Another maker, who was producing achromatic lenses at this time, was Joseph Frauenhofer. He incorporated achromatic doublets in an instrument which with respect to its mechanical construction was clearly influenced by the "drum" microscopes of Benjamin Martin. Frauenhofer's early achromatic lenses do not seem to have possessed very good definition and it is probable that they were inferior in this respect to the lenses of Harmanus van Deyl.

Around the turn of the century, fresh attempts were obviously made in Leningrad to construct an achromatic microscope; Sobol in a recent article claims that in 1939 he discovered an instrument which was constructed from designs found among the papers left by Epinus after his death. Epinus had been noted for his interest in the microscope and he had reported to the Leningrad Academy a new form of achromatic microscope which he had invented. Apparently this instrument had a total length of four feet and a lens with a focal length of about seven inches (17·5 cm) which provided a power of sixty to seventy diameters.

George Adams was somewhat scornful of this development, commenting in his *Essays on the Microscope* that these new instruments:

> were nothing more than an application of the achromatic perspective to microscopic purposes . . . botanists might find some advantages in attending to this instrument; it would assist them in discovering small plants at a distance, and thus often save them from the thorns of the hedge, and the dirt of a ditch.

Despite this unfavourable opinion from one of the foremost opticians of the day, Epinus carried on with his calculations and designing. After his death two new microscopes were constructed from his last designs and it seems to have been one of these which came to the notice of Sobol. He gives a detailed description of the lenses of the microscope, telling us that the objective had a focal length of 18 mm or just under three quarters of an inch. The maximum magnification was $180 \times$ and the resolution was of the order of $2 \cdot 5$ microns, which was a very reasonable figure for the time. Nothing appeared to come of this development in Russia, however, which may reflect the slow communications of the time and the general difficulties in the rapid dissemination of information of any kind.

Other abortive attempts to develop achromatic objectives seem to have been made in France by M. Charles, who does not appear to have been very successful, for Chevalier, writing in 1839, tells us that his lenses were very badly constructed and practically unusable! It is obvious that in the first year of the nineteenth century the imagination of the opticians and instrument makers had been fired by the possibility of constructing workable achromatic lenses of reasonable power. Such a development would have been of the utmost importance for microscopy. It would have helped to raise its standing as a separate discipline and overcome to a certain extent the disrepute into which microscopy had fallen. In the eighteenth century many errors of interpretation of biological structures had been perpetrated, largely because the instruments had a high degree of magnification but a low resolving power and their lenses suffered severely from both spherical and chromatic aberration. There is little wonder that the images which such microscopes produced were so often misinterpreted. Much of this confusion arose as a result of the diffraction halos which surrounded all the objects due to the very small aperture of the lenses and in consequence it was commonplace for the general appearance of the object to be described as being "globular" or "fibrillar". So common were these artifacts that whole systems of thinking were based upon them. Swammerdam, who was such a good observer of the structure of insects, comments on the globular appearance of the viscera of the louse and Leeuwenhoek in 1674 reporting on the structure of hair round it

> wholly to consist out of conjoined globules which by my Microscope appear'd so manifestly to me, as if they could be handled.

It is probable that in this instance Leeuwenhoek was looking at the scales of the hair, each surrounded with a diffraction halo. Towards the end of the eighteenth century a biologist named Prochaska produced figures of globules in brain tissue. According to J. R. Baker, who made a most thorough examination of the writing of these upholders of the "globulist" theory of the structure of biological material, these globules found by Prochaska in brain and in nerves were about one-eighth the size of a mammalian red blood cell; this calculation would put the size of the globules at something under one micron, a figure almost certainly below the resolution of the uncorrected lenses of low aperture which were in use at that time. The "globulist" theories probably reached their zenith in the views and writings of Joseph and Carolus Wenzel and in the works of Milne Edwards who in 1823 reported globules in connective tissue, muscle, tendon, skin and many other tissues. It is interesting that most of the globules which he reported were about three microns in size. As we are accustomed to our vastly improved microscopes of today, and what is equally important, to our carefully controlled techniques of preparing the specimens for examination with the microscope, it is difficult to assess exactly what Milne Edwards was seeing. His results were not confirmed, however, by Hodgkin and Lister who in 1827 were unable to find globules but only fibres in preparations of striated muscle. They were using Lister's new microscope, which will be described later, and attributed the discrepancies between their results and those of Milne Edwards to the deficiencies of the latter's microscope. The situation is well summed up in the words of Baker who wrote:

> There can indeed be little doubt that many of the globules reported by the early microscopists were images of minute particles, smaller than any ordinary cells, but surrounded by haloes. The fact that the excesses of the globulists were exposed by Lister's microscope seems significant; for the particular advantage of his instrument was that spherical aberration was corrected and the "ring" appearance round small particles thus reduced.

Bichat, who may be regarded as one of the founders of the science of histology, was especially sceptical of the image produced by the microscope: so much so that he preferred to avoid falling into error and avoided microscopical work entirely. He expressed his reservation in the following phrase written in 1800:

> Quand on regard dans l'obscurité chacun voit à sa manière et suivant qu'il est affecté.

While these pioneer workers were attempting to produce a workable achromatic lens, attention was still being given to the development of the reflecting microscope. One of the famous experimenters in Italy, Gianbattista Amici (1786–1863) is particularly remembered for his efforts in this direction. Amici was a student of physics and mathematics and also had a considerable reputation as a botanist. In the early years of the nineteenth century he devoted considerable effort to the reduction of the spherical aberration of achromatic lens combinations, for he clearly realized that although the chromatic aberration had been largely eliminated, the lens was still not producing an acceptable image because of the large amounts of spherical aberration introduced by the extra lens elements.

Amici eventually despaired of ever achieving this ideal and resorted to the use of mirrors as microscope objectives. In this field he had a great deal of success by using an elliptical mirror; if any object is placed very close to one of the foci of an elliptical mirror then an enlarged image will be formed at the second, more distant focus. Because a reflecting system is in use the image will be completely achromatic, and for points near the axis, almost completely aplanatic. This means that the definition in the centre of the field should be very good. In order to simplify the construction and allow easy access to the object itself, Amici placed a small reflector within the tube of the instrument so that the object was placed to one side of the optical axis. In order to make the microscope convenient for a seated observer to use, Amici mounted the whole instrument with the tube horizontal on the lid of its box; the light path of this microscope is shown in Fig. 5.10. The chief drawback of this microscope is the difficulty in the production of an accurate elliptical mirror surface and the alignment so that its optical axis accurately coincides with that of the microscope. A number of Amici's reflecting microscopes still survive in working order and for low powers the image they produce is surprisingly good. The only method of altering the power with this system was to provide interchangeable eyepieces.

Amici was followed in England by Cuthbert, who upon the advice of Dr. C. R. Goring, began the construction of reflecting microscopes. Cuthbert's microscopes differed from those of Amici in that whereas the latter relied upon different eyepieces to provide the changes in power, Cuthbert provided each instrument with a whole series of elliptical mirror–objectives of different focal lengths. The actual construction of the Cuthbert instruments which have survived is probably superior to that of the Amici microscopes. Although there were other efforts to develop the reflecting system still further, progress in this direction did not come until the early years of the present century. Despite the fact that the reflecting microscopes of Amici and Cuthbert performed just as well as the crude achromatic lens combinations which were in use at that time, developments in the 1820's led to a marked advance in the design of lens systems and the reflecting microscope passed into disuse.

The great problem with the first achromatic lenses was that they could be only made satisfactorily to give low magnifications, and as all the really interesting objects required much higher powers to reveal the details of their structure, prospects seemed bleak. The working of the large curvatures required by high–power achromatic combinations did not yet seem feasible so that about 1823, Selligue, a famous French microscope maker, reverted to the system introduced by Adams in his "Variable" microscope and increased the power by simply screwing together extra lenses. Whereas Adams had simply added more uncorrected lenses, Selligue, however, intended that each succeeding combination should be itself chromatically corrected. The instrument was in fact built in 1824 by Vincent and Charles Chevalier in Paris. It was provided with four achromatic doublet lenses each of which screwed into the other (Fig. 5.11(c)). Fresnel the physicist was commissioned to report on this microscope and on comparing it with the best of the non-achromatized microscopes then available, he found that up to a magnification of about $200 \times$ the new achromatic instrument was definitely superior. Above this magnification there was no improvement in the definition of the achromatic instrument and Fresnel himself preferred the non-achromatic microscope for long observations because of the greater field of this latter instrument.

At this time most of the optical design and construction was still highly empirical; nowadays it is obvious that the basic premise of making a strong objective by combining more and more weaker lenses, each perfectly corrected in itself, was incorrect. The accumulated spherical aberration proved far more detrimental to the image quality and greatly outweighed the advantages gained by the colour correction. The Chevaliers had made the lenses for this microscope of a diameter of about $\frac{1}{2}$ inch, but they had been forced to place a diaphragm with an opening of only $\frac{1}{10}$ inch over the topmost lens in order to keep the spherical aberration within reasonable bounds. This drastic restriction of the aperture of the system inevitably affected the resolution very much indeed. Van Heurck in his well-known book on the microscope comments that although the image was well achromatized, the objective was hardly capable of resolving any fine detail. Scales of *Macroglossa stellatarum* (the Humming Bird Hawk moth) did not show any detail when used as a test object although earlier non-achromatic microscopes were capable of showing the longitudinal lines. J. J. Lister, the father of the celebrated surgeon, in his famous paper in 1830 which provided the solution to this problem of accumulated spherical errors in lens combinations, commented on Selligue's lenses that

> The chromatic aberration was thus in a considerable degree corrected, but the glasses were fixed in their cells with the convex side foremost, which is their worst position, and the spherical error was in consequence enormous, showing itself even through the contracted opening, to which it was necessary on that account to limit them.

Chevalier, who actually made these lenses, seems to have realized that a large amount of the trouble with Selligue's microscope was due to the position of the lenses. He himself in his own microscopes, therefore, retained the same method of construction but mounted the elements with the plane sides towards the object and at the same time slightly shortened the focal length of the combination. This arrangement, which is represented diagrammatically in Fig. 5.11(d), would give rise to a considerable improvement in the quality of the image, although Lister commented that his glasses were still

> restricted to apertures too small to show difficult test objects.

Again, E. M. Nelson in his contribution to the seventh edition of Carpenter's book on the microscope, noted with respect to Chevalier's objectives:

> Everything in the history points to happy accident as the principal step in achromatized objectives, and this, with very high probability, applies to the work of Chevalier, for Selligue's attempt was a blunder against the commonplace knowledge of his time.

At about this time (1825) we can discern the beginnings of a more logical approach to the design and construction of microscope objectives. The use of special test objects to enable their performance to be assessed accurately and compared with the productions of other opticians was to some measure responsible for this, as well as the most important work of J. J. Lister which gave a proper understanding of the theoretical principles behind the combination of achromatic doublets without increasing the spherical errors of the whole. The credit for the introduction of test objects into microscopy belongs to Dr. C. R. Goring. Goring, a medical practitioner in Edinburgh, first of all had a microscope constructed by a Mr. Adie of Edinburgh. No expense was spared but the instrument, even after extensive modification, was not completely achromatic. Finally, suspecting the competence of Adie, Goring consulted Tulley of Islington who

> soon convinced me of the impossibility of obtaining achromatism . . .
> otherwise than by the action of concaves of flint glass.

This was not Tulley's first essay into the construction of achromatic lenses, however, as he had previously tried to make them in 1807. Troughton had then asked him to make some achromatic lenses to act as objectives for the microscopes used to read the graduations on the Greenwich circle in the observatory. Tulley made the lenses, each of a focal length of one inch, which proved to be well corrected for chromatic aberration but retained a great deal of spherical aberration so that they were considered a failure.

Goring now acted as Tulley's sponsor and set him to work with the aim of producing a practical achromatic objective in which the spherical aberration was reduced to acceptable proportions. Goring was a prolific writer and he explains his interest in the development of the compound microscope in the following passage:

> I was always addicted to the use of single magnifiers, in my micro-
> scopical studies, which I felt to be far superior to all other microscopes
> in use; yet I always had a lurking fondness for compound instruments,
> with whose large field of view, and facilities for illumination of opaque
> objects, as well as the application of micrometers and graphic eyepieces
> etc., I could not help being much smitten; though I was fully sensible of
> their great imperfections in point of perfect vision; I thought it would be
> a glorious improvement if they could be rendered equal in point of optical
> performance to single microscopes, because they would then have a most
> decided superiority over the latter, from the accommodations they afford for
> the observation of every species of object. The eyes of very few individuals
> are, by nature, gifted with such energy as to endure the use of deep single
> lenses with impunity for any length of time; and even the most favoured
> observers must allow that these show so small a portion of an object, and

are so disagreeable to use from their very minute aperture, that it is a downright labour to employ them, even when we have been habituated to them for years.

In another passage Goring explains his dissatisfaction with the usual type of achromatic lens current at this time:

It is but a small point gained to render these lenses free from colour, for they may, notwithstanding, be no better, *or even a great deal worse*, with regard to distinctness, than common ones, as is the case also with the chromatic object glasses of telescopes.

Tulley accepted Goring's commission and set to work. He encountered numerous difficulties and, according to Goring, the

repeated failures and disappointments which occurred were so very disheartening, that the project was nearly abandoned more than once, not as a physical impossibility in itself, but merely as impracticable in point of execution.

Tulley developed his lenses entirely by trial and error methods using Goring's test object — the scales of the butterfly *Morpho menelaus* — as the standard by which the performance of the various experimental lenses could be judged. This use of a standard object was of vital importance in stimulating the subsequent improvement in lens performance and the development of better methods of lens manufacture. The use of natural test objects was much extended in subsequent years by the use of insect scales which possessed even finer markings, and by the introduction of diatom frustules with their periodic patterning. Such natural objects, however, suffer from the drawback that they are slightly variable so that results obtained with their aid are often not strictly comparable. In the later years of the nineteenth century the test objects which were most used were in fact artificial; Friedrich Adolf Nobert of Barth in Pomerania discovered the secret of producing very regular rulings on glass slides and these rulings, of known periodicity, served as reproducible tests of resolution.

Goring was very much to the point when he wrote in 1829:

The discovery of a set of objects for ascertaining the defining and penetrating powers of microscopes, has founded a new era in the history of those instruments.

Tulley and Goring proceeded empirically with the development of the lens with the result that Goring was not able to develop the theory, a fact which he readily admits.

As these small aplanatics have been worked entirely by trial upon new microscopic objects, exactly as a telescopic object glass is worked upon distant ones, very little can be said about their theory; experience has shown that the thinner the component lenses can be made and the more closely curves compacted together, the better.

Tulley produced two partially successful combinations for Goring, which had focal lengths of a third and a fifth of an inch respectively. Later he was able to produce a triplet lens of just under an inch focus with an acceptance angle of 18°. At this time the theory behind the optical performance of a lens was not understood and the detailed relationship of the angle of acceptance (that is the angle embraced by the two extreme rays of light from the object which can be encompassed by the objective lens; see Fig. 5.12) and the resolution was only

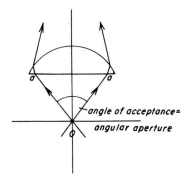

FIG. 5.12. Diagram to illustrate the angular aperture of a lens. The acceptance angle or angular aperture is the angle aoa.

vaguely appreciated. It was not until the 1870's that Ernst Abbe, working with Carl Zeiss, succeeded in rationalizing this and introduced the concept of "numerical aperture" to enable the performance of different lenses to be compared more easily. What is meant by the "numerical aperture" of a lens will be explained in the next chapter.

Goring gave full credit for these achromatic objectives to Tulley, but in his characteristic fashion he contrived to promote his own part in the enterprise.

> The honour of the discovery and execution of its curves belongs entirely to Mr. W. Tulley: yet the public will, I hope, pardon my egotism when I assert that, without my agency, it would never have been made; for at my instigation, and at my expense, was this valuable present to the observer of nature produced.

Goring was instrumental in introducing several changes into the mechanics of the microscope stand, despite the criticism of the more conservative scientists, which he stigmatized as the

> Inveterate hatred and contempt of all innovation whatever, which seems to form part of our nature, when arrived at a certain period of life.

He published his ideas at length and stipulated what he regarded as the essentials of a practical microscope stand. He concluded with pride with what now seems to us an extremely rash prophetic passage:

> This seems to be the golden age of microscopes, the finishing stroke has been given to their exaltation among scientific instruments, by the formation of aplanatic lenses of adequate depth and aperture to become effectual in performance, — by the perfection of the Amician reflecting microscope, — and the formation of single lenses from the diamond. No improvements at all commensurate to these in magnitude and importance can, I predict, be ever made hereafter.

By this time, Dollond was producing achromatic microscopes and Goring began to transfer his patronage to him. Apparently, Dollond was a better workman and produced lenses of a much higher standard of finish than did Tulley. Dollond's lenses were held in their mounts by being burnished into their cells, whereas Tulley's were only screwed in and so on. Goring, writing in 1829, concluded:

> Mr. Tulley will, I am sure, consider it no disparagement to his own talents to admit that as Mr. Dollond can work the small aplanatics with certainty and dispatch (which Mr. T. confessedly cannot) the said Mr. D. is the better man and more consummate artist, by whom it is no disgrace to be beaten.

Dollond was now producing achromatic lenses, probably of triplet construction, of less than one inch focal length. Most of these lenses were probably not of cemented construction, but retained a layer of air between their components, whereas the Continental practice had been for some time to cement the elements together with canada balsam.

In general, it may be stated that the decade of the 1820's resulted in the production of practical objectives in which the chromatic aberration had been corrected by the addition of concave components of flint glass. Such doublets could then be combined to increase the power of the lens, but the resultant spherical aberration could only be minimized by careful selection and arrangement of the positions of the lens elements by trial and error. No theoretical treatment of this subject had yet been attempted.

The success of Selligue's work had led Amici to resume the construction of achromatic lenses about 1824 and he soon produced some fine lenses which were later to be commended by J. J. Lister in 1827. Amici overcame the accumulated spherical aberration of his lens combinations not by combining separate combinations which had each been carefully corrected in itself, as was the custom of all the other workers, but by combining lenses in such a fashion that the inherent spherical errors of the second achromatic component of his lens cancelled out those introduced by the first achromatic doublet of the lens. In other words, the spherical errors of each doublet or triplet were so arranged empirically as to give rise to a cancellation of the errors of the whole. It thus proved possible for Amici to use larger apertures with his lenses and so not only was the resolution of his lenses better than those of his contemporaries, but the image also appeared much brighter as a result of the increased light transmission. At this time Amici was making lenses of shorter and shorter focal lengths and by 1827 he had produced an achromatic objective with a focal length of 1·25 mm which is in fact a shorter focal length than that possessed by any lens current today.

Although some considerable success was achieved by workers such as Amici purely by trial and error methods, the great problem of the residual spherical aberration in compound lenses formed from achromatic doublets and triplets was finally solved in a completely different way by the important work of J. J. Lister which was based on sound theoretical grounds. Instead of empirically correcting the errors of one lens by opposing those of another, Lister showed how to combine fully corrected achromatic doublets so that no further errors were introduced by subsequent elements into the system as a whole. His paper, published in 1830 in the *Philosophical Transactions* proved to be the turning point in the design of microscope objectives; indeed, it may be said that as a result of this work the *design* of microscope objectives became possible, whereas before they could only be constructed on an empirical basis. The starting point in Lister's investigations was the assumption that the microscope objective should consist of a plano-concave element of flint glass cemented to a convex lens of crown glass. For such a lens, shown in Fig. 5.13, Lister deduced that it would possess two focal points (f and f_1) on its axis for which points both the chromatic and spherical aberration would be corrected. For rays emanating anywhere in the space between or beyond these two points these corrections would no longer hold. For rays originating in the space between these foci the combination would be chromatically corrected but *over* corrected for spherical aberration, whereas for the rays which arose beyond these foci there would be a spherical *under* correction. It is not possible here to go into the optical theory behind

FIG. 5.13. The two aplanatic foci, *f* and *f'*, of a doublet lens. Spherical and chromatic aberrations would only be properly corrected for rays originating from these two points.

this, which may be found by those interested in any standard text-book; it is sufficient to note in Lister's own words:

> These facts have been established by careful experiment.

He goes into considerable detail in his paper, which must rank as one of the most important ever published on microscopy and concludes:

> Of the several purposes to which the particulars just given seem applic-able, I must at present confine myself to the most obvious one. They furnish the means of destroying with the utmost ease both aberrations in a large focal pencil, and of thus surmounting what has been hitherto the chief obstacle to the perfection of the microscope. And when it is con-sidered that the curves of its diminutive object-glasses have required to be at least as exactly proportioned as those of a large telescope, to give the image of a bright point equally sharp and colourless, and that any change made to correct one aberration was liable to disturb the other, some idea

may be formed of what the amount of that obstacle must have been. It will, however, be evident, that if any object-glass is but made achromatic, with its lenses truly worked and cemented so that their axes coincide, it may with certainty be connected with another possessing the same requisites and of suitable focus, so that the combination shall be free from spherical error also in the centre of its field. For this the rays have only to be received by the front glass B from its shorter aplanatic focus f'', and transmitted in the direction of the longer correct pencil fA of the other glass A.

It thus follows that the two completely corrected combinations could be placed at such a distance apart that the resultant rays are entirely free from both chromatic and spherical aberration. The great significance of this discovery, perhaps the most important single feature of Lister's work, was that this distance could be calculated and lens designers were no longer dependent upon a lucky chance arrangement in which the components of their lens happened to be placed at or near this optimal distance.

Lister also formally enunciates the principle on which Amici's lenses had been constructed; it is probable that he arrived at this quite independently from Amici:

> In combining several glasses together, it is often convenient to transmit an under-corrected pencil from the front glass, and to counteract its error by over-correction in the middle one. Slight errors in colour may in the same manner be destroyed by opposite ones; and on the principles described, we not only acquire fine correction for the central ray, but by the opposite effects at the two foci on the transverse pencil, all coma can be destroyed, and the whole field rendered beautifully flat and distinct.

Lister had Tulley make him some lenses to his own design so that he could experiment further. One of these with a focus of $0 \cdot 7$ of an inch and an angular aperture of $50°$ gave

> the most distinct microscopic vision that I have yet met with; and I anticipate no serious impediment to the carrying of defining power much further.

Lister found that his ideas did not meet with much support immediately; so little enthusiasm was shown that he decided to learn how to grind and polish lenses himself in order that he could proceed with his experimental work. He achieved a great measure of success in this field, so much so that one of his lenses, which he made to his own design, had the very short working distance of a tenth of an inch and was rated by him as the best of its time. Several of Lister's trial combinations and early efforts at lens grinding are still preserved in the collection of the Royal Microscopical Society. Lister was somewhat surprised that his work led to no rapid development of the microscope objective, and for some years the lens makers carried on in the old way, by means of trial and error. Lister wrote (in a paper which was not, however, published during his lifetime)

> After succeeding fairly well in a trial combination, with this view I left the subject for a while, hoping it would be pursued by opticians but the glasses produced by the makers continued to be on the first simple construction of two or three plano-convex compound lenses till the beginning of 1837.

One of the foremost microscope makers at this time was Andrew Ross. In 1831 he began the construction of achromatic lenses and it is interesting to list some of his achievements in this field during the consequent years in order to show how the angle of aperture was being rapidly extended at this time even though the lenses were still designed empirically.

According to E. M. Nelson, Ross produced the following lenses:

1832	1 inch	14°	two doublets
1833	1 inch	18°	single triplet
1834	1/4 inch	55°	three doublets

In 1837 Ross produced two lenses to the formulae of J. J. Lister who tells us:

> At that time I called on Andrew Ross ... and at his request I gave him a projection for an 1/8 inch objective of three compound lenses ... which he soon worked out successfully, and it became the standard form of high power for many years.

The details of these historic lenses are as follows:

1837–41	1 inch	22°	triple front, two double backs
1837–41	1/8 inch	63°	triple front, two double backs.

Ross carried on improving the higher powered lens and in 1842 he produced a $\frac{1}{8}$-inch lens with an angular aperture of 74°. These lenses of Ross, produced to the designs of Lister, proved to be of great success. They produced such a good quality image that it was soon discovered that the covering of an object with a very thin plate of glass (or coverslip as it was known), a technique which was just coming into vogue, was sufficient to reintroduce considerable spherical errors into a well-corrected object lens. The theoretical studies of Lister suggested that this could be eliminated by altering the distance between the lenses which composed the objective, so in 1838 Andrew Ross produced an objective in which the front element was mounted in a tube which was able to slide over a tube of smaller diameter containing the rear element of the lens combination. Screws were provided to clamp the outer tube at any position on the inner one when the desired correction had been obtained. In principle this crude device worked very well but it soon gave way to a screw arrangement in which the outer tube was moved up or down by the rotation of a collar, and so the lens elements were separated or brought closer together.

This device, with very slight modifications, was used until about 1855 when F. H. Wenham produced an improved type of correction collar. In the old version by Ross, the adjustment of the collar caused a movement of the front lens of the objective and unless the greatest of care was taken it was possible to force the front lens of the objective through the coverslip of the actual preparation. Wenham so altered the mechanism that the collar acted upon the rear element of the combination, with the result that the working distance of the whole remained constant. This form of correction collar has survived to this day and it should be regarded as essential on all high-quality dry lenses which possess a large aperture. With the modern tendency to sacrifice quality for speed and ease of operation it is unfortunate that this most useful refinement is only present on the most expensive lenses. It is true to say that the correction of the final remnants of spherical aberration is not practised by the average user of the microscope and the majority of microscopists today would not know what to do with the correction collar if it were fitted! The correction of the final traces of spherical aberration either by the use of the collar if fitted, or by variation of the tube length is one of the skills which should be acquired by anyone who claims to be a microscopist; the careful performance of this final correction will often cause a most marked improvement in the quality of the image.

One of the first English achromatic microscopes is shown in Fig. 5.14. It represents the microscope commissioned in 1826 from Tulley by J. J. Lister, and was to be built from the working drawings supplied by Lister. It seems that the actual construction of this instrument was passed on to James Smith by Tulley and it was completed in May 1826. It shows several features of interest, such as the mounting of the eye-piece in a screwed mount and the provision of full movements to the stage. These movements were controlled from milled knobs, one of which may be seen mounted vertically just in front of the limb; the substage condenser is compound and fits into a sleeve just below the stage.

FIG. 5.14. The achromatic microscope constructed by W. Tulley for J. J. Lister.

One of the most important departures from tradition is the fact that this microscope was constructed only as a compound instrument. All the early Marshall and Cuff microscopes were only compound instruments, but the microscopes of Martin, Adams, Jones and Powell up to this time were all intended to serve as both simple or compound instruments. Such was the confidence of Lister in the superiority of his achromatic lenses that he did not include the facility of use as a simple microscope which had hitherto been regarded as essential if fine detail was to be studied. The other feature which is worthy of comment is

FIG. 5.15. The microscope which Ross constructed to Valentine's design in 1831. The fine-focus control is at table level, below the tripod foot; the screw visible at the level of the stage is one of the mechanical controls.

he device for supporting the limb. Lister realized the importance of tability and steadiness in a microscope stand and he arranged for the ody tube to be supported by struts which passed from the tube to he folding tripod base. This feature in a modified form was adopted by other makers in the following years. The workmanship of this microscope had to be of good quality and it is interesting to note in this connection that Lister did not make any provision for the fitting of a fine focus screw, relying entirely upon the smooth running of the main rackwork to focus his relatively high aperture lenses.

(a) Oberhauser's pattern.   (b) A similar design due to Nachet.

FIG. 5.16. The Continental drum microscope in the early nineteenth century.

A slightly later instrument by Ross which was made by him to the order and to the design of W. Valentine of Nottingham, is shown in Fig. 5.15. This microscope may be dated at about 1831 and to our eye seems rather ungainly; as it could not be inclined, it must have been rather uncomfortable to use when placed on a table of normal height.

The fine focus thread of this instrument is contained within the central stem and acts on the triangular bar which may be seen in the picture. This is an interesting reversion to the practice of Adams in 1746 in which the fine focus milled head is placed below the tripod approximately at table-top level. One of the most interesting features of this microscope is the long tube which served to hold the condensing lens. The mirror was also fitted in this tube at its lower end, opposite the cut-out portion, and the whole design probably originated with Wollaston who used it in the construction of the stand intended to carry his celebrated doublets. This stand, and the models of a slightly later date to be described in the next chapter, represent the English trends in microscope design. The tripod foot was favoured, together with a long body tube and a mechanical stage in which both the top and bottom plates were movable. On the optical side it was noticeable that nearly all English models were provided with a substage condenser. Allied to these features was superb craftsmanship and a truly fine finish which characterized the best of English instruments throughout the nineteenth century.

The microscope on the Continent in the early years of this century, however, showed considerable divergence in design, the general pattern being directly descended from the drum microscope of Benjamin Martin. Figure 5.16(a) shows an early instrument of Oberhauser and the differences from the English model are immediately apparent. The foot is circular and heavily weighted with lead in order to provide the necessary stability. It carries a large tube to support the stage within which is enclosed the mirror. Light enters by means of an oblong opening cut into the side of the large tube. The support for the compound body is attached to the side of the stage and this support pillar contains both the fine and coarse focus adjustments, the former working by a screw thread, whilst the latter acts by means of rackwork. A very similar instrument by the French maker Nachet is shown in Fig. 5.16(b). From these early instruments the microscope on the Continent developed along quite independent lines to that in England so that by the latter part of the nineteenth century there were two completely different patterns of microscope extant, with all the resultant confusion from the proliferation of different accessories to suit each type. The later development of these microscopes, however, will be considered in the next chapter.

CHAPTER 6

THE MICROSCOPE IN VICTORIAN
TIMES

As we have seen in the previous chapter the achromatic lens was a practicable proposition by the 1830's. It was now possible to construct a lens in which the chromatic errors had been eliminated and, which as a consequence of Lister's work, was also spherically corrected. This progress meant that objects were now clearly distinguishable under the microscope, whereas before they were blurred and their images surrounded by coloured fringes. Thus there was fresh interest in the microscope as a tool for biological study and as a result of increased interest, the optical progress continued.

Much important development work was carried out on the Continent at this time, by such workers as Chevalier, Nachet and Amici. The work of Amici has already been mentioned and it will be remembered that he attempted the correction of the spherical aberration in his lenses by balancing the errors of one partially-corrected combination against those of another. This contrasted with the more precise theoretical approach of Lister who used highly corrected combinations and carefully placed them so that the lenses lay at the aplanatic foci and so minimized the aberrations in that way. Although Amici's approach was very empirical, he was nevertheless very successful. By 1844 he had constructed an objective with a focal length of $\frac{1}{7}$ inch which, when he brought it to this country, astonished microscopists by its angular aperture of 112° (corresponding to a numerical aperture of 0·83 in our present terminology). This aperture was much larger than that of British objectives of a comparable focal length. Studies of the microscopic structure of animal and plant tissues were now beginning to flourish, especially on the Continent; as a result of the very clear images furnished, by the new achromatic compound microscopes many workers, especially medical men and physiologists, were stimulated to enter the exciting new fields of animal and plant histology.

Some of these microscopists continued to use the simple microscope — one of the most famous was Robert Brown who has already been mentioned in this respect. All his studies on the motion of very small particles in a liquid and on the nuclei in the leaves and staminal hairs of *Tradescantia* were carried out with single lenses of very short focal length. He was not, however, unaware of the new achromatic compound lenses; Lister in his famous paper of 1830 on the aplanatic foci, says with reference to Frauenhofer's lenses:

> My friend Mr. Brown has kindly lent me a series of five glasses of this description, purchased by him in Munich a few months ago from the establishment of Utzschneider and Frauenhofer, which range from 1·8 to 0·43 inch in focal length, and are of excellent workmanship.

It seems that Brown preferred to use his single lenses rather than the new achromatic lenses which he had bought on his Continental trip, possibly because he was more certain of their capabilities and placed more reliance upon his interpretation of the image furnished by a single lens. Another research worker who actually preferred the simple microscope was William Sharpey, the histologist, who is remembered today for the fibres passing from the periosteum or covering membrane of bone into its substance, and which are still called "Sharpey" fibres. In 1835 Sharpey was working on the beating of cilia, following up investigations reported by Purkinje and Valentine, and he tells us that

> For the most part I used a doublet lens of 1/35 of an inch focus though the phenomenon could sometimes be seen with a lens of 1/20 of an inch focus.

In general, however, the Continental workers displayed no such conservatism and led by Johann Purkinje, the Professor of Physiology at Breslau, who bought one of the new instruments by Ploessl of Vienna, they all changed to the use of the new achromatic microscope. Müller at Berlin was one of these workers who used the new microscopes and stimulated by Purkinje's work on the structure of bone, he began serious microscopical work studying the deposition of minerals in tissues. This proved to be very significant for the future of such histological studies as Müller had previously been of the opinion that the microscope was only of value for the examination of isolated particles or transparent textures and he did not believe that physicians

needed to acquire the ability to undertake microscopical examinations
for themselves. Müller had a very great influence on his assistants and
students, one of whom was to become a very great figure in the
development of the concept of the cell as the structural unit of living
organisms. Theodor Schwann, who was Müller's assistant, also came
under the influence of Schleiden who was at this time developing the
ideas of the cell as the unit of plant anatomy. Schwann extended the
work of Schleiden to the animal tissues, building up a whole classification on a cellular basis. He passed on and expressed his general belief
in the cellular origin and structure of both animals and plants and in
so doing laid the foundations for the greater part of the work of
histologists and cytologists up to the present day. It was also on
the basis of his ideas that Virchow was able to lay the foundations
of the science of cellular pathology with its important practical
aspects.

It is not certain which type of microscope was used by Schwann as
he does not mention it by name in his book, but it is very likely that
it would have been supplied either by Ploessl in Vienna or by the firm
of Pistor and Schiek of Berlin. The instruments supplied by both of
these firms had a high reputation in France and Germany at this time;
Frison, in a recent evaluation of certain contemporary accounts of the
optical performance of Ploessl's lenses comments that in 1829 both
Jacquin and Ettlinghausen examined them and found that they were
of very variable quality. By 1846, however, Nobert the instrument
maker of Griefswald (later of Barth) produced his artificial test plate
of lines ruled on glass at ever closer spacings. He himself said that the
lenses made by Ploessl dating from 1840 were the best of their time
and were capable of resolving the sixth or seventh band on his own
ten-band test plate. Recent measurements (made with the electron
microscope) of the spacings of a Nobert ten-band plate by G. L'E.
Turner and the author, enable us to say that this lens must, therefore,
have had a resolving power of about 1 micron.

Another famous histologist who was working at this time was Henle.
He is known today for his description of parts of the tubules in the
kidney, but also studied epithelia and made many other contributions
to the rapidly developing science of histology. It is known that the
microscope which he used was made by Schiek and resembled those
of Ploessl very closely.

There was great activity in the 1830's from the French microscope
manufacturers, especially Chevalier, Oberhauser and Trecourt, and it

was at about this time that the Oberhauser drum microscope illustrated (Fig. 5.16) in the last chapter appeared. According to Mayall:

> the success of this model was, I believe quite unprecedented in the history of the microscope. The design was copied by the Ingenieur Chevallier, Lerebons, Soleil, and Nachet, senior with modifications principally with reference to the mechanism of the substage.

These French instruments were imported into this country and soon accounts appeared in contemporary scientific works of their use in our laboratories and medical schools. This popularity of the Continental instruments among the working scientists was largely due to the fact that they combined good lenses and construction with a very reasonable price. The English microscopes which were being produced at this time were second to none in design and in workmanship but they were large and very elaborate instruments, intended for the

> rich and influential amateurs whose view prevailed in the microscopical societies. These gentlemen, who regarded their costly and monumental instruments as precious toys rather than as the tools for work and study, amused themselves by resolving test objects.

Such microscopes as these were obviously beyond the reach of practising medical men and teachers in the universities, so it is not surprising that they turned to the much cheaper and equally efficient Continental stands by such makers as Oberhauser, Ploessl, and others.

The instruments of the 1830's and 1840's were obviously superior to their predecessors from the pre-achromatic days, but they still had a maximum resolution of only about 1 micron. This figure, which was obtained from measurements made by van Cittert with a Nobert test plate, may be compared with a modern student's microscope of today; on this instrument the $\frac{1}{6}$ inch high-power objective would be easily capable of resolving two points separated by a distance of half a micron. The importance of the study of microscopic anatomy was becoming more and more evident; so much so that by the late 1840's efforts were being made to introduce such studies into the formal medical training. John Quekett, who was Professor of Histology at the Royal College of Surgeons, even went to the extent of contriving a system by which the students could examine a microscopical preparation during the course of one of his lectures. In his famous *Treatise on the Microscope* he publishes as the frontispiece an engraving of the lecture theatre at the Royal College of Surgeons. In this picture one can see that each tier of the theatre had its microscope mounted on a slide or tray so that it could be circulated, together with its own lamp, to each student in turn. A similar system was used by Acland in the Anatomy School at Oxford.

The period between 1830 and 1850 is very important because it was during these years that the foundations of modern cell biology, of cellular pathology and of normal histology were being laid. There was a great revival of interest in the applications of the microscope to science and medicine and it is very significant that much of this actual stimulus came before the technical developments which led to the greatly increased resolutions of the microscopes used in the second half of the century. It was the achromatic lens which almost certainly provided the initial impetus and once the process was actually under way the other improvements in instrumentation followed on very rapidly.

The fact that the main centres of activity in the new sciences involving the use of the microscope were on the Continent of Europe has already been noted. This may well have been due to the more enlightened attitude on the part of scientists there, but also to a large extent the availability of cheap well-made microscopes in France, Germany and Austria must have played a large part in maintaining the lead of these countries. The best English microscopes were so elaborate and expensive that microscopy, with the few exceptions already noted above, remained very largely the province of the well-to-do amateur.

On September 3rd, 1839, a historic meeting took place in the house of Edwin Quekett, the elder brother of John who has already been mentioned for his interest in microscopy. Seventeen gentlemen gathered at 50, Wellclose Square, in London to consider

> the propriety of forming a society for the promotion of microscopical investigation, and for the introduction and improvement of the Microscope as a scientific instrument.

Some of the names of those who approved that resolution are now very famous in the history of microscopy in the nineteenth century. Among them were Joseph Lister, George Jackson, Cornelius Varley, Nathaniel Ward, as well as others less well known. As a result of this meeting the "Microscopical Society of London" was formed and a public meeting was arranged. Soon the society could boast 115 members and the famous anatomist Richard Owen was elected to be its first president. At first the society numbered many professional scientists among its members, no fewer than twenty-two being Fellows of the Royal Society, although later the membership was to become largely amateur. This society was later to receive a Royal Charter when it became known as the Royal Microscopical Society, a body which came to rank foremost in microscopical affairs by the turn of the century. Today the Royal Microscopical Society is still active in the field of microscopy, although now catering rather more for the professional worker in this field than for the amateur.

In its early days the amateur members were often "amateurs very near to the border of the professional" as was said of James Scott Bowerbank, one of the founder members and later its president; such men contributed very largely to the scientific knowledge of the day especially in various fields of natural history. At a later date, however, many of the amateur members devoted their entire efforts to the resolution of various test objects, competing with one another to see who could "dot" a given diatom frustule or who could resolve more bands of a Nobert test plate with a given lens. Such workers, often referred to as devotees of "brass and glass", often tended to display extreme conservatism as far as microscopy was concerned; their influence was such that when they participated in some of the violent controversies which were to rage in the microscopical world their view came to prevail and may in some cases actually have retarded the progress of the science. Sir Frank Crisp was led to complain in 1878 that

> out of the entire scientific world there is probably no body of men who devote so little real attention to the principles that lie at the root of that branch of science of which they are disciples, as do the English microscopists.

It must, however, be added in fairness that very often the wealthy amateurs of this country, with their urge to possess the finest equipment possible and to attain the best possible resolution, even if only to score off their rivals, did encourage superb instrument making and optical work by supporting such men as Andrew Ross, James Smith and Hugh Powell. These men were directly responsible for most of the progress in this country around the mid-nineteenth century. Before passing on to consider some of their achievements it is necessary to pause briefly in order to consider microscopy in America.

Up to about 1830 such microscopy as had been carried out in American colleges and universities had been with instruments imported from Europe. The first real development in American microscopy seems to have been the work of Edward Thomas who published a paper on the microscope in 1830. He stressed several points, among them the fact that the residual spherical aberration in achromatic objectives was much more detrimental to image quality than any residual chromatic aberration, and that blue light gave a better resolution than ordinary daylight. Thomas understood the theory of the microscope and he was aware that the larger the aperture of the objective the better it would be for showing fine detail in the object; he also made the statement that better lenses could only be constructed when other materials, differing in refractive indices and dispersions from crown and flint glass, became available.

Thomas, unfortunately, died in the year following the publication of his paper so that no real follow-up of his results took place. About ten years later Charles Achille Spencer began work as a maker of optical instruments. Not only microscopes but many other types of instrument were produced from his workshop and from early examples of his work which have survived, it can be seen that he favoured a style made popular by Amici and Chevalier in which the stage was mounted horizontally on a pillar and a right-angled prism was used above the objective lens to enable the tube to be mounted parallel to the table. This system allowed the use of a large heavy stand and a long tube but without causing inconvenience to the observer. Spencer was particularly famed for the excellence of his objective lenses. In 1847 he made an achromatic microscope for Dr. C. R. Gilman of New York, and on his way to deliver it he showed it to Dr. Jacob Bailey who was the Professor of Chemistry at the United States Military Academy, West Point. Bailey was an enthusiastic amateur microscopist and an expert on diatoms so it was natural for him to try out Spencer's microscope on some of these objects. He found that the lenses of Spencer's microscope easily resolved all his difficult test objects much better than the best of the European objectives that he had in his possession. Bailey was eager to buy Spencer's instruments and soon his fame as an instrument maker spread widely and his works grew in size. He passed his skill and enthusiasm to his two sons and to his apprentice Robert Tolles, who was in later life to prove an even better lens-maker than his teacher.

From the late 1830's other firms began to enter the business of microscope manufacture and it is to this period that most of the great American optical firms can trace their origin. Such firms as the American Optical Company, and the firm of Bausch and Lomb of Rochester, New York, began as small concerns at this time. The real stimulus to the development of microscopy in the universities and medical schools came out of the visits of the lecturers and professors to Europe; the introduction of microscopy into the curriculum of the Harvard Medical School only came after Dr. Oliver Wendell Holmes returned from his own studies in Paris in 1835. He brought a microscope back with him and used it extensively in his own teaching. When he became Professor of Anatomy and Physiology in 1847 he fitted up a room in the attic of the Grove Street medical building as a "Microscope room". Later he devised a special class microscope designed to be passed from student to student in order to illustrate

A   *B*

Fig. 6.1.
(a) The "Lister" limb construction.
(b) The "bar-limb" type of construction.

the points made in the lecture, in much the same way as John Quekett had done at the Royal College of Surgeons in London.

To return to the progress of the microscope in England: it has already been mentioned that much of the activity centred around the activities of three people — Andrew Ross, Hugh Powell and James Smith. Andrew Ross first became noted as a microscope maker when he built an instrument to the design of W. Valentine who lived in Nottingham. This microscope (which was figured in the last chapter, Fig. 5.15) was, like the majority of instruments of its day, capable of being used both as a single or a compound microscope. It resembled Adams's Universal microscope of 1746 in that the pillar was upright and not inclinable; both instruments had flat folding tripod feet and both fitted the screw head for the fine focus mechanism at the base of the pillar. The other interesting feature of this first microscope of Ross was the use of a substage illuminating system which was very similar to that used by Wollaston in his doublet microscope.

The next large stand which Ross produced was illustrated in an article which he wrote for the *Penny Cyclopaedia* of 1839; this

Fig. 6.2. Ross microscope of 1839. The upper part of the limb is of triangular section, while the mirror is mounted on an extension of the same casting, but of circular section. The nosepiece carries the short-lever type of fine focus mechanism.

microscope is very significant as a landmark in instrument design as the limb had the form of a single casting which supported the body on its upper part and below the stage, on the same casting was mounted the tailstock with the condenser and mirror. This construction is shown diagrammatically in Fig. 6.1, where it is contrasted with the "bar limb" construction which was the favoured alternative. The former design is generally believed to be the work of Joseph Jackson Lister, in consequence of which it is generally referred to as the "Lister" limb, and it has been extensively used up to the present day.

The Ross microscope of 1839 is shown in Fig. 6.2 from which its general form may be seen. The debt which later microscopes owe to this instrument is clearly obvious. The body tube is supported at two points by a cradle which is driven up and down by the rack and pinion focusing mechanism working on the triangular upper part of the limb casting. The tailstock and mirror mounted on the continuation of this same casting should be noted, as well as the fact that here the cross-section of the limb is now of a circular shape. It is very

A   *B*

Fig. 6.3.
(a) Ross's short-lever fine focus mechanism.
(b) Powell's long-lever fine focusing device.

likely that this microscope was fitted with achromatic lenses, which were probably made by Ross to Lister's formula, whilst the higher power lens of $\frac{1}{8}$-inch focus incorporated Ross's coverglass correction collar.

The development of corrected lenses with ever-increasing angles of aperture led to the reintroduction of fine focusing mechanisms and this particular instrument by Ross shows for the first time his short lever nose piece focusing. This mechanism involves the use of a lever of the second order and is shown diagrammatically in Fig. 6.3 together with the form of fine focus which was eventually to supersede it. The object of these devices was to use a lever system to reduce the amplitude of the movement and so make the focusing of high aperture lenses with a very short working distance much easier. The other lever device, shown in Fig. 6.3, is Hugh Powell's long-lever which was much more practicable than the invention of Ross; both types, however, do suffer to some extent from flexure and lateral movements

Fig. 6.4. The 1843 model of Ross. Notice the trunnion mounting of the limb, and the adoption of the bar-limb type of construction.

which are due to the temporary stresses applied by the pressure of the screw. Ross's microscope was subsequently modified by the adoption of a plan devised by Jackson for grooving the limb for the body slide and fitting the rackwork to the body tube. At the same time the sub-stage was mounted on a rackwork and the groove for this was cut in the same machining operation as that of the body so that they were absolutely in line. This development, which probably dates from around 1841 was adopted by both of the other manufacturers.

Subsequently Ross adopted another of Jackson's suggestions, which was to mount the limb of the instrument between two trunnions so that the centre of gravity is lowered and a much better balance obtained. An example of such an instrument is shown in Fig. 6.4 dating from 1843 in which the short-lever focus has been abandoned and the tube is now mounted on the end of a traverse arm which contains the lever of the fine focus mechanism. This form of "bar-limb" model, as it became known, was adopted from Powell and Lealand and was used by most English makers for some considerable time. The microscopes, which Andrew Ross made from this time up to his death in 1859, only differed from this form in minor details, such as the omission of the back support stay for the tube, alteration in the position of the mechanical stage controls, and the provision of a complete substage with rectangular and rotary movements.

In 1841 the Microscopical Society of London ordered sample microscopes from Andrew Ross, Hugh Powell and James Smith. Although the Smith and the Powell instruments are still in the possession of the Society, the Ross microscope was exchanged in 1863 for a binocular model made by Thomas Ross who had continued in his father's business. It is unfortunate that this early microscope is no longer extant, but as its delivery was not effected until 1843, it seems very likely that it did not differ in essentials from the instrument shown in Fig. 6.4.

Hugh Powell, like Andrew Ross, was an instrument maker in London. Up to 1840 he had made several microscopes for Cornelius Varley, one of the founder members of the Microscopical Society and a well-known artist. It was not until he was asked by the Society, along with Ross and Smith

> to furnish a standard instrument made according to their own peculiar views,

that he became one of the three leading manufacturers. His microscope was delivered in December 1841 and except for the fitting of a binocular body in 1862, it is still in its original state. This microscope is very solidly built, as can be seen from Fig. 6.5, and it has a system of mounting the body on a triangular bar which is obviously influenced by the Ross microscope of 1839. The single pillar, the tripod foot and the

FIG. 6.5. Hugh Powell's microscope, commissioned in 1841 by the Microscopical Society. This particular instrument was fitted with a binocular body in 1862. Notice the triangular limb, obviously influenced by the earlier design of Ross.

compass joint method of inclining the body are all very reminiscent of the practice of the instrument makers of the years immediately preceding the introduction of the achromatic microscope.

Hugh Powell's microscope is fitted with an achromatic condenser, which was almost certainly one of the first ever made in this country, as this was first used in France about three years previously by Chevalier and Felix Dujardin. Powell provided his microscope with a very large solid stage, furnished with a movement (designed by a mechanic named Edmund Turrell) in which the actuating milled heads are concentrically mounted. The fine focusing mechanism of this microscope acted upon the stage, a clever system of three inclined planes being actuated by the screw. This produced a very slow and smooth motion but as the stage moved with respect to the objective and as the substage was not carried with it, this arrangement produced alterations in the focus of the substage condenser. As the illumination of the object assumed more importance this loss of focus of the condenser on changing the objective focus proved an insuperable handicap to the general acceptance of this form of fine focusing. This design feature has recently reappeared in many current research microscopes produced within the last twenty years, but now the whole of the substage mechanism is moved at the same time so that the focus of the condenser is not disturbed.

At about the time that Hugh Powell constructed his microscope for the Microscopical Society of London, he took into partnership his brother-in-law, P. H. Lealand, and so started one of the most famous associations in the history of the microscope. They continued to manufacture this large model of stand with its characteristic triangular limb; as all of their products are signed and dated it is relatively easy to follow the evolution of their designs. As one of these microscopes is in the Museum of the History of Science at Oxford and bears the date 1849, it seems that this model had a period of production of about ten years. Powell and Lealand began to experiment, however, and even at the beginning of their partnership in 1841 they produced a stand with the Lister limb and the Jackson groove in which the limb was supported between twin pillars, yet another of George Jackson's inventions. This microscope had a fine focusing device mounted on the side of the limb actuated by a cone driven by a micrometer screw; this was not very successful as it had to carry the full weight of the tube and the coarse adjustment and was soon abandoned. The cone drive did reappear later at the suggestion of E. M. Nelson as a fine focus for the substage rackwork. The trunnion mounting, however, did prove valuable and was retained in essentially the same form by other makers.

In 1843, Powell and Lealand departed completely from this design and produced a stand based on the "bar-limb" model and with a true

FIG. 6.6. Powell and Lealand's No. 3 microscope. The struts supporting the tube are very characteristic of this model. There is a strong resemblance to the later models of this firm.

tripod suspension for the limb. They introduced for the first time their long lever focusing (Fig. 6.3) which was incorporated inside the transverse bar carrying the microscope body. This lever acted only upon the nosepiece and the objective and proved so successful that Powell and Lealand used the same system unchanged for the rest of the century. There can be little doubt that the bar-limb microscope with this pattern of fine adjustment was far superior to the short-lever movements which had to be fitted to the Lister-Jackson limb models until the 1880's. Later changes led to the appearance of the instrument shown in Fig. 6.6, subsequently known as the "P. and L. No. 3" stand. There was the usual Turrell stage, by now standard on all Powell and Lealand microscopes, and a full centring substage fitting. At first these instruments were fitted with a side screw fine focus, but very soon the long lever took its place and the most characteristic external feature, the struts connecting the bar-limb to the tube, were added. Still later, the struts were found to contribute nothing to the stability of the monocular tube and were omitted. In this last form the stand was manufactured up to 1870, when by minor changes in matters of detailed design (increasing the spread of the tripod foot, fitting a longer bar and adding a rotating object holder to the stage) it was transformed into the "No. 2" stand.

In 1860, Powell and Lealand brought out what was to become the direct predecessor of their most celebrated microscope, the famous "No. 1", which marked the summit of microscope design and manufacture in this country for over fifty years. This forerunner of the "No. 1" was characterized by the presence of a large gun-metal ring attached to the limb. The Turrell stage was fixed to a second ring which was mounted inside that attached to the limb and so arranged that the whole stage could be rotated within the outer ring by means of a rack and pinion. One of the popular features which was introduced with this model was the provision for unscrewing the monocular body above the bar so that it could be replaced very quickly by a second binocular body. This latter had just come into favour as a result of Wenham's invention of his beam-splitting prism. The large ring fitted to the early models of this microscope did not prove a success with the users, so it was abandoned in 1869 and the "P. and L. No. 1" then appeared in the form in which it remained for so many years (see frontispiece); the only changes incorporated later were three minor additions — fine focusing on the substage, rackwork on the draw tube and a modification to the coarse focus rackwork — which were fitted at the suggestion of E. M. Nelson. The P. and L. instruments were so well constructed that they are still highly prized today not as collector's items but as actual working microscopes. They can still be used with great success for every type of microscopical research, although naturally they are not so convenient to use as a modern research instrument.

The Powell and Lealand "No. 1" stand may well be regarded as the highest peak of achievement of English microscope construction and is of such importance in the development of microscope design that it justifies quoting Powell's own description of it in full:

> This instrument on the bar-movement pattern is supported on a tripod stand. A wide spread is given to the legs of the tripod, viz. 7 × 9 inches, so as to give perfect steadiness in every position of the instrument. Cork is inserted in the feet of the tripod, as it has been found to give additional steadiness to the instrument and protection to the table. When the instrument is inclined in a horizontal position, the optic axis is 10 inches from the table. The body is of such a length as to give, as nearly as possible, the standard optical interval of 10 inches between the posterior principal focus of the objective and the anterior focus of the eyepiece: the variation in the optical tube length does not exceed $\frac{1}{4}$ inch with objectives of $\frac{1}{2}$ inch and upwards. The No. 2 inch eyepiece has the largest field glass that can be used with a binocular, viz. $1\frac{1}{4}$ inch full. The arm on which the body is fixed is $5\frac{3}{4}$ inches long, which not only gives a clearance of $3\frac{1}{2}$ inches from the optic axis, but also permits the use of a long fine adjustment lever. The movable nosepiece is 3 inches long; it is held at both ends, so that any rocking movement is simply impossible. The fine adjustment screw is placed immediately behind the pivot which holds the bar; this prevents it communicating vibration to the bar. The stage is supported by a very strong bracket; it has 1 inch of motion in rectangular directions by screw, rack and pinion. The milled heads do not move with the stage. When the stage is racked either way to its full extent, there is $\frac{1}{4}$ inch of clearance between it and the milled heads. A milled head is placed on each end of the pinion that moves the stage in a vertical direction, so that it may be moved by either hand; while the milled head which moves the stage in a transverse direction, is placed at the right hand side, and on the same spindle as the pinion that gives the vertical movement. The stage, when in any position, can be rotated through a whole circle. The optic axis passes through the centre of rotation. The instrument has a graduated arc made of gun-metal, silver or platinum, for measuring angles. The stage plates are graduated to 0·01 inch, which enables the position of an object on any slide to be registered. The opening in the stage is large, so that the finger may be inserted for the purpose of feeling the working distance of an objective. This enables the observer to rack down an objective on to the thinnest cover by the coarse adjustment without risk of breakage. The substage has full mechanical movements, viz. rectangular and rotary. The milled head of the substage focusing pinion is conveniently placed for the right hand. The 3 inch plane and concave mirrors are fitted on a double jointed arm. All the moving parts are sprung; they can be tightened up if at any time they should wear loose. The instrument can be instantly converted to a

binocular by unscrewing the monocular body at the arm, screwing on the binocular tubes in its place, and inserting the prism.

It can be seen from this description how carefully Hugh Powell had thought out the requirements of the microscopists and had incorporated them in his design. E. M. Nelson, one of the foremost microscopists of his day, thought very highly of the Powell and Lealand "No. 1". He wrote with respect to this microscope:

> Beginning with the highest types we place first on the list Powell and Lealand's No. 1. The instrument may claim a seniority over all the foremost instruments, because for nearly fifty years it has practically remained the same. All its principle features were brought to their present perfection nearly fifty years ago, while all other microscopes during this period have been redesigned and materially altered over and over again. This is no small commendation, for during that period, as the reader so well knows, the apertures of objectives have been enormously enlarged, and with this has come a great increase in focal sensibility. As a result the majority of the microscopes of forty years ago are absolutely useless for the objectives of today, but the focusing and stage movements of Powell and Lealand's microscope still hold the first place.

The remaining member of the three great instrument makers of the early Victorian era was James Smith; although he had been making microscopes for the trade in the 1820's (it will be remembered that he actually built Lister's microscope for Tulley in 1826) Smith did not set up in business on his own until around 1840. He too provided one of his microscopes for the Microscopical Society in 1841 and this microscope is illustrated in Fig. 6.7. It has the typical Lister limb, with the foot and single pillar and is provided with a short-lever type of fine focus. There was an achromatic condenser which was not, however, carried in the typical substage mounting, but which slid into prepared grooves on the underside of the main specimen stage. The objectives provided with this microscope were rather unusual; the basic lens, of $1\frac{1}{2}$-inch focus, carried mounted on its front a diaphragm which could be removed when a higher power was required. A new front lens was then substituted which altered the focus of the whole to $\frac{8}{10}$ inch. By exchanging this front for yet another, the combination was altered to one of $\frac{1}{2}$-inch focus. This latter front element was provided with a correction collar divided into ten divisions, as was the collar provided on the completely separate $\frac{1}{4}$-inch objective; at this time this represented a very advanced feature for it was only usual to

FIG. 6.7. James Smith's microscope of 1841, commissioned by the Microscopical Society. This instrument has a typical Lister limb and short-lever fine focus acting on the nosepiece.

mark the correction collar with two lines, one representing the "covered" position, the other the "uncovered" setting.

In 1846 Smith entered into partnership with Richard Beck and so the famous firm of Smith and Beck came into being; they produced a microscope very similar to that shown in Fig. 6.7, but which had incorporated Jackson's trunnion mounting of the limb between two pillars and with a slightly different drive mechanism for the mechanical stage. For the Great Exhibition of 1851 they prepared a new model in which at the suggestion of Jackson the grooves for the substage were cut at the same time as those for the body slide. This practice, which was to become universal for all models with a Lister limb, marked an important advance in the mechanical construction of the microscope. The first models to incorporate this amendment were not provided with any means of centring the substage, as Jackson's invention was thought to render this unnecessary. Later, when developments in illumination techniques resulted in the use of wide cones of axial light, it proved essential to reintroduce such centration devices for the condenser.

In 1852 Joseph Beck joined the firm, which then became known as Smith, Beck and Beck; large microscope stands were still manufactured on the lines of those already produced, but in order to meet the large and ever-growing demand for a cheap microscope the firm introduced additions to their range. Two of these models are illustrated in Fig. 6.8. At this time great interest was shown in the binocular microscope, as a result of the invention of various types of beam-splitting prisms by Ridell and Wenham. For low powers especially the advantage of using both eyes proved considerable and this type of binocular became very popular. In fact, "Popular" was the name applied by Smith, Beck and Beck to one of their new cheap stands. It was intended to give good service at a reasonable price. This was achieved by simplification of the design and by eliminating many of the over-elaborate refinements which were so common on the large microscope stands of the period. The "Popular" microscope (Fig. 6.8a) used a triangular casting as the base, to which was hinged a broad supporting piece (G) which carried the microscope stage. By placing the tail post (H) in any one of a series of holes in the base, the angle of inclination of the body could be easily changed to any one of several selected positions between vertical and the horizontal. A complete set of accessories, such as dark-field condensers and polarizing apparatus was available for this instrument and could be purchased separately as required.

The other instrument shown in Fig. 6.8b was, as Richard Beck describes it in his book (*The Achromatic Microscope*, 1865)

> the result of an endeavour to make a very low-priced Compound Achromatic microscope by reducing its construction to the simplest possible form, still retaining all that a really useful instrument requires,

together with such an arrangement as would admit of considerable additions being made without returning the stand to the maker.

The microscope was mounted on a circular base, the limb itself being carried at the top of a strong pillar, labelled B in the figure. This

(a)   (b)

FIG. 6.8. The Smith and Beck designs intended for wide appeal.
(a) The "popular" microscope. One of the first cheap binocular microscopes to be placed on the market.
(b) The "Universal" microscope. Notice the square section body tube casting and the fine focus lever, labelled F.

microscope possessed several interesting mechanical features of design, such as the coarse focus control which was mounted on the same axis around which the microscope body pivoted in order to change its inclination. The knob which operated the focus was linked by means of a chain drive to the body E, itself unusual in having a square section, and provided a rapid motion for obtaining the approximate focus of the objective. Chain drive mechanisms for this purpose have been little used in the construction of microscopes; the only maker to adopt this idea was Ladd who used it extensively and developed it to give a very smooth and certain control.

FIG. 6.9. The combined body for the Universal microscope. Any one of the three objectives or eyepieces could be brought into the optical axis by pressing the button on the right hand side of the mounting disc.

Beck's "Universal" microscope also had an unusual fine focus. Hanging free upon the coarse focus knob D was a long lever marked F in the illustration; when this was held at its lower end and pressed sideways, either towards or away from the pillar, it obtained a grip on the axis of the focus knob and allowed it to be turned very slowly indeed. In this way, the need to provide a conventional fine focus (which would of course increase the manufacturing costs very considerably) was avoided. The stage was a simple form of gliding stage which allowed the object to be positioned by sliding the whole with the fingers, after which it was retained in position by means of spring tension.

At the time when this microscope was designed most microscopes were provided with the universal thread for the objective lens screw which had been sponsored by the Microscopical Society in order to promote greater interchangeability between the lenses of different makers. With the "Universal" microscope, however, Beck reverted to a smaller size of thread for the objectives and at the same time set the lenses in as short a mount as possible, so effectively preventing their use on any other instrument. It will be noticed that the body tube of this microscope was much shorter than the normal English practice of the time, so the makers provided a "lengthening tube" to fit the stand in order that the initial magnification provided by their lenses could be increased to suit the inclinations of the buyers, who were accustomed to the much greater magnifications which were obtained with lenses worked on the longer tube of the standard English microscope. Beck provided five lenses, of focal lengths 2 inches, 1 inch, $\frac{1}{2}$, $\frac{1}{4}$ and $\frac{1}{8}$ inch together with three eyepieces; these latter were unusual in that they were of the Kellner type which provide a flatter and more extensive field than the normal Huyghenian eyepieces.

One novelty which could be added as an accessory to this instrument was the "combined body" (Fig. 6.9). This fitted onto the stand in place of the normal body tube and carried three objectives and three eyepieces permanently mounted on swivelling holders. Only one of each was of course in the optical axis at any one time, but any of the others could be very rapidly brought into use by pressing the head of the pin labelled B in the illustration. The disc C was then free to revolve until the required objective or eyepiece was in position when it was located by the pin springing into the next notch. This accessory was commended to the user in the following words:

> This arrangement may be appreciated by those who are deterred from making a casual use of the microscope, either from the trouble of putting an instrument up, or from the delays which the necessary changes involve, whilst it will considerably assist in the investigation of objects which are undergoing a change either in their position or structure, and when a great range of power is required with the least possible delay.

In its basic form this microscope retailed for the sum of £9 and considering the quality of the workmanship it must be regarded as a bargain at this price. The provision of such cheap instruments filled a very considerable demand at the time, when there was a growing interest in the microscope which was stimulated by lectures and by the appearance of such periodicals as *Science Gossip* and the *English Mechanic*. The influence which these papers had in the latter half of the nineteenth century on the amateur microscopy of this country has not yet been properly assessed but many of the most eminent microscopists chose to contribute extensively to their pages and many of the controversial issues of the day were hotly argued by correspondence in their columns. Among the microscopists who were active contributors, passing on their considerable technical knowledge were Nelson, Eliot-Merlin, and many others equally eminent who chose to write under such pseudonyms as "F.R.M.S." or "Country Solicitor". It has proved possible in some cases to identify these correspondents and their writings help to build our knowledge of the technical attainments of the period. Frey, writing in 1865 was able to say:

> the use of the microscope has spread widely among the educated section of the public,

and such popularity was on the increase. In an effort to provide suitable microscopes to meet the demand, the Royal Society of Arts organized a competition in 1855 for the design of a microscope to certain specifications. The competition was won by Field and Co. of Birmingham, the model which they produced became known as the "Royal Society of Arts" stand and was sold for three guineas. Most of these stands were unsuitable for really exacting microscopy at high powers, but they were produced and sold in considerable numbers, judging by the number which are still offered for sale by second-hand dealers today! These microscopes must have provided the introduction to microscopy for many people and provided hours of pleasure to their owners.

As we have seen, the microscope in England had evolved by the middle of the nineteenth century into a very large superbly-made piece of mechanism. The best instruments were either Jackson-Lister limb or bar-limb types with a body tube ten inches in length, for which all the objectives were corrected, and with the remainder of the stand of comparable proportions. They were nearly all provided with elaborate achromatic substage condensers carried in an equally elaborate centring and focusing mechanism. The development of the microscope stand on the Continent had, however, proceeded along entirely different lines. The basic pattern on which the Continental designers based their efforts was the Oberhauser model of about 1835 (see Fig. 5.16a). This stand was developed by the substitution of a horseshoe-shaped foot and twin supporting pillars for the drum base, an innovation which has been attributed to Hartnack, the nephew of Oberhauser. This change was most probably prompted by the desire to use the mirror to obtain oblique illumination. It had been noticed that the resolution of periodic structures was enhanced if the light was not striking the object on the optic axis of the microscope but was at an angle. This condition, which was usually operated without any sub-stage condenser at this time, was very difficult to achieve with the drum-type base in which the mirror was firmly fixed and therefore unable to provide light with an obliquity of more than a few degrees.

In Hartnack's new design the mirror was mounted on a swinging tail piece so that any desired obliquity of the illumination could be very easily and quickly obtained. In the early designs the fine focus was as before, at the lower end of the limb, so that it was not possible to incline these models. Very soon Hartnack changed this and moved the milled head to the top of the stem, where it remained for the rest of the century. This allowed the introduction of a horizontal pivot joint below the level of the stage so making it possible to incline the whole microscope.

All the Continental lenses were constructed to work with a short body tube, and very often the only form of coarse focus provided was a sleeve in which the body tube was inserted. Focus was obtained by sliding the tube up or down and relying on friction to hold it in place. Most of the microscopes manufactured on the Continent up to about 1870 did not possess a substage condenser but for the illumination of the object relied entirely on a concave mirror with a wheel of diaphragms mounted underneath the stage to control the angle of the illuminating cone of light. The value of the substage condenser was not appreciated by the Continental opticians — to them it was just an elegant plaything, fit only for the English amateurs and wealthy dilettanti, and not for the busy professional scientist who was busy applying the microscope to the rapidly expanding science of histology! Nelson goes so far as to remark:

> the condenser was regarded on the Continent as a superfluous, if not a foolish appliance.

The English microscopists had discovered empirically that better results were obtained from a given microscope objective when a corrected substage condenser was used, although the theoretical reasons for this were not fully appreciated. The continental prejudice against substage condensers was not abolished until the 1870's when the work of Ernst Abbe and of Carl Zeiss established the value of the substage illuminator designed by Abbe and which came to bear his name.

An example of the microscope stand as it developed on the Continent is shown in Fig. 6.10 which represents the small "No. IV" stand of Reichert. This microscope incorporates the sliding body tube method of coarse focusing and a lever type of fine focus operated by the milled head at the top of the pillar. The horseshoe foot (which was the popular design on the Continent), the wheel of diaphragms and the concave mirror on its jointed arm can all be seen in the illustration. Towards the end of the nineteenth century, such a microscope, together with three objectives and two oculars would have cost about £6. It was this type of small microscope which was extremely popular with the professional workers. Similar stands were also produced by all the leading makers such as Zeiss, Leitz, Seibert, Nachet and others.

Following upon the researches of Abbe into the theory of the microscope superior lenses became available, which in turn necessitated corresponding improvements in the techniques of illumination and in the mechanics of the stands. We, therefore, find about the year 1880 that the Continental designers moved gradually towards the incorporation of some of the features of English design, although the short tube was still retained. The direct-acting screws much favoured on the Continent for providing the fine focus gave a very rapid motion to the tube when compared with the English long lever motion; however, the new lenses of Zeiss, in particular, demanded a very delicate fine focus in order to allow them to operate in a satisfactory manner. In consequence, the new Continental microscopes had to be provided with a much modified fine focus. Again they had to be fitted with a substage to carry Abbe's new illuminator and in order to provide for oblique illumination it then became necessary to add centring screws and a complicated device for moving the iris diaphragm out of the optic axis. Most of these instruments were also fitted with a substantial mechanical stage. Although this late nineteenth-century version of the Continental microscope was a very fine microscope (the large stand of

FIG. 6.10. A small Continental stand of the late nineteenth century. There is no substage condenser, some control over the illumination was gained by the use of the wheel of diaphragms to be seen under the stage. Coarse focus is by sliding the whole body tube within a sleeve.

Carl Zeiss is shown in Fig. 6.11) many English microscopists refused to accept it; others, however, thought it far surpassed the products of the English makers, and a considerable controversy arose. As usual E. M. Nelson had a very strong opinion which he was not slow to express. Writing in the well-known book *The Microscope and Its Revelations*, part of one of the revisions of which he had helped to prepare, he says:

> The more recent instruments are marvels of ingenuity . . . . There is no fault in the workmanship; it is the best possible. The design only is faulty; there is nothing to command commendation in any part of the model, and seeing that Messrs Zeiss have now progressed so far as to furnish their first class stand with the English mechanical movement, and even stage rotation, and fine adjustment to their newest and best sub-stage condenser, we can but believe that the advantages of these improvements will make plain the greater advantage that would accrue from an entirely new model. To all who study carefully the history of the microscope and have used for many years every principal form, it will, we believe, be manifest that the present best stand of the best makers of the Continent is an overburdened instrument.

Despite these criticisms on the part of the majority of the English microscopists the Continental stand, as represented by the Zeiss model Ia (Fig. 6.11) proved to be a tremendous success. Many of the English professional scientists at the universities adopted these Continental models very readily, largely on the grounds that they were used by the best Continental workers who were setting the pace in histology and cytology at this time and so they must be the best instruments for this purpose. At the same time these microscopes were considerably cheaper than the large English stands. The amateur microscopists fought a rearguard battle and Nelson remarked rather sourly:

> Yet it is the Continental model that has become the darling of English laboratories, and that still receives the appreciation of professors and their students.

Despite such comments it generally became agreed that the short tube was generally more convenient in use and all present day instruments are made with a tube length of 160 mm, the long English tube having become completely obsolete. With the development of the Continental model of microscope to its final form, as exemplified by such instruments as that shown in Fig. 6.11, there were thus two completely independent designs current at the end of the nineteenth

FIG. 6.11. The large Continental research stand in the late nineteenth century. The horseshoe foot is typical of this type of instrument, as also the position of the fine-focus control. This microscope was fitted with Abbe's substage illuminator.

century, both equally perfect as regards mechanical design and construction.

We should now trace the development in optical design and see the progress which was achieved in this field. In the early 1840's in England the three major makers (Powell, Ross and Smith) were producing a wide variety of lenses. Lister was responsible for the design of some of these lenses, which are listed together with their optical features and angular apertures in Table 1. For comparison the apertures of a few lenses of the Continental makers of the same period are given in Table 2. In general, it may be said that if we compare lenses of approximately the same focal length and of about the same date, then the English opticians were producing lenses of much larger aperture (which, other things being equal, were of correspondingly higher resolving power) than their counterparts on the Continent. The explanation for this may well lie in the class of users for whom the lenses were intended; on the Continent the lenses would have been used by medical research workers who were studying histological preparations.

At this time such preparations would have been largely macerated material, as sectioning techniques which are so widely used today were still in their infancy, and for preparations of whole cells high aperture lenses would have been of no advantage. What these scientists needed was a well-corrected lens which provided good definition at a lower aperture and which provided a large depth of focus or "penetration" as it was then termed. Such lenses could be made in large numbers and at a reasonable price. The wealthy English amateurs on the other hand, who amused themselves by resolving ever finer and finer test objects such as the markings on the frustules of diatoms and the artificial rulings of Nobert, demanded higher and higher apertures. Such lenses which had to be produced by the instrument makers to satisfy their customers, were difficult to make, correspondingly expensive and furthermore they were very tricky to use. In order to exploit their high angular aperture to the full, expensive achromatic condensers were needed and very often as the lenses were of such short focal lengths the objects had to be mounted under very special thin covers.

Despite their interest in attaining high resolving powers, the English microscopists overlooked for many years a very important advance which was widely accepted on the Continent and which was eventually to allow of the attainment of the maximal resolution from the optical microscope. This was the so-called "immersion principle". It was not,

Table 1. Focal lengths and apertures of English "dry" lenses of the mid-nineteenth century.

		date	focal length	angular aperture	N.A.
(A)	Ross	1837	$1''$	22°	0·19
			$\frac{1}{8}''$	64°	0·53
		1843	$\frac{1}{6}''$	66°	0·55
			$\frac{1}{12}''$	90°	0·71
		1851	$1''$	27°	0·23
			$\frac{1}{2}''$	60°	0·50
			$\frac{1}{8}''$	107°	0·80
			$\frac{1}{12}''$	135°	0·92
		1852	$\frac{1}{4}''$	105°	0·61
			$\frac{1}{12}''$	150°	0·97
		1855	$\frac{1}{2}''$	65°	0·54
			$\frac{1}{4}''$	120°	0·87
			$\frac{1}{6}''$	135°	0·92
			$\frac{1}{8}''$	150°	0·97
			$\frac{1}{12}''$	170°	0·99

(B) Powell (later Powell and Lealand)

	date	focal length	angular aperture	N.A.
	1838	$1''$	29°	0·25
		$\frac{1}{2}''$	26°	0·22
		$\frac{1}{4}''$	40°	0·34
		$\frac{1}{8}''$	60°	0·50
	1840	$\frac{1}{2}''$	40°	0·34
		$\frac{1}{16}''$	74°	0·60
ca.	1857	$\frac{1}{4}''$	89°	0·70
		$\frac{1}{12}''$	137°	0·93
		$\frac{1}{10}''$	175°	0·99
	1860	$\frac{1}{25}''$	175°+	close to 1·0
	1864	$\frac{1}{50}''$	?	?
		$\frac{1}{80}''$	?	?

(C) Smith (early objectives were made under Lister's directions and these therefore did not differ appreciably from those of Ross)

	date	focal length	angular aperture	N.A.
	1852	$\frac{2}{3}''$	27°	0·23
		$\frac{4}{10}''$	66°	0·54
		$\frac{1}{4}''$	70°	0·57
		$\frac{1}{8}''$	110°	0·82
		$\frac{1}{10}''$	121°	0·87

of course, new in the nineteenth century; Hooke had used it with simple lenses and he wrote in his Cutlerian lectures of 1679:

> If further, you would have a Microscope with one single refraction, and consequently capable of the greatest clearness and brightness that any one kind of Microscope can possibly be imagined susceptible of, when you have fixt one of these little Globules as I have directed, and spread a little of the liquor upon a piece of Looking-Glass plate, then apply the said plate with the liquor, next to the Globule, and gently move it close to the Globule, till the liquor touch; which done, you will find the liquor presently to adhere to the Globule, and still to adhere to it though you move it back again a little; by which means, this liquor being of a specifique refraction, not much differing from glass, the second refraction is quite taken off, and little or none left but that of the convex side of the Globule next the eye; by which means as much of the inconvenience of refraction as is possible is removed, and that by the easiest and most practicable expedient that can be desired.

It is surprising that this idea was not pursued any further until the nineteenth century. Amici is generally credited with the introduction of immersion lenses at that time, but Sir D. Brewster preceded him by suggesting in 1812 that the front element of a microscope objective lens might actually be brought into immersion contact with the fluid in which an object is mounted. Brewster was interested in this as a means whereby he could obtain an achromatic lens combination. At the same time the object would be examined while in more or less its natural state and without suffering any of the distortion introduced by drying.

Table 2. Focal lengths and apertures of "dry" lenses of three Continental makers.

	date	focal length	angular aperture	N.A.
(A) *Amici*	1850–60	22·8 mm (*ca.* 1″)	26°	0·22
		8·47 mm (*ca.* $\frac{1}{3}$″)	37°	0·32
		3·92 mm (*ca.* $\frac{1}{6}$″)	57°	0·48
		3·5 mm (*ca.* $\frac{1}{7}$″)	77°	0·62
(B) *Ploessl*	1829	—	24°	0·2
	1840	—	48°	0·4
	1846	—	52°	0·45
	1860–68	—	82°	0·65
(C) *Oberhauser*				
	1848	3·22 mm (*ca.* $\frac{1}{8}$″)	58°	0·48
		2·5 mm (*ca.* $\frac{1}{10}$″)	60°	0·5
		1·7 mm (*ca.* $\frac{1}{14}$″)	63°	0·51

He explains his idea in a section of his work, published in 1813, *A New Treatise on Philosophical Instruments.*

> Several small glass vessels must then be provided, having different depths, from one inch to three inches, and having their bottom composed of a piece of flat glass, for the purpose of admitting freely the reflected light which is intended to illuminate the object. The fluid in which the object has been preserved or prepared, is next put into the vessel; and the object itself, placed upon a glass stage, or if necessary fixed to it, is immersed in the fluid. The glass vessel is now laid upon the arm of the microscope which usually holds the object, and the lens is brought into contact with the fluid in the vessel. The rays which diverge from the object emerge directly from the fluid into the object glass, and therefore suffer a less refraction than if it had been made from air; but the focal length of the lens is very little increased, on account of the great radius of its anterior surface. The object may now be observed with perfect distinctness un-affected by any agitation of the fluid; — its part will be seen in their finest state of preservation; delicate muscular fibres, and the hairs and down upon insects, will be kept separate by the buoyancy of the fluid; and if the object when alive, or in its most perfect state, had a smooth surface, its natural polish will not only be preserved but heightened by contrast with the fluid. Aquatic plants and animals will thus be seen with unusual distinctness, and shells and unpolished minerals will have a brilliancy communicated to their surface which they could never have received from the hands of the lapidary.
>
> The method of fitting up and using the compound microscope, which has now been described, enables us, in a very simple manner, to render the object glass perfectly achromatic, without the assistance of any additional lens. The rays which proceed from the object immersed in the fluid, will form an image of it nearly at the same distance behind the lens, as if the object had been placed in air, and the rays transmitted through a plain concave lens of the fluid combined with the object-glass. If we, therefore, employ a fluid whose dispersive power exceeds that of the object-glass, and accommodate the radius of the anterior surface of that lens to the difference of their dispersive powers, the image will be formed perfectly free from any of the primary colours of the spectrum.

Brewster employed various essential oils to achieve this end, and his specimens were mounted in such fluids as oil of cassia, oil of anise seeds, and oil of cloves. Brewster repeated his views in an article published in 1837 in which he repeated his earlier words and summed up by affirming:

> Almost all objects are seen to the greatest advantage when immersed in a fluid, even the finest test objects such as the scales of the Podura.

Brewster's arrangement may be seen in Fig. 6.12, which shows the object in the bath of oil with the front lens of the objective immersed in the liquid. The application of the device to the achromatization of a compound lens is also shown. It can be seen that the liquid passes in between the glass components (labelled A, B and E in the figure) and effectively acts as a concave lens. With the advent of glasses of differing dispersive powers, this rather clumsy system passed into disuse.

Fig. 6.12. Brewster's immersion lenses, 1813. The lower system involves the penetration of the fluid between three of the convex lenses, so forming liquid negative lenses.

Amici, however, probably working quite independently, came to use the idea of immersing the front lens of the objective not to correct the chromatic aberration but to diminish the loss of light in high-power lens systems and to improve the definition of the image. The exact date of the adoption by Amici of immersion systems is not known with certainty, but it was probably somewhere in the late 1840's; Harting tells us that one of Amici's microscopes which was provided for Professor Donders of Utrecht in 1850 was provided with immersion lenses. The immersion lenses were not officially launched until they were exhibited at the Paris Exhibition of 1855. Amici tried many fluids, such as glycerine, and mixtures of various oils. These latter he did not consider to be practicable at that time as they apparently attacked the cement of the mounts which were in common use. He therefore reverted to water as an immersion medium and his lenses were designed to work with this. They were not provided with a correction collar, however, and so they only gave really good spherical correction when used with a coverglass of a certain definite thickness. This drawback, together with the fact that their resolving power was probably not so high as the best "dry" objectives of the time resulted in the immersion lenses only having a partial success.

It was left to Edmund Hartnack, a very practical optician, to combine the water-immersion principle with the fitting of a correction collar. He began to supply such lenses somewhere around 1859. Hartnack showed that the loss of light increases with the obliquity of the incident rays falling upon the front element of an objective; when objectives of high aperture are used "dry", that is with air intervening between the front lens and the cover slip, the advantages of increased aperture are largely offset by the reflection of a large proportion of the rays falling on the peripheral portion of the lens. If, on the other hand, rays of the same obliquity enter the peripheral portion of the lens from water, then the loss by reflection is greatly reduced and more benefit is gained from the larger aperture. In addition, the use of the immersion principle allows a greater working distance (the distance between the front lens of the objective and the coverglass when the lens is in focus) than would be possible for a dry lens of equal aperture. This is obviously important as it makes the lens much easier to use. Most important of all, however, an immersion lens allows a far greater portion of the light diffracted by the object, which we now know to be important in the formation of the detail in the microscopical image, to enter the lens and so the image quality of an immersion lens is much better than that of a dry lens of equal power.

Hartnack had a great success in Paris with his highly corrected water-immersion lenses. About 1860 his "No. 10" lens of approximately $\frac{1}{16}$-inch focus was produced; this had an angular aperture in air of 172° (corresponding to a numerical aperture of 0·99) whilst three years later his "No. 11" lens had a focal length of $\frac{1}{18}$ inch and an angular aperture of 175°. It was with this lens that Harting succeeded in the resolution of the diatom *Surirella gemma* using oblique light but no condenser. Harting had been experimenting with this lens since

1860 and the early results which had filtered out created such a sensation among the microscopists of the day that they had been putting their names on a waiting list for when the lens should eventually go into commercial production. It is true to say that Hartnack was the first maker to have water-immersion lenses in regular production and from the beginning his lenses achieved a reputation for their very high quality. It was not very long before all the Continental opticians were producing water-immersion lenses; Nobert in Germany was making a $\frac{1}{14}$ and a $\frac{1}{16}$ and later a $\frac{1}{20}$ which could be used either "dry" or immersed by simply adjusting the correction collar. Nachet, Zeiss and Gundlach were also making this type of lens. In the 1860's there was a vogue for lenses with a very high initial magnifying power. This, probably, was due to the special requirements of the English microscopists and it was true both of dry lenses and of immersion systems. Most of the opticians produced the type of lens that their customers demanded and hence lenses of $\frac{1}{25}$, $\frac{1}{30}$ and even $\frac{1}{50}$ inch focus were produced, especially in England. Such lenses with their restricted apertures gave an excessive initial magnification at the expense of image quality and excellence of corrections. Nevertheless, their production was continued for some time until the researches of Abbe showed that their use could not be justified on theoretical grounds.

In England there was great opposition to the use of immersion lenses. Frison, in a recent paper, lays the blame for their rejection squarely on the shoulders of the rich amateurs who by the 1860's were very influential in the microscopical societies and who set the fashion in the microscopical methods. It was probably because the water-immersion lenses could only be used *as such*, i.e. they were not suitable for any other purpose, and because equally good results could be secured by the use of dry lenses employed with better methods of illumination than were in use on the Continent, that the English microscopists did not take up the immersion system. Carpenter, a very eminent microscopist at that time, had himself tried Hartnack's lenses and he agreed that they were capable of showing difficult test objects by means of simple oblique illumination from the mirror alone "with a brightness and definition which are only equalled by the best English objectives when used in combination with condensers and stops". He urged that as the apparatus used in microscopical studies should be as simple and as easy to use as possible, the English workers should adopt this system and demand that the English makers produce immersion lenses at least as good as the Parisian ones.

His pleas fell on deaf ears, however, and even a few years later after Powell and Lealand had begun to make water-immersion lenses and J. J. Woodward in America had used an immersion one-sixteenth of theirs to resolve and photograph the very fine rulings of the nineteenth band of Nobert's test plate, some of the conservative die-hards in the Royal Microscopical Society would not be convinced of the superiority of immersion lenses. The President of the R.M.S. at that time, the Rev. Joseph Reade, who was noted for his pioneering experiments with photography, cast doubts on the value of such lenses by suggesting in his Presidential Address that the

> high praise which is given to the immersion system will perhaps be received with caution until more extended observations have been made upon its powers.

He concludes:

> Still we have yet to learn, notwithstanding these acknowledged advantages whether there are considerable drawbacks looming in the microscopic future which may in some measure counterbalance the employment of water refractions. Of one thing we may be sure, that absolute perfection is unattainable. The ghost of aberration will never be entirely exorcised even by cold water.

Frison attributed the extreme conservatism of the English microscopists largely to the influence of one man — Francis Wenham, who possessed a tremendous practical knowledge of microscopy but only a limited grasp of the theoretical principles involved. He designed many accessories for the microscope, such as a perfected correction collar for objective lenses and perhaps most important of all, his beam-splitting prism for the stereoscopic binocular. Wenham had convinced himself that the immersion principle was a bad one; his views may be summarized by the following quotation from an article which he published in the *Monthly Microscopical Journal* during 1869:

> Recently some excellent glasses have been made, as the so-termed "immersion lenses". These combinations are under-corrected, and not suitable for use in any other way. The plan is an old one, and objectives were constructed on this principle by Amici and Ross many years ago. That such lenses give brighter and clearer definition, with the highest powers, from the 1/12th upwards is unquestionable; but the effect of the water and the covering glass is precisely the same in its corrective action *as additional thickness thrown* onto the front lens. The interposition of water doubtless tends to neutralize errors of surface and polish, and more light

is transmitted in consequence; but, as preparations are generally not so minute in their structure as to require the habitual employment of such object glasses (which are useless without the water film), it will probably be found, that the inconvenience attached to their use will not compensate for their advantages. Allowing that they perform better on the *Diatoms* and other tests, it would be preferable to mount these objects, in which special discovery is required, without any covering glass, and have an objective of 1/50th constructed with a thick front, specially corrected for uncovered objects only. This having no adjustment, the best definition would always be a matter of certainty, which cannot be the case when the covering-glass, with its varying thickness and errors, forms part of the optical combination.

It seems clear from this extract that Wenham was under a misapprehension as to the reason for the increased light transmission of a water

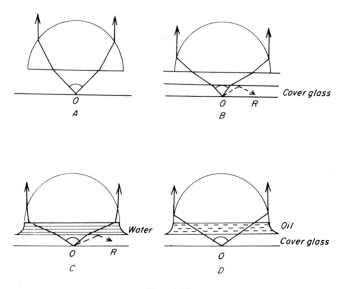

Fig. 6.13.

(a) The maximum angular aperture of a dry lens, working with an uncovered object.
(b) The effect of adding a cover glass.
(c) The maximum angular aperture of a water immersion lens is 140°.
(d) A homogeneous-immersion system, with no refraction between the upper surface of the coverslip and the immersion medium, has the angle of aperture increased still further.

immersion objective, thinking that it was solely due to the overcoming of surface finish irregularities, rather than to the presence of a fluid of higher refractive index than air between the cover and the objective front. The scheme of the water-immersion lens may be seen in Fig. 6.13.

At A in the figure we see the path of light rays emerging from an object mounted in air, with air between the object and the front lens of the objective. The maximum angle of the cone of rays which can be accepted by the lens is about 170°, very occasionally slightly more. The situation where an object is mounted in a medium of equal index to the coverslip is shown at B in the figure. The only rays which can enter the objective are contained within an angle of 82°, because of the refraction or bending of the light rays which takes place at the air/glass interface; the remainder are lost by total reflection, as shown with ray R on the right of the figure. The pencil of rays on emerging into air, however, becomes exactly equivalent to the 170° pencil in the dry-mounted object shown in Fig. 6.13(a). It follows that all the rays which travel from the object mounted in such a medium, say in canada balsam, which have a greater angle than 82° cannot enter the objective. If, however, they could in some way be brought within its compass it is obvious that they would contribute to the detail in the image and its luminosity. By using a medium of high refractive index between the front lens of the objective and the coverslip this can be achieved. In the case of water, with a refractive index of 1·33, the critical angle for reflection at the upper surface of the coverslip it reduced so that the objective can now accept a larger cone of rays from the object. Theoretically, the maximum angle would be expected to reach 140°, as shown in Fig. 6.13(c), but in practice this value is never achieved. It is still possible for some reflection of the rays to occur and only if the refractive index of the medium actually equals that of the glass will there be maximal light transmission. This was eventually found to be possible as we shall see.

The American opticians were not slow to follow the lead given by the Continental workers and soon they were making very fine water-immersion lenses, which soon acquired a high reputation. The lenses made by R. B. Tolles in particular were held in high regard. It was not long before the water-immersion lenses had an angular aperture which surpassed that attainable with a dry lens. In modern terminology the numerical aperture (a term introduced by Abbe, and which will be discussed later, see p. 242), which cannot practically exceed $0 \cdot 95$ for a dry lens, was very soon made to exceed 1, and it was not long before numerical apertures of $1 \cdot 2$ were commonplace.

The next logical step in the sequence would be to make the refractive index of the medium equal to that of the glass, a situation shown diagrammatically in Fig. 6.13(d). At the time of which we are speaking (1860) even the leaders of the optical profession and the most skilful users were ignorant of microscopic theory and so this decisive step was not immediately taken.

In the same year that Wenham was criticizing the use of water-immersion lenses, one of his own countrymen, John Mayall, was making a strong plea for their adoption. It is ironic to note that his article appears in the same volume of the *Monthly Microscopical Journal* as Wenham's criticisms! Mayall was using one of Nobert's new test plates as his object. He writes:

> With the 1/18th and 1/12th by Ross and the 1/20th by Smith, in the possession of this Society, and with a 1/9th, a 1/12th, a 1/16th and a 1/25th by Powell and Lealand, all dry objectives (not to mention others which gave similar or inferior results), on a new nineteen band plate, all the bands beyond the 12th seemed imperfect — the lines were not separated.
>
> But with a 1/10th and a 1/18th by Hartnack, of Paris, a 1/16th by Merz, of Munich, and a 1/20th by Nobert, all immersion objectives, straight and well-defined lines were separated as far as the fifteenth band inclusive. In the last four bands true consecutive lines were seen; but they are so extremely slightly ruled, that the eye fails to appreciate their increased fineness.

Mayall concludes that the immersion objectives maintained their superiority by all methods and that

> Continental opticians and men of science have been aware of the merits of the Immersion system during several years past; and to such purpose that knowing how little attention it has received here, they do not scruple to say that the English no longer take the lead either as opticians or microscopists.

Soon after this was written, and perhaps largely as a consequence of it, Powell and Lealand produced their first immersion lens. In an effort to compromise they made it of $\frac{1}{16}$-inch focus and fitted it with a dismountable front lens which enabled it to be used either as a water-immersion or as a dry lens. Soon Ross began to produce immersion objectives, probably at the insistence of Professor Henri van Heurck the famous Belgian diatomist who was a personal friend of Ross. This must have been a bitter blow to Francis Wenham who, according to Frison, was retained as the optical adviser to the firm of Ross and who had so recently been condemning the immersion objective. Although Wenham had great practical skill, he had come to erroneous conclusions in this particular instance and he was later to enter into another even more bitter series of arguments with Robert Tolles over the apertures of the lenses produced by the latter when the new "homogeneous immersion" system was introduced. Again Wenham was proved to be in error, although he never would admit this fact.

Before discussing the introduction of homogeneous or "oil" immersion as it is now called, we must digress for a moment because in 1866 one of the more significant events in the development of the microscope took place. This was the appointment of Ernst Abbe as the technical adviser to the firm of Carl Zeiss. Ernst Abbe, born in Eisenach, a little town in the Grand Duchy of Saxe-Weimar, was the son of a foreman in a spinning mill. He showed considerable scholastic ability as a boy and eventually attended the University of Jena and later that of Göttingen. It was at this last University that he presented his thesis to obtain his degree. After graduation Abbe taught, first at Frankfurt, and later at Jena University where he was appointed Lecturer in Mathematics, Physics and Astronomy in 1863, when he was only twenty-three years of age. Three years later he was invited to be the optical consultant to Zeiss, who had set up in Jena as an instrument maker in 1846. So began one of the most famous partnerships in the history of the microscope. In 1875, Abbe was made a full partner in the firm and in 1888 after the death of Carl Zeiss he became the sole proprietor.

Abbe abandoned all the preconceived ideas about the design of microscope objectives and set to work to establish the whole process of design and manufacture on a firm basis of theoretical calculations, and to standardize the processes used in the manufacture of microscope lenses. This programme was successful and by 1870 all the lenses which came from Jena were made from standard, pre-calculated designs instead of being produced (as elsewhere) solely by the skill of the individual craftsman. During these early years Abbe carried out numerous experiments and must have acquired a sound grasp of both theoretical and practical optics; it was at this time that the beginnings of the understanding of the influence of the *aperture* of the objective upon resolution (irrespective of its *magnification*) came to him. The results of his studies led him to develop his great theoretical work on the formation of the microscopic image which he published in 1873.

This theory had a great success, despite some opposition, again largely from the English amateurs! It explained how the resolution of fine detail in a microscopic object demanded lenses of large aperture, and why if the structure was periodic (as in a diatom frustule) the use of oblique light with lenses of high aperture appeared to be more effective in obtaining resolution. It is not possible to go into the details of Abbe's theory here, but essentially he showed that a periodic object

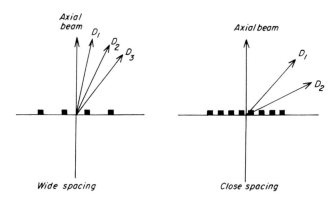

FIG. 6.14. The diffracted beams produced by regularly spaced objects. With a wide spacing the diffracted beams (D_1, D_2, D_3) are close together but with a fine object-spacing the beams are much further apart and separated from the axial beam and each other by a much greater angle.

gives rise to a series of diffracted rays of light on either side of the main illuminating or axial beam. The angular dispersion of these diffracted rays depends on the spacing of the structure of the object; the closer the structure or periodicity, then the wider the separation of the diffracted beams. This is shown in Fig. 6.14. Abbe proved that in order to resolve the structure of the object, the microscope lens must accept not only the axial light rays, but also at least one of these diffracted beams; the more diffracted light which entered the objective, then the more faithful would be the representation of the structure. If the periodicity of an object is so fine that the first of the diffracted beams is so far from the axis that it cannot be admitted to the lens, then there will be no resolution of the structure. By the use of oblique light, however, the axial beam is directed into one side of the lens and thus there is then a good chance that at least one of the diffracted beams will enter the aperture of the lens and so allow resolution of the structure to take place. This is shown diagrammatically in Fig. 6.15. This explains the empirical observations that the larger the aperture of a lens, the better was its resolution of fine, regular structure in an object, other things being equal.

It is obvious that by the use of immersion lenses a much larger aperture can be obtained and so a larger amount of diffracted light can be admitted to the lens, hence the superior resolving power of such lenses. From his theory of image formation, Abbe was led to the concept of expressing the light accepting power of a lens by what he termed the "numerical aperture". Previous to his work there was general agreement that the more oblique the light, the finer the resolvable detail; it was thought, however, that this was directly related to the obliquity of the direct rays of light and that the larger the angular aperture the more suited the lens for accepting such oblique rays. Abbe brought home the point that it was the ability of such high aperture lenses to accept the *diffracted* light, originating at the object, which accounted for their superior resolution. He showed that this relationship could be better expressed not in terms of the angular aperture, measured directly, but to the sine of *half* the angle of acceptance multiplied by the refractive index of the medium between the front lens of the objective and the mount. This quantity Abbe designated the "numerical aperture" or N.A. In the case of a dry lens the expression becomes simply

$$\text{N.A.} = \sin \alpha$$

where the value of α is equal to half the angular aperture, as the refractive index of air is (by definition) equal to 1. This mathematical expression has the great advantage over the older direct form of comparison in terms of degrees of aperture that the resolution of any two lenses may be directly compared simply by comparing their numerical apertures. For example, any lens of an N.A. of 0·8 would be expected to have twice the resolving power of one of N.A. 0·4. Such a direct relationship does not exist if only the angular apertures are compared. One further consequence of Abbe's work (which up to the middle of the 1870's was largely theoretical) was that he was able to develop a formula for calculating the resolving power of the

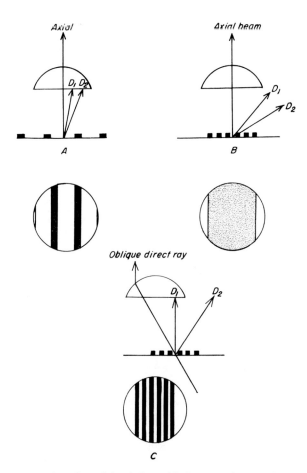

FIG. 6.15. The effect of the diffracted light in resolution of the fine structure of a microscopic object.

(a) Coarse spacing; the diffracted beams D_1 and D_2 are admitted by the objective lens and the grating is resolved.

(b) Fine spacing; no diffracted light enters the lens and no detail is seen in the final image.

(c) By the use of oblique light, the first diffracted beam D_1 is admitted by the lens and the fine grating is now resolved.

objective so that a theoretical yardstick was then available by which its actual performance could be assessed.

Very soon, however, Abbe was responsible for the practical development of a new advance in microscopy. This was the use of "homogeneous immersion" which was suggested to him by J. W. Stephenson, an eminent English microscopist. Stephenson was interested in obtaining a lens in which the correction collar could be dispensed with; in the *Journal of the Royal Microscopical Society* for 1878 he wrote:

> The origin of the correcting collar as shown by the late Andrew Ross, was the imperative necessity of compensating the error arising from the difference between the refractive index of the covering glass and that of the air between the front of the lens and the thin cover, whenever a high power was used.
>
> Now it is evident that if some fluid, of which the refractive and dispersive powers are the same as those of the covering glass, were substituted for air in the intervening space, the end in view would be attained.

This is the situation represented in the diagram presented as Fig. 6.13(d). Stephenson lacked the necessary technical knowledge and facilities to carry this any further so he wrote to Abbe suggesting this as a possibility. Abbe followed up the idea and the results were published in his famous paper "On Stephenson's system of homogeneous immersion for microscope objectives", which appeared in the *Journal of the Royal Microscopical Society* in 1879. In this paper Abbe mentions that the same idea had actually occurred to him, but that he was of the opinion that there was no value in it and so he did nothing further with it.

> The idea of realizing the various advantages of such a kind of an immersion lens by constructing objectives in this system had for some time presented itself to my mind, but I thought that there was not much to be expected in regard to the scientific usefulness of such objectives since I believe their use would be limited on account of using oil or some other inconvenient material as the immersion fluid. It appeared to me that, except perhaps for the examination of diatoms, scarcely any other scientific value remained than photographic research which would afford a scope for realizing the optical advantages of such objectives.

Abbe pointed out that not only would the use of homogeneous immersion eliminate all refraction at the front of the lens, but also it would limit the loss of light by reflection. He continued:

> What is still more important, a very considerable amount of spherical aberration is at the same time prevented which otherwise would have to be corrected in the upper portion of the objective.

At the same time the use of homogeneous immersion would have the effect which Stephenson wished to achieve, namely the elimination of the influence of cover thickness on the spherical corrections, and hence there would be no need to fit such immersion objectives with a correction collar. The search for the ideal immersion medium gave Abbe a great deal of trouble. He tells us that he personally examined the refractive indices and dispersive powers of over a hundred different liquids, and that Dr. Töpel of Jena studied a further two hundred. Eventually they chose cedar wood oil (to which they sometimes added fennel seed oil to alter the dispersion slightly) and all their objectives were calculated to work with this. The first oil immersion objectives made by Zeiss had a focal length of $\frac{1}{8}$ inch, but very soon further lenses of $\frac{1}{12}$-inch focus were made. All of these lenses had an angular aperture of 114° (equivalent to an N.A. of 1·25), which as Abbe commented, was the

same angular magnitude as can be attained without any great difficulty within the film of water in the usual immersion lenses, or within the stratum of air in dry objectives. But since the "numerical" equivalent of the angle of aperture (the measure which determines the number of rays taken in by the objective) is proportional not only to the sine of half the angle of aperture, but also to the refractive indices of the respective media employed, and since all the functions of the angle of aperture, and this numerical equivalent, it follows that, according to theory, the capacity of the new objective, compared with that of ordinary immersion lenses, is increased in the proportion of 1·50 to 1·33, and as compared with the highest dry objectives, as 1·50 to 1.

These first homogeneous-immersion lenses were very successful and Abbe considered that this system would allow the computation of lenses with considerably larger apertures and short focal lengths, without making too great demands on the designer in order to ensure correction of their residual aberrations.

Meanwhile, in America, Robert Tolles had been steadily progressing with the construction of immersion objectives. At first these were water immersion, like all the European lenses, but about 1873 he made a $\frac{1}{10}$-inch lens designed to be used with soft canada balsam as the immersion medium. This was, therefore, a homogeneous-immersion objective as the refractive index of balsam approximates to that of glass. There was at this time a great controversy in the pages of the *Journal of the Royal Microscopical Society* between Wenham on the one hand, and Dr. Piggot and Robert Tolles on the other. In this argument

Wenham, although now agreeing with the whole principle of homogeneous immersion, denied that this system would allow the use of an angular aperture of more than 82° in glass or balsam (equivalent to 180° in air). He stated categorically:

> The same optical law that limits the aperture of any object glass to near 82° in a balsam-mounted object also determines the angle *in the lens* at which the rays diverge after being refracted from the plane surface of the front . . .
>
> I challenge Dr. Piggott, or anyone else, to get through the object-glass with the immersion front, a greater angle, or any portion of the extraneous rays that would in the other case be totally reflected, *as no object-glass* can collect image-forming rays beyond this limit.

The balsam-immersion lens which Tolles had now produced had an aperture of 110° (equivalent to an N.A. of 1·25) a figure which Wenham firmly refused to believe. J. J. Woodward showed that this lens was capable of giving very high resolutions by using it to resolve and photograph both the 19th band of Nobert's test plate and the diatom *Amphipleura pellucida*. In the following year a detailed computation of the ray paths through the lens was published by Keith in an effort to vindicate Tolles, and Stokes showed theoretically that Wenham was wrong in his arguments and that the aperture of 180° was theoretically possible in glass. Tremendous feeling was aroused by this controversy and although Tolles was eventually vindicated and his claims for his lens substantiated, Wenham never apologized to him in any way. So great was Wenham's prestige in England that Mr. Brook, the current President of the Royal Microscopical Society, defended him valiantly in the Presidential Address for 1874; in fairness it must be mentioned that other influential members of the society, such as Sir Frank Crisp and John Mayall, were wholeheartedly in support of Tolles.

It thus seems that Tolles deserves the credit for first devising and constructing a workable homogeneous-immersion lens, although his system was rather clumsy and involved a very messy and intractable immersion medium. The achievements of Stephenson and Abbe must be rated equally high, for it is to their work that we owe the practical homogeneous-immersion system, using oil as the liquid medium between the lens and the coverslip. In addition to their practical achievement was added the great theoretical studies of Abbe which defined once and for all the meaning of the aperture of a lens and established its importance in microscopical resolution. Abbe's grasp of the theory prevented any futile controversy from surrounding his discovery and tending towards its disparagement. To a certain extent the achievement of Robert Tolles is clouded by controversy; although he was able and he too understood the theory extremely well, his writings were in such a terse style that his opponents often mistook his meaning and failed to appreciate his point of view.

The new lens of Abbe and Zeiss was keenly studied in England and its performance was described in 1878 by W. H. Dallinger in a letter to the periodical *Nature*. Dallinger, who was very well known for his studies of saprophytic organisms with the microscope, tells us that the lens performed well with the Powell and Lealand condenser or with the

> small plano-convex lens which the maker sends with it to be fastened to the under surface of the slide with the oil of cedarwood.

Dallinger compared it with a new formula $\frac{1}{8}$-inch lens just issued by Powell and Lealand:

> It is but justice to say that all my most crucial tests were equally mastered by the lens of Carl Zeiss. I have not been able to do more with it than the English glass, *but the same results* can be accomplished much more readily. . . . . On the whole, I think it in many senses the finest lens, of its power, that I have ever seen; and in every sense it is an admirable acquisition. . . . . It may perhaps be right to note that this lens, although not provided with the complex arrangement of "screw-collar" adjustment, and although *only* "immersion", is higher in price than the most costly 1/8th by any English maker, although the latter lens may have the screw collar correction, and be both "immersion" and dry.

This new development soon caught the attention of the microscopists and within two years Powell and Lealand themselves were producing homogeneous-immersion lenses; within a very short time an oil-immersion lens became an essential part of the equipment of any microscopist. The professional users of the microscope eagerly sought after these new lenses and it is largely due to the improved images and better resolution of the oil-immersion lens that rapid progress was made in histology in the latter part of the nineteenth century. These lenses were especially valuable in the studies which were carried out in the new science of bacteriology and microbiology; however, we must not forget that the great progress made at this time was not entirely due to these optical advances.

E.M.—R

The techniques of preparing the material were also being developed and a technical breakthrough in this field often stimulated a flood of discoveries. One of the main problems with biological material is that tissues and cells are transparent and it is therefore very difficult to discern any structure in the object unless the aperture of the illuminating system is very much reduced so that contrast is provided at the expense of resolution. This problem, of lack of visibility due to lack of contrast, was troublesome until the development of the phase-contrast microscope (see Chapter 7, p. 293) and was first really appreciated when the new high aperture oil-immersion lenses were introduced. The discovery of the aniline dyes was a great step forwards, as it was found that many biological objects could have their visibility in the microscope considerably enhanced by staining with these substances, which rendered them strongly coloured and so made the details, of their structure apparent.

The bacteriologists very soon realized the potentialities of the aniline dyes in microtechnique. Robert Koch, who may be considered as one of the founders of modern bacteriology, developed many methods of using these dyes to colour the micro–organisms strongly whilst leaving the background of the tissue unstained. When the high aperture homogeneous-immersion lens was used on such material the occurrence of the bacteria within the tissues was easily seen and their location within the tissues determined. The development of high resolution lenses, together with such methods of differential staining, proved invaluable to bacteriologists and to the cytologists who were using these new methods to elucidate the detailed behaviour of the chromosomes in the cell nucleus at the division of the cell.

At the same time as these existing developments were taking place in the optics of the microscope, equally rapid progress was being made in the techniques of preparing material for microscopical study.

In the eighteenth century it was generally only the surfaces of objects which were examined microscopically, using incident light; sometimes whole objects, if small enough, were dried and mounted dry for examination by transmitted light, but naturally owing to the poor quality of such mounts, very little internal detail could be seen.

One alternative approach is to cut the object into such thin sections that light can easily pass through them. This was in fact done by John Hill in 1770 who (as mentioned on p. 140) used a machine or microtome designed by George Adams for cutting wood into sections thin enough to study on his "Variable microscope". This approach to the study of biological material was not generally possible until some means of supporting the soft tissues whilst they were being cut had been devised. Many workers about 1860 realized the advantages of this method of preparation and a great search started for suitable "embedding" materials which would support the tissue whilst it was cut into thin slices. Frison has recently traced the development of the various agents which have been used for this purpose; the most important was hard paraffin introduced about 1869 by Klebs who melted it around the object to provide the support during cutting. Later several workers adapted the technique to include actually soaking the dried tissue in melted paraffin in order to allow complete penetration of the wax, and so obtaining still better support. This technique revolutionized micro-anatomy as it enables serial sections to be obtained through a complete organism and permits the visualization of the entire structure by a process of reconstruction. Paraffin sectioning is still probably the most used microtechnique today.

The great advances in micro anatomy and cell biology which stem from the period 1870–1900 may thus be attributed on the one hand to the technical advances in the microscope and its lenses, but also on the other hand to the equally important developments in the preparative techniques.

In particular, the bacteriologists made discoveries of great practical significance, as the causative agents of many infectious diseases were soon described. Koch himself discovered the bacillus which causes tuberculosis, which he described in 1882, whilst in the following year he was able to see the agent responsible for cholera. Klebs described the diphtheria bacillus, and Pasteur had characterised the staphylococci and streptococci. In the period immediately after the discovery of the differential staining method by Weigert and a little later after Gram's work on his specific staining technique which enabled the bacteria to be placed into two easily-recognizable categories, more and more organisms were described and the part they played in disease processes was recognized. It may truly be said that the period between 1880 and the turn of the century may be classed as the "golden age of descriptive bacteriology". To this development the new lenses of Abbe were indispensable and together with the development of staining reactions, they may be said to have played a major role in the scientific study of disease.

Most of the medical workers, however, used the oil-immersion lenses without any form of substage condenser thus depriving these lenses of the greater part of their resolution. The view was current at one time that one actually saw *more* if there was no condenser! These faulty conclusions can almost certainly be traced to workers who were studying unstained biological material of low contrast; to see any image at all under these circumstances would have been impossible with a large cone of axial light.

In an interesting study of the development of microscopy in the late nineteenth century, Hughes has analysed the numbers of publications on various topics which appeared during a given period; these numbers can then serve as an index of the research activity involving the microscope in that field. He concludes that cytology of the nucleus and chromosomes and general studies on the structure of the cell only showed a marked rise in popularity after 1875. This increase, however, *preceded* the introduction of the homogeneous-immersion lens, and it seems likely that here the interest stems from developments in preparative techniques (in this case the use of staining methods) rather than as a consequence of optical progress. When the study of diatoms is considered the significant increase in the number of papers did not come about until after the establishment of the oil-immersion lens; here it seems obvious that the optical developments were the direct stimulus of the research.

Before the importance of wide aperture lenses was established in the latter part of the century, it had been noticed that the fine periodic structures, such as are found on the frustules of diatoms, were more easily resolved if the light were extremely oblique with respect to the axis of the microscope. This discovery led to the design of some extraordinary microscopes, often of great complexity, in which the substage mechanism was so conceived as to facilitate the production of illuminating rays of great obliquity. All these stands were characterized by a swinging substage, often with the controls elaborately graduated into degrees.

One of the first of these stands was shown by Zentmayer of Philadelphia at the Exposition which was held in that city in 1876. The general pattern of this instrument, including the swinging substage, is shown in Fig. 6.16, which represents an instrument made by Ross to one of Zentmayer's designs. The principle appealed to the Victorian microscopists and later microscopes were made in which not only the substage, but also the object stage was provided with a swinging movement, in order to further the production of oblique illumination. Most of the leading makers produced such instruments and these stands were often of great complexity, every movement being driven by a rack and pinion and provided with a carefully calibrated scale of degrees. Although this complexity does in fact detract from their value as practical microscopes, their construction often showed a very high order of craftsmanship.

FIG. 6.16. The swinging substage Ross/Zentmayer microscope. The stage could also be inclined in order to increase further the obliquity of the illuminating light.

Perhaps the extreme form of microscope with such varied movements was reached with the production of the "Ross Radial" microscope to a design of Francis Wenham. The idea behind this instrument (shown in Fig. 6.17 taken from an example in the collection of the Royal Microscopical Society) was to provide complete inclination of the limb and body, together with the substage and mirror system, by sliding it in a sector attached to a rotatable base-plate. This in its turn provided a rotation movement about the optic axis of the whole instrument. There was also a lateral inclination of the limb on either side of the optic axis, so that a wide range of obliquities of the light could be provided in all directions of altitude and azimuth. Mayall, in the Cantor Lectures, wrote of this instrument:

> I am not prepared to say that any one of the movements is essentially useless in practical microscopy. I understand from Dr. Dallinger, the President of the Royal Microscopical Society, that in some of his most difficult investigations in tracing the evolution of minute forms of life, no facilities hitherto devised for controlling the illumination, according to methods capable of being recorded and repeated, have proved valueless; and I believe he has tested this Radial microscope by practice more thoroughly than any other microscopist.

Despite his deference to the opinion of Dallinger, Mayall held the view that this type of instrument was needlessly complex and subsequent events proved him to be correct. With the development and with the spread of an understanding of Abbe's theories, the demand for oblique illumination gradually disappeared; by the end of the century the view was clearly established that for the best resolution a so-called "critical" image was desirable. This came about largely through the writings and demonstrations of E. M. Nelson, who was an enthusiastic advocate of the use of large aperture lenses used with axial illumination provided by a well-corrected illumination system of an aperture slightly less than that of the objective. Abbe himself provided a simple two lens "illuminator" for use with his lenses; it was first developed in 1873, but was followed in 1888 by an achromatic version which was preferable for the more highly corrected lenses. The bacteriologists, especially, soon found that this illuminator gave them a greatly improved image quality and within a few years the Abbe illuminator or condenser as it became known, was the standard fitting for the substage of the Continental microscope. In deference to the still widely-felt need for oblique illumination, Abbe made provision for the iris diaphragm to be moved off the optical axis of the instrument by means of a small rackwork so that the light in its turn became oblique.

In England the development of high quality condensers had been in hand since the introduction of Gillet's achromatic condenser in 1850.

FIG. 6.17. The ultimate of the trend for oblique-light illumination is shown here in the Ross Radial microscope. In this instrument a complete inclination of the limb and body and substage system was possible in all directions.

Powell and Lealand were marketing a whole series of highly corrected condensers of ever-increasing aperture; by 1878 they had one such condenser which would deliver a cone of light of N.A. 0·99, whilst three years later they produced an immersion condenser which worked at a numerical aperture of 1·3 and which far outclassed the Abbe illuminator in the excellence of its spherical and chromatic corrections. Still later Powell and Lealand were to produce *apochromatic* condensers and, just as objectives were fitted with a correction collar, so these condensers of Powell and Lealand were also fitted!

It thus can be seen that by the year 1880 the microscope stand had reached the form in which it has essentially remained until very recently, although various bizarre models were still appearing at intervals, and the lenses had been brought to a very high standard by the work of Abbe and the firm of Carl Zeiss. The scientists on the Continent were enthusiastically seizing all the opportunities which their new lenses provided and were rapidly opening up new fields of study for the microscope. In England, once the centre of microscope design and development, conservatism was such that Crisp, writing in 1878 on the "Present condition of microscopy in England", could say:

> In recent years no substantial progress has been made in this country either in the knowledge of the theoretical principles of the microscope itself, or in the systematic investigation of microscopical phenomena.

He concluded:

> It may I think be truly said that out of the entire scientific world there is very probably no body of men who devote so little real attention to the principles that lie at the root of that branch of science of which they are disciples, as do the English microscopists.

These were harsh words, and to a great extent they were well deserved. It may be that the conservatism of the English microscopists (who, banded together in the microscopical societies, exercised such a tight control on the development of the subject) was responsible for this. Certainly the microscopical societies had played a very valuable role in the development of microscopy in England; perhaps at this time they were too conscious of their power and position to view fresh developments objectively. Despite this the British makers were producing instruments of a standard of workmanship unequalled anywhere else in the world. Although the lead in optical design unquestionably lay with Abbe and the Zeiss factory, our own opticians soon were able to produce immersion lenses as good as those of the best Continental makers. Abbe, however, was not content to let his achievements rest with the homogeneous-immersion lens and he sought continually for yet better lenses. These further developments will be described in the next chapter, which brings the story of the optical microscope up to the present day.

CHAPTER 7

THE OPTICAL MICROSCOPE
SINCE 1880

THE acceptance of Abbe's homogeneous-immersion lens was very rapid on the Continent, although as mentioned in the last chapter there was some reluctance on the part of English workers to regard it as a valid development. It has been stressed that some of this hesitancy may well have been due to sheer prejudice, but to some extent also to the fact that makers such as Powell and Lealand were producing water-immersion lenses of such a high quality that they at least equalled the first oil-immersion lenses in aperture and probably excelled them in optical corrections. It soon became apparent, however, that the oil-immersion lens had come to stay and the English opticians began to produce their own versions, which were of the standard that had become associated with the best makers of the country. Most of the oil-immersion lenses produced about 1880 had apertures of about 1·3, a figure already in excess of that which was attainable with the water-immersion lens.

Abbe's formula for the resolution of fine periodic detail in a microscopic object pointed to the importance of aperture. There could be no resolution unless the objective admitted at least some of the diffracted light. The spacing of these diffracted rays depends on the closeness of the object spacing, being much further apart for objects with fine detail; in order therefore to allow diffracted rays from such an object to enter the lens, the aperture must be large. There was thus a very strong tendency to increase the numerical aperture or N.A. of the lenses, as the only other way to increase resolution suggested by Abbe's formula was to use light of shorter wavelength which cannot be carried beyond a certain point. This tendency for the increase in the aperture of immersion lenses is shown in Table 3, which lists some of the lenses of the period together with their focal lengths and apertures.

Powell and Lealand, in particular, soon discovered that it was possible, by making the front element of a microscope objective with

Table 3. Achromatic immersion lenses

approx date	maker	systems	focal length	numerical aperture
1867	Hartnack	Water-immersion	No. 9, $\frac{1}{12}''$	$1\cdot00+$
1867	Hartnack	Water-immersion	No. 12, $\frac{1}{21}''$	$1\cdot00+$
1873	Tolles	Balsam-immersion	$\frac{1}{5}''$	$1\cdot27$
1873	Tolles	Balsam-immersion	$\frac{1}{10}''$	$1\cdot27$
1874	Gundlach	Water-immersion	$\frac{1}{16}''$	$1\cdot00+$
1875	Tolles	Water-immersion	$\frac{1}{10}''$	$1\cdot20$
1875	Powell & Lealand	Water-immersion	$\frac{1}{4}''$	$1\cdot18+$
1875	Powell & Lealand	Water-immersion	$\frac{1}{8}''$	$1\cdot15+$
1875	Zeiss	Water-immersion	$\frac{1}{8}''$	$1\cdot05+$
1875	Zeiss	Water-immersion	$\frac{1}{15}''$	$1\cdot05+$
1875	Zeiss	Water-immersion	$\frac{1}{25}''$	$1\cdot05+$
1877	Powell & Lealand	Water-immersion	$\frac{1}{8}''$	$1\cdot26$
1877	Powell & Lealand	Water-immersion	$\frac{1}{12}''$	$1\cdot22$
1878/9	Zeiss	Oil-immersion	$\frac{1}{8}''$	$1\cdot20$
1878/9	Zeiss	Oil-immersion	$\frac{1}{18}''$	$1\cdot20$
1878/9	Zeiss	Oil-immersion	$\frac{1}{12}''$	$1\cdot35$
1879	Powell & Lealand	Oil-immersion	$\frac{1}{12}''$	$1\cdot20$
1879	Tolles	Oil-immersion	$\frac{1}{8}''$	$1\cdot20$
1879	Tolles	Oil-immersion	$\frac{1}{10}''$	$1\cdot30+$
1879	Tolles	Oil-immersion	$\frac{1}{12}''$	$1\cdot30+$
1879	Zeiss	Oil-immersion	$\frac{1}{8}''$	$1\cdot40$
1880	Powell & Lealand	Oil-immersion	$\frac{1}{25}''$	$1\cdot38$
1880	Powell & Lealand	Oil-immersion	$\frac{1}{50}''$	$1\cdot38$
1880	Powell & Lealand	Oil-immersion	$\frac{1}{12}''\star$	$1\cdot43$
1885	Powell & Lealand	Oil-immersion	$\frac{1}{8}''\dagger$	$1\cdot50$
1885	Powell & Lealand	Oil-immersion	$\frac{1}{12}''\dagger$	$1\cdot50$
1885	Powell & Lealand	Oil-immersion	$\frac{1}{50}''\dagger$	$1\cdot50$

$\star$ Hyper-hemispherical front element
$\dagger$ Flint glass front element

a hyper-hemispherical configuration, to increase the N.A. to about 1·43 for an oil-immersion lens of $\frac{1}{12}$-inch focal length. They had some difficulty in mounting such a front element in the metal holder; this they eventually overcame by the simple trick of cementing the actual lens to a plane piece of glass which then served as the actual front of the combination and which could be used to hold the lens firmly in its metal setting. At a later date the same makers had the idea of inverting the whole combination so that instead of making the front element of crown glass and using the flint in the subsequent components, they made the front element of *flint* glass with the crown glass needed to complete the correction of the aberrations in the other combinations. This system allowed the lens to have its aperture increased still further to a value of 1·50, which approaches very closely the theoretical maximum of 1·52 permitted by this method of construction. Such lenses were made with focal lengths ranging from $\frac{1}{8}$ inch to $\frac{1}{50}$ inch — some of the English amateurs had a special delight in using lenses of extremely short focal leng hs and of consequent high initial magnifying power. Frison, in his discussion of this subject in his memoir on the microscope in the nineteenth century, believes that these lenses of extremely high aperture were of little practical value as

> the enormous aperture was practically unusable, its aberrations being unable to be corrected with the glasses that were available to the English manufacturers.

As a direct result of Abbe's teachings, the view that magnification without resolution of detail was useless spread very rapidly and was loudly proclaimed

> empty amplification is a folly of lenses of the past.

W. H. Dallinger expressed similar views in respect of the work that he carried out with Drysdale on the structure and life cycles of saprophytic organisms.

> Now the objectives with which the earlier work done by the present editor and his colleague, Dr. Drysdale, was effected — to which allusion is made only as being the instance with which we have most practical familiarity — are still in our possession; what was revealed by them fifteen, twelve or ten years ago we can exactly repeat today; and in the general features of the work — in the broad characteristics of the life histories of the saprophytic organisms, minute as they are, revision with objectives of N.A. 1·50 and other lenses of the best English and German

makers, reveals no positive error, even in the *minutest* of the details then discovered and delineated. But the later lenses of great aperture and beautiful corrections have opened up *structure absolutely invisible before*,

It became increasingly apparent that what was needed in a microscope objective was ever-increasing perfection of corrections, allied with increase in the numerical aperture. With the crown and flint glasses which were available to the lens designer of the 1870's and early 1880's it proved impossible to obtain a complete correction of the chromatic aberration. All the coloured rays which formed the

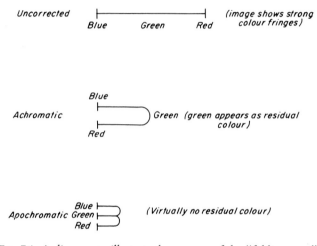

Fig. 7.1. A diagram to illustrate the concept of the "folding over" of the spectrum by an achromatic lens, and the "double folding" by an apochromatic combination.

image could not be brought to the same focal point because of the fact that the dispersion of the various wavelengths of light by these two different types of glass was not proportional. This meant two colours (usually the extremes, red and blue) were brought together with the consequence that there was a residual colour in the image. This residual colour was of the wavelengths which form green light so that dark objects still appeared to have a *very slight* border of greenish-yellow light. In an achromatic lens made up of elements of these two types of glass the basic colour correction had, therefore, been effected, but there was still this "secondary spectrum", as it was called, resulting from the folding over of the primary spectrum as shown diagrammatically in Fig. 7.1. A further difficulty was that such correction was only possible for rays passing through one zone of the objective. Again, the spherical aberration in such lenses made only of crown and flint glass could be properly compensated for only one colour. The result was that the achromatic lenses were provided with colour correction for two colours, which were brought together in one zone of the lens, and spherical correction for one colour, usually the residual colour. This gave very satisfactory images, in (say) the central rays but the peripheral rays often produced very pronounced colour fringes at the borders of an object of high contrast, especially if oblique light was used.

Abbe was very sensible of these theoretical restrictions upon the full correction of microscope objectives, and he devoted a great deal of thought to the problem. It seemed impossible to him to correct the errors when the same lens surface would have to be computed to correct both the spherical and the chromatic aberration at the same time. He therefore turned his attention to the possibility of correcting each of these errors independently. This was a completely new approach and required, as he wrote in 1879:

> at least two kinds of glass having optical relations different to those now in use, — either low refractive index combined with high dispersive power or high refraction with low dispersion.

No such glasses were known in the 1870's, so Abbe tested his idea by constructing objectives which contained fluid elements acting as lenses. One such objective was made by Carl Zeiss in 1873 (with a focal length of $\frac{1}{4}$ inch and a numerical aperture of $0 \cdot 83$) at the direct suggestion of Abbe:

> in order to obtain a clear view of the direction in which further improvement in the dioptric performance of objectives ought to be made, Mr. C. Zeiss, on my suggestion undertook a very interesting and important experiment, not hitherto publicly recorded, by constructing some systems with *fluid* lenses, based on the principle of independent correction. For this purpose we availed ourselves of the low refractive indices of certain of the highly dispersive fluids which are to be found among ethereal oils and artificial chemical preparations, selecting those fluids similar to crown, or light flint, in respect to refraction and equal to heavy flint in respect of dispersive power.

The liquids were enclosed in the posterior element of a microscope objective, between a crown and a flint glass lens; for this first lens the liquid was a mixture of aniseed and cassia oils. Three years later Abbe and Zeiss made another of these experimental lenses, which was of $\frac{1}{9}$-inch focus and which contained cinnamon aldehyde as the liquid. This objective proved to have a numerical aperture of $1 \cdot 15$. They were very fragile, however, and were never made on a commercial basis. Abbe was pleased with the results which they yielded

> both objectives — which are still preserved in Mr. Zeiss' workshop — perform exceedingly well when their fluid contents are kept in good order. They yield images almost perfectly colourless on every kind of preparation and with every kind of illumination, with very superior definition — demonstrating the great improvement in dioptric performance which is attainable by a really perfect correction of spherical and chromatical aberration.

Abbe regarded these lenses as tests of his theoretical speculations, or as he put it, as "a glance at the microscope of the future". In this respect they may be considered successful, as they showed that it was possible to obtain almost perfect chromatic corrections with very little residual colour and at the same time to obtain good spherical correction for two colours instead of only one. This experimental work pointed very clearly to Abbe the way in which future developments lay and he began to turn his thoughts towards interesting someone into carrying out research into the scientific aspects of glass-making, with the particular object of modifying the properties of the final product in the desired direction. Many years later Abbe wrote:

> for years we have been dealing besides true optics, with as it were imaginary optics. We have been considering designs with hypothetical glass which did not exist at all, and discussed the progress which could be feasible if raw material producers were to be brought to the point of interesting themselves in the advanced tasks of optics — which they refused to do.

When he visited the Loan Exhibition in England in 1876, Abbe indicated in his report that, from the point of view of the owners of the great glass works, experiments designed towards the creation of new types of glass were not considered practicable; Abbe suggested that the State Academies might be induced to help in the solution of this problem. One immediate result of the publication of this report in Germany was that Otto Schott sought out the acquaintance of Abbe. Schott was the son of a glass maker and fully understood the manufacturing processes involved; at the end of 1879 he wrote to Abbe and told him that he had succeeded in formulating a lithium-based glass which possessed different optical properties from the normal types then in use. Abbe encouraged Schott to persist in his experiments and to develop systematically the manufacture of new varieties of glass; Schott persevered and in 1881 Abbe was able to report to him that two new borate glasses had properties which would make them of use in lens manufacture.

About this time Schott was persuaded to move to Jena and he was established with the aid of financial help from Zeiss in a small research laboratory. Abbe and Zeiss were well aware of the importance of Schott's research, but they also realized that it would prove extremely expensive and so they approached the government for help. Abbe established contact with an official of the Prussian Ministry of Culture, named Wehrenpfennig, who visited Abbe at Jena and who proved sympathetic towards Abbe himself and towards his ideals. As a result of Wehrenpfennig's influence, the Prussian government granted them 25,000 marks in April 1884, and a year later a further 35,000 marks; these payments enabled the first large-scale melting experiments to begin.

Before this, however, in 1882, Schott had given Abbe small samples of optical glasses with properties which were widely different from those of ordinary crown and flint glass. From these samples Abbe made two lenses, one of which had a focal length of 1 inch and an N.A. of $0 \cdot 3$ whilst the other had a focal length of $\frac{1}{6}$ inch and was of $0 \cdot 86$ N.A. The Berlin instrument maker Bamberg, who was closely associated with Carl Zeiss, tells us that the first of these lenses gave a definition

> as has perhaps not been accomplished before combined with great brightness and complete correction of every trace of chromatic aberration.

Abbe himself reported later (1884) with respect to both of these lenses

> with both objectives, that which hitherto could not even be attempted with any similar lens system has now been almost absolutely achieved, namely equality of the spherical aberration for two different colours (i.e. elimination of the chromatic difference of spherical aberration). In the weaker one it has at the same time been possible to completely eliminate the secondary chromatic aberration at the axis, in other words bring the exact union of rays of three colours, and this is probably the first instance where this condition has been satisfied by an optical construction of any kind which has actually been made. In the stronger objective, on the other hand, the uncorrected remnant of the secondary spectrum has been reduced to slightly less than half the amount which must remain at the given angular aperture with other available types of glass.

He tells us that in these lenses a total of not less than seven new types of glass were used.

With the government subsidy to Schott's Jena glass works, Abbe and Zeiss were in a position to consider the commercial production of these new objectives, as the supply of the new glasses which made them possible was ensured. With the help of a young assistant, Paul Rudolph, Abbe calculated the data for some new lenses and they were announced to the world at a lecture given by Abbe himself to the "Jenaische Gesellschaft für Medizin und Naturwissenschaft". An English translation of his paper soon appeared and was published in the *Journal of the Royal Microscopical Society* for 1886 with the title "On Improvements of the Microscope with the aid of New Kinds of Optical Glass". This paper described in detail the properties of the new lenses, stressing their excellent definition and at the same time describing the special eyepiece which could be used with them to enhance their performance. Abbe called his new lenses "apochromatics" (meaning "away from colour") in order to emphasize the fact that the elimination of the secondary spectrum resulted in

achromatism of a higher order than has hitherto been attained.

In an apochromatic lens three colours are united for two zones and its spherical aberration is corrected for two colours. As shown diagrammatically in Fig. 7.1, the union of three colours at one focus results in the spectrum being "folded" twice, so that the resultant image is almost entirely free from residual colour.

What practical advantages did the use of these new and necessarily very expensive lenses confer on the user? For the greater part of microscopical studies it must be admitted that the advantage would be so small as to be unnoticeable; for careful researches involving the use of the highest powers of the microscope at the limits of resolution then the image quality would show a definite improvement. With the ordinary achromatic lenses, for example, the working aperture of the lens had always to be reduced, as the light passing through the poorly-corrected outer zones spoilt the quality of the image. Apochromatic lenses, however, allowed the use of their full stated aperture; in addition their corrections were so good that it proved possible to use eyepieces of very high power ("deep" eyepieces as they were called at the time) and so obtain a more easy visualization of all the detail that their resolution afforded. It was also stressed that the almost perfect achromatism of these new lenses would be valuable for photomicrography which was rapidly developing at this time as a means of recording the microscopic image.

The use of special eyepieces with these lenses has already been mentioned. The reason for this is that in all objectives of large aperture the front element consists of a single piece of glass which cannot itself be achromatized. This means that even when all the most careful corrections have been made in the subsequent elements, some residual colour still remains at the periphery of the field of view. The image formed by the blue and violet rays is larger than that of the red and yellow rays; although they coincide at the centre of the field of view the blue image extends over the red more and more as one goes towards the margin. In the ordinary achromatic lens the amount of this difference in the size of the image (called the "chromatic difference in magnification") is not the same at the centre of the field and at the periphery, so that little can be done to correct it; with the apochromatic lens, however, the chromatic difference in magnification is approximately constant over the entire field. This makes it easy to correct by constructing the eyepiece in such a way that it has an equal but *opposite* magnifying effect for the two extremes of colour. In effect this is to make the eyepiece deliberately non-achromatic by a known and controlled amount. If this system is to be used then it follows that in order to make the eyepieces completely interchangeable with all objectives, as obviously one must, then *all* the objectives must exhibit this chromatic difference in magnification. With low aperture lenses, where the front lens is itself an achromatic combination, this difference in magnification of the various colours is not usually present. Abbe, therefore, deliberately made his low-power apochromatic objectives to show the same chromatic difference of magnification as the high power ones. This allowed him to use the system of correcting the last traces of colour at the periphery of the image field by means of the special eyepiece. Abbe called these "compensation" eyepieces, but this has now been changed to "compensating" in all modern works on microscopy.

The Zeiss works produced a series of eleven apochromatic lenses, which are summarized in Table 4; these lenses were produced in forms which were corrected both for the long English tube and for the shorter version favoured on the Continent. The price of these new lenses ranged from about £5 for the 16 mm to £27. 10s. 0d. for the 2 mm oil immersion lens of N.A. 1·4. The apochromatic objectives owed their existence entirely to the new types of optical glass developed by Schott and Abbe; fresh formulations were being produced all the time and in 1886 they were able to issue a pamphlet listing over 44 different types of glass with varying properties of refractive index and dispersion. Figure 7.2 shows in diagrammatic form the complexity of the lens elements in one of the high aperture apochromatic lenses, and compares them with the lenses as found in a simple achromat.

Table 4. Apochromatic lenses

Date	Maker	System	Focal length	Numerical aperture	Comments
1883	Abbe	Dry	$1''$ (25 mm)	0·30	Experimental lenses
1883–4	Abbe	Dry	$\frac{1}{6}''$ (4 mm)	0·86	not made for sale
1886	Zeiss	Dry	$1''$ (25 mm)	0·30	
	(designed by	Dry	$\frac{2}{3}''$ (16 mm)	0·30	
	Abbe)	Dry	$\frac{1}{2}''$ (12 mm)	0·60	First series; unstable
		Dry	$\frac{1}{3}''$ (8 mm)	0·60	glass in some ele-
		Dry	$\frac{1}{4}''$ (6 mm)	0·95	ments and lenses
		Dry	$\frac{1}{6}''$ (4 mm)	0·95	were not reliable
		Water-immersion	$\frac{1}{10}''$ (2·5 mm)	1·25	after a time in some
		Oil-immersion	$\frac{1}{8}''$ (3 mm)	1·30	climates
		Oil-immersion	$\frac{1}{12}''$ (2 mm)	1·30	
		Oil-immersion	$\frac{1}{8}''$ (3 mm)	1·40	
		Oil-immersion	$\frac{1}{12}''$ (2 mm)	1·40	
1888	,,	Dry	$\frac{1}{4}''$ (6 mm)	0·95	Second series; re-
		Dry	$\frac{1}{6}''$ (4 mm)	0·95	calculated and with
1889	,,	Dry	$\frac{1}{8}''$ (3 mm)	0·95	better corrections
		Oil-immersion	$\frac{1}{16}''$ (1·5 mm)	1·30	
1894	,,	Dry	$\frac{1}{8}''$ (3 mm)	0·95	Third series; con-
		Oil-immersion	$\frac{1}{12}''$ (2 mm)	1·30	structed from new
1895	,,	Dry	$\frac{1}{6}''$ (4 mm)	0·95	durable glass
1897	,,	Remainder of the series			
1889	,,	Naphthalene monobromide immersion	$\frac{1}{10}''$ (2·5 mm)	1·63	Only few made; cost £40 in 1893
1892	Powell &	Oil-immersion	$\frac{1}{8}''$	1·40	
	Lealand	Oil-immersion	$\frac{1}{10}''$	1·40	
		Oil-immersion	$\frac{1}{12}''$	1·40	
		Oil-immersion	$\frac{1}{20}''$	1·40	
		Oil-immersion	$\frac{1}{10}''$	1·50	van Heurck thought this to be a very fine lens; cost £50 in 1893
		Oil-immersion	$\frac{1}{12}''$	1·50	
		Oil-immersion	$\frac{1}{20}''$	1·50	

Very soon the new lenses were constructed by other makers; Powell and Lealand in England were listing them by the year 1892 and soon Reichert, Leitz and others were making them on the Continent. It is surprising that Abbe did not even trouble to protect his invention by taking out a patent. No sooner had the apochromatic series appeared on the market than Abbe began work on yet another idea, the development of the use of fluorite as a material for the construction of microscope lenses. Fluorite is a natural crystalline material with a much lower refractive index and dispersion than any known optical glass and it had been realized by Abbe about 1881 that this substance possessed optical properties which would make it of use in correcting some of the residual spherical and chromatic aberrations in microscope objectives.

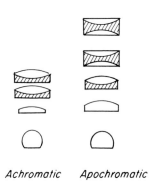

Achromatic   Apochromatic

Fig. 7.2. The lens elements of a typical achromatic objective compared with those of an apochromat.

In the published descriptions of the new types of apochromats, the stress was laid on the use of Schott's new varieties of optical glass and nothing was said about the use of other compounds such as fluorite, although it is likely that this substance was in fact used in the first apochromatic objectives. Abbe devoted a lot of time and effort to procuring supplies of fluorite and to developing its use in lenses; in 1890 he published detailed information as to its use in combination with the Jena glasses. This proved to be a very important development as nowadays "fluorite" lenses are extensively produced with corrections intermediate between those of an ordinary achromat and the much more expensive apochromats.

The new apochromats were soon in great demand by microscopists, who appreciated the superb quality of image which it was possible to obtain by their use. One difficulty soon became apparent — the new Jena glasses were not very stable, and in hot or humid climates especially they soon began to devitrify and eventually became completely opaque, so making the lens useless. The manufacturers actively pursued research to discover yet more types of glass which would not suffer from this fault. In the meantime, Zeiss issued a new set of lenses (in 1888) which had been recalculated and in which the number of lens elements had in some cases been increased to give superior corrections, especially of the marginal rays. Finally, in 1894, Zeiss began to introduce yet a third system of apochromats, this time manufactured of glasses which were much more durable; by 1897 all the apochromatic lenses were being produced to these improved formulae.

These lenses were much favoured by the bacteriologists, who had been among the first to appreciate the value of the homogeneous-immersion system a few years earlier. Among the many discoveries which were made with the new lenses perhaps the observation of the unstained syphilis organism by Schaudinn may be singled out for mention. By the aid of the very high resolution the *Spirochaeta pallidum* was clearly visualized for the first time. Such was the enthusiasm for these lenses, which of course demanded the most meticulous attention to the arrangement and alignment of the microscope for their successful operation, that some workers wished to use them for any and every purpose, often under the most unsuitable conditions! The microanatomists and the histologists and cytologists also became aware of the enormous potentialities of these new lenses and as an example of the superb results to which they gave rise, one has only to look at the description of the spermatozoa published by the Swedish anatomist Gustav Retzius, which have not been surpassed by any optical microscopist since With proper use, the apochromatic objective allows the attainment of the ultimate resolution of the optical microscope. By 1890 these lenses were allowing expert microscopists to resolve structures which lay at the theoretical limits of visibility (about $0 \cdot 25 \, \mu$). Workers such as E. M. Nelson in this country, van Heurck in Belgium, Retzius in Sweden and others were pushing forwards the limits of the optical microscope. Nelson was very impressed with the new lenses and wrote in 1889:

> The achievements which the microscope has accomplished, owing to achromatism, are truly marvellous, far surpassing the expectations of its most sanguine votaries. Who shall say what conquests are in store for it now that it is apochromatized?

On another occasion he commented:

> Thanks to the Abbe Zeiss apochromatics, the curtain which hides the
> very small from our gaze has been drawn up a little higher.

One has only to study the catalogues of the leading manufacturers at
the end of the nineteenth century in order to see how many superb
lenses were produced, often with extremely high apertures and of
apochromatic quality. Powell and Lealand, for instance, in 1893 were
offering such a lens of $\frac{1}{10}$-inch focus with an N.A. of 1·5, a truly
remarkable figure. Such a lens, regarded as extremely fine by van
Heurck was, it is true, very expensive, costing £50; at this time
such a sum of money would have put this lens beyond the reach of
most people. With the aid of such high aperture lenses it was perfectly
feasible to push the resolving power to its limit. Booth, in a recent
article in the *Journal of the Royal Microscopical Society* comments on
this in the following words:

> The amateur microscopists of the nineteenth century were responsible
> for the great technical virtuosity of the opticians of the time. It is a salutary
> comment on scientific progress that whereas between 1890 and 1914 one
> could buy either from Charles Spencer in the United States, or from
> Messrs Powell and Lealand in the United Kingdom, a 1/16th, 1/10th and
> 1/20th inch objectives of numerical aperture of 1·5, at the present time
> there is great difficulty in finding lenses whose aperture is even 1·4 and
> none with the preceding high aperture is now made.

It seems that the current design tendencies in optical microscopy are
working against the achievement of the ultimate in resolution; with
modern equipment it is very difficult and perhaps even impossible to
equal some of the feats of microscopic resolution which were reported
half a century or so ago. The modern objectives, in addition to being
of lower aperture, are often computed so as to deliver a truly flat field
in order to make them more suitable for photomicrography and this
may well mean the sacrifice of ultimate performance as far as resolution
is concerned. With the development of the electron microscope,
which will be considered in Chapter 8, the stimulus to push the performance of the optical instrument to its limit seems to have decreased
so much that it is not now commercially worthwhile for the manufacturers to provide equipment which could necessarily be of interest to
relatively few workers and would in all probability be extremely
expensive. The keen microscopist, still often an amateur worker as in
the nineteenth century, who can obtain a second-hand Powell and

Lealand stand No. 1 in good condition, and who can find one of their high aperture apochromatic objectives which is still in good working order is fortunate indeed. With such equipment, and a high degree of manipulative skill it is possible to obtain better results at the limits of resolution than with modern objectives, although for the majority of routine work in a laboratory the modern stand is much to be preferred on account of its ease of operation.

In 1889, Abbe and Zeiss produced a further lens which is worth mentioning on account of its exceptional numerical aperture of $1 \cdot 63$. This remains to this day the highest N.A. of any objective ever made; it was designed with a focus of $\frac{1}{10}$ inch and to apochromatic standards. There were five elements in its construction, the front element consisting of a hyper-hemispherical flint lens of refractive index $1 \cdot 72$, followed by a series of single and composite elements, some of which incorporated fluorite. This lens was intended for use with immersion in naphthalene monobromide and in order to obtain the full advantage of its huge aperture it had to be used with a slide and coverslip of glass with a very high refractive index (of at least $1 \cdot 6$). At the same time the object itself had to be mounted in a medium of at least the same refractive index. For the most critical work Zeiss provided a special ocular and a condenser with a front lens made of flint glass. This lens was particularly suited to the observation of objects by means of incident illumination. Henri van Heurck obtained one of these lenses and after extensive trials commented that it was difficult to use and hence

> its practical use for ordinary work is not very great.

By the use of this lens, however, he succeeded in photographing one of the most famous of the test objects then in use — the markings on the frustule of the diatom *Amphipleura pellucida*, quite clearly resolved all over its extent into separate "beads", "as clearly as we can see the *Pleurosigma* with the best objectives in our possession". (*Pleurosigma* is a diatom with much coarser markings on its frustule which are relatively easy to display.) The naphthalene monobromide objective was of little use for the study of biological material, for as already mentioned the tissue must be mounted in a medium of very high refractive index which is not feasible as the only available fluid, naphthalene monobromide itself, was very destructive to the structure. Again the flint glass slides and coverslips proved to be excessively costly, a further factor against the general use of this lens. Only a few were ever made but one is still preserved in the collection of the Royal Microscopical Society and was in excellent working order when last examined.

By the end of the nineteenth century we have seen that the optics of the microscope had been brought to such a pitch of excellence that they have never been surpassed. The large microscope stands of the English makers were triumphs of the art of the instrument maker, and were much sought after by connoisseurs; they, however, proved to be too cumbersome and elaborate for the professional scientist, who preferred the lighter (and equally efficient) Continental instrument with its shorter tube length and Abbe illuminator in place of the elaborate and highly-corrected condensers of the English stand. Towards the end of the century, however, there was a tendency for English makers to move towards the Continental style of instrument; Powell and Lealand and Watsons, who were both producing excellent large stands, proved an exception to this trend. The large stands of Watsons had established an excellent reputation, and they combined in one stand the good features of the Jackson-Lister limb and its compactness, with the solidity of the tripod foot and the smoothness and certainty of the long-lever focusing system. One of their stands, that designed to the specifications of Henri van Heurck and bearing his name, is shown in Fig. 7.3 from which the main features of its construction are apparent. The instrument was furnished with two draw tubes, so that lenses corrected for either the English long tube or the Continental short tube could be used; there was a fine focus to the substage movement and the stage itself was provided not only with the full mechanical movements but also with rotating movements which are often very valuable in photomicrography. Such microscopes, and the rather simpler "Royal" and "Edinburgh Students" models of the same maker, although no longer in production may still be found in numerous amateur and professional laboratories in use and giving excellent service.

In the early years of the present century many English makers abandoned the traditional long (ten-inch) tube and adopted and standardized on the short tube of the Continental makers (160 mm); at the same time there was a tendency to adopt the Continental type of mechanical stage in which the whole top plate moves to give the vertical motion, whilst the lateral traverse was effected entirely by means of two small "fingers" which carried the microscope slide. This system is found in most research microscopes of the present time, and

FIG. 7.3. The Watson "Van Heurck" microscope. Note the fine-focus adjustment for the condenser (located just behind the controls for the mechanical stage).

although it provides for a very easy coverage of the whole slide it does suffer from the disadvantage that the lateral motion which receives most of the wear is the weaker one, whereas the vertical movement which is much more robust, is much less used.

The period around the turn of the century proved to be a most important point in the development of the mechanical aspects of the microscope. Before this date many microscope users had been the amateur workers who were concerned with observing pond life at low magnification or in seeking to prove by "diatom dotting" that the resolution of their latest high-aperture objective was better than that of the lens belonging to the next man. The twentieth century, how-ever, resulted in a vast increase in the professional use of the micro-scope by medical students, scientists, and specialist workers in all fields of industry. Their needs proved to be quite different from those of the "diatom dotters"; they were usually content with lenses of a lower aperture, with a stand which was more manageable, and above all with apparatus which was sold at a reasonable price. It was this above all which led to the adoption of the Continental model, but one further change in the whole way of production of instruments also was involved. This was the change from hand construction methods to the machine-made, mass-produced article.

Formerly, microscopes were fashioned by hand, either by a single craftsman or by a very few workers, each specializing in his own particular aspect of the work. Powell and Lealand microscopes were hand-made from the very beginning and continued to be so until they ceased being made about ten years before the death of Thomas Powell in 1925. These microscopes were produced by a very small staff of highly skilled workmen and it has been estimated that at least 600 man-hours were required for the production of one stand. So skilled were the P. and L. craftsmen that it is said that no general drawings existed for the famous No. 1 stand and that each instrument was individually made, often with the result that parts of the stand were not inter-changeable with any other instrument. However, with the outbreak of the First World War in 1914 and the industrial demands then im-posed, there were great advances in the methods for the mass-produc-tion of all types of instruments. Large numbers of gun-sights, tele-scopes, range finders and other instruments had to be made by rela-tively unskilled labour; at the same time high standards of accuracy had to be preserved. By the use of precision tools a great deal of the responsibility was removed from the operator. At the same time an advantage was obtained in that the microscopes or other instruments were all produced to standard tolerances and the individual parts were subjected to a careful inspection to ensure that they conformed to the requirements; this resulted in interchangeability of parts from one microscope to the next.

The development of standardization and mass production was a logical outcome of the moves leading to the interchangeability of component parts which had been initiated by the Council of the Royal Microscopical Society in 1857 when the advisability of having standard sizes for objective threads and for eyepieces and condenser mounts had been first suggested. The RMS standards and their modifications, which were added at a later date, were successfully instituted and eventually adopted by all the makers throughout the world. With the development of mass production the microscope could be purchased as a simple stand with the minimum of lenses and accessories, which could be added to as the occasion arose with the certain knowledge that all the extra parts would fit. This was the eventual fulfilment of the ideal attempted in the middle of the last century by Beck with the "Popular" microscope but which did not ever really succeed because of the lack of standardization in the manufacturing procedures. A good example of a model of microscope which fulfilled the requirements of precision quantity production at a reasonable cost was the "Service" microscope of Watsons which was introduced just after the First World War. To the basic stand such accessories as a centring substage, a rotating multiple nosepiece, binocular body and mechanical stage could be added any time as the need arose, so extending the scope of the instrument.

The trend for English makers to "go Continental" was also stimulated by the tendency (especially prominent in the Edwardian era) to regard everything German, and especially their optical instruments, as desirable. The older English bar-limb instrument of Ross and Powell was superseded almost entirely by Jackson's modification of the Lister limb which was also adopted by the leading Continental instrument makers; in 1903 Leitz, for example, abandoned their vertical prismatic slide carrying the vertical micrometer spindle for the fine focusing in favour of a typical C-shaped Lister limb. At the same time they changed the old direct-acting micrometer screw with the vertical milled head which served to drive the fine focus, to a form in which the operating knobs were on the sides of the limb.

Many modifications of the fine focus adjustment of the microscope have been introduced in the last fifty years and their details are of interest only to the specialist. It will be sufficient here to note the four main types into which these various mechanisms may be grouped (Fig. 7.4). Firstly, we have the older direct-acting micrometer screw; this was going out of favour in the early 1900's as it was considered that this form was not sufficiently accurate to work a high-aperture apochromatic lens. Some makers, such as Reichert, modified the

FIG. 7.4. Diagrams to show the principles involved in various fine-focus mechanisms used in microscopes.

(a) The Continental direct screw.
(b) The English long-lever system.
(c) Two types of side levers used by Swift.
(d) Two variants of the inclined-plane principle.

direct-acting screw by placing levers between the end of the screw and the slide in order to slow down the movement, and this version was incorporated in their microscope for some time. The second main type of fine adjustment constituted the long lever of the English makers. Here, as in the direct screw, the control knob was placed vertically behind the limb. This form was retained only by a few makers, who developed it to one of the most satisfactory fine focus mechanisms ever used on microscopes. It was, for example, used by Watsons for many years in their Edinburgh, Royal and Van Heurck series microscopes.

The third main type of mechanism owes its origin to a device originally used by Swift in their "Best Challenge" microscope of 1881 which they perfected in 1886. This form, known as the side-lever, is shown in two of its versions at C in Fig. 7.4. There was a single milled control knob which could be placed on either side of the limb; in various modified forms this mechanism is still used today. The fourth group of mechanisms all use some form of the inclined plane. This may take the shape of a micrometer screw forcing a hardened steel ball along between two inclined surfaces, as used by Leitz in 1913, or more commonly by the action of a heart-shaped cam. In this latter form, also due to Leitz, a wormwheel is rotated on a horizontal axis by means of an endless screw on the operating shaft of the focusing rod. The heart-shaped cam is fixed onto the face of the wormwheel and rotates with it. A small hardened steel wheel attached to the slide ways of the microscope served as a follower and rolled on the edge of the cam so that as the latter rotated, an up-or-down motion was given to the fine adjustment slide of the microscope. This action is represented in Fig. 7.4(d). By the use of hardened steel parts, and later by the introduction of ball bearing mechanisms, the wear in fine focus mechanisms was kept to a minimum and very smooth and reliable actions were obtained.

One notable tendency in microscope design during the last fifty years has been the increasing use of binocular tubes, which are now standard on almost every large research model. The use of a binocular tube allows both eyes to be employed simultaneously which is important as it eliminates a considerable amount of the fatigue during the prolonged periods of observation which are often needed for research or diagnostic work. For low-power work there is the added advantage that some systems of adapting the microscope to binocular vision allow a stereoscopic effect to be obtained. This can be useful in understanding the morphology of certain small types of object such as the shapes of Foraminifera shells (Protozoa which are found in large numbers in the deposits of the ocean floor).

The binocular microscope has a long history, dating back to at least 1671 when Cherubin d'Orleans described such an instrument in his

A. *Ridell* 1854   B. *Wenham* 1860

C. *Powell and Lealand* 1865   D. *Abbe* 1880

FIG. 7.5. The optical elements of four of the early binocular microscope systems.

book *La Dioptrique Oculaire* and illustrated one six years later in his subsequent *La Vision Parfaite*. His microscope was in fact two separate microscopes, with completely independent optical systems, united with their tubes fixed at an angle so that they both focused on the same part of the object. No interest was shown in this system (which, together with its inventor, was criticized by Robert Hooke) until many years later when fresh interest was aroused by the publication of Wheatstone's paper on binocular vision in 1838. This started a search for the stereoscopic binocular microscope, which according to E. M. Nelson, was won by the Americans. Professor J. A. Ridell of New Orleans developed a workable system in 1854 which used two prisms placed behind the objective in the manner shown in Fig. 7.5(a), so that the light from the objective was split and deflected up the two parallel eyepiece tubes.

Perhaps the most popular and successful of the nineteenth-century binocular systems was developed by Francis Wenham in 1860; his instrument employed convergent tubes with a beam-splitting prism inserted just above the objective lens to send light from half the aperture up the second tube to its own eyepiece. Wenham was associated with the firm of Ross, so that they manufactured many of these microscopes over the succeeding years. As no patent was taken out the system was soon extensively copied and most of the makers soon were offering binoculars constructed on this system. The arrangement of the prism (shown in diagrammatic form in Fig. 7.5(b)) is such that half of the aperture of the lens is occupied by the beam splitter which limits the usefulness of this system to objectives of low power. With these, however, a very beautiful stereoscopic effect is obtained. One advantage of this type of binocular is that the image in one of the eyepiece tubes is not altered at all or impaired in quality, whilst the effect on the other is only slight; the prism may easily be removed if desired, so converting the microscope back into a monocular with complete utilisation of the full objective aperture.

Powell and Lealand soon produced a modification of their own (see Fig. 7.5(c)) as also did Ross, which allowed the use of the binocular tube with the highest magnifications and with the full aperture of all lenses. With these systems, however, there was no stereoscopic effect and the only advantage was the lessening of fatigue. Many ingenious binocular systems, often involving numerous prisms and consequent light losses, were proposed and constructed in the latter half of the nineteenth century. Abbe himself designed a binocular eyepiece (Fig. 7.5(d)) which used two right-angled prisms, separated by a very thin film of air. The great drawback to this system, as to many of the other high-power binocular devices of this period was the unequal optical path in the two tubes which made some form of correction essential. Abbe provided dissimilar eyepieces to carry out this task. Another disadvantage of most of these early high-power systems was the unequal intensities of light in the two eyepieces; the Abbe binocular eyepiece suffered very much from this defect, as one eyepiece provided over two and a half times as much light as the other.

The first really successful high-power binocular system was introduced by Conrad Beck in 1913. It owed its inspiration to an invention

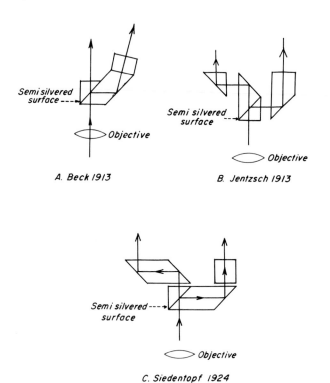

FIG. 7.6. Later binocular systems. Those due to Jentzch and Siedentopf are still in use.

by F. E. Ives in America in 1902 and used the so-called "Swan cube" as a beam-splitting device. This cube consists of two right-angled prisms cemented together after one of them had been coated with silver on the cemented face to such a thickness that approximately half the incident light was transmitted and half reflected. The Beck system is illustrated in Fig. 7.6(a), from which it may be seen that this form of binocular also demanded the use of convergent eyepiece tubes; this

Beck firmly believed to be the best system, as the eyes naturally converge for viewing near objects. In the same year Leitz produced their own system, designed by F. Jentzsche, which again used a beam-splitting prism embracing the whole aperture of the lens.

In this form of binocular microscope the two eyepiece tubes are parallel, with the great advantage that a simple separation of the two outer prisms caused a corresponding variation in the interocular distance; the optical path difference could be very simply equalized by making the right-hand prism longer than the left-hand one (Fig. 7.6(b)). This system was so successful that it is still used today as the basis of most of the binocular microscopes now produced. Another variant which found some favour is due to Siedentopf and was invented around 1924; this is shown in Fig. 7.6(c), and it will be seen that the interocular distance can be varied by a simple rotation of the left-hand prism. This has no effect on the optical path difference and so with this system variation of the interocular distance has no effect on the tube length of the microscope.

Another twentieth-century trend has been the adoption of more or less complicated prism systems so that the eyepieces may be inclined whilst the limb is vertical and the stage of the microscope remains horizontal. Such devices provide a very convenient viewing position for the operator allowing the instrument to be used on a table whilst the operator remains seated normally. A microscope by Zeiss is shown in Fig. 7.7. From this illustration the appearance of a modern research biological microscope may be gauged. The inclined eyepiece tubes are clearly visible and the general solidity of the main limb casting will be noticed. This is a very important trend in modern microscope design and the solidity of such stands (preventing excessive flexure of the limb during use, which may be troublesome with high-power lenses) is a great advance over the earlier instruments. Indeed, in some of the more elaborate microscopes this is carried so far that the weight of the casting makes it very difficult to lift the microscope from the table! The contrast with the microscope of fifty years ago, as represented by the van Heurck instrument shown in Fig. 7.3 is very marked.

It will be noticed that the microscope of today does not have any provision for altering the tube length; the lack of such a refinement is to be regretted in instruments which now cost many hundreds of pounds; provision of tube length adjustment would often be valuable in attaining the best possible image from a given lens. An alternative solution which would be welcome in today's expensive research

instruments would be the inclusion of a Jackson tube-length compen-
sator which also enables the best optical performance to be obtained
from high-aperture dry lenses. Perhaps the manufacturers work on
the assumption, which may well be true, that the majority of users
neither know nor care how to use such a device and hence it is not
worth adding to the already complex instrument! In general the
standard of current microscopy is not commensurate with the standard
of the instruments which are in use and there is a very good case
for the extension of education in the use of the microscope at all
levels.

In the current research microscope, as for example in those illustrated
in Fig. 7.7, it can be seen that the focus controls, both coarse and fine,
have been made concentric so that they are very convenient to use
and they have been brought down to a low level; here we have in
effect a reversion to the idea of George Adams the Elder, where he
made the focusing arrangement of his "New Universal" microscope
of 1746 at table level (see Chapter 4, Fig. 4.8). In the instruments
illustrated in Fig. 7.7, the body tube and the lenses do not move in
order to focus the object; in the interests of stability, the limb and the
lenses have been fixed and the focus is varied by the movement of
the stage. It is claimed that this allows a much steadier focusing
motion and facilitates the use of very high-aperture lenses.

One further feature of modern practice which is universal in research quality stands and is rapidly spreading to simpler microscopes
of the student category, is the incorporation of the lighting unit into
the base of the microscope. The low-voltage bulb is housed in the base
of the instrument and its light concentrated by a lens system and reflected onto the condenser by means of a right-angled prism. This has
the advantage that the whole microscope system is rendered much
more portable and it is easier to set up and align for use. The low-
voltage bulbs used in these lamps have a filament composed of several
coiled strands of wire arranged side by side in order to provide a large
or "solid" source. It is thus easy to form an image of the source that
fills the full aperture of the condenser. The low-voltage lighting unit
gives a very intense light which is suitable for observation at the
highest powers and also for photomicrography. For normal visual
observations the light is dimmed by reducing the voltage by means
of a suitable rheostat or variable transformer.

Such modern microscopes are provided with relatively few accessories. If one looks at a large research microscope of even sixty years

(b) By Wild.

(a) By Zeiss.

FIG. 7.7. Two modern Continental research microscopes.
Both of these microscope stands possess built-in illumination; the focusing movement of (b) is effected by moving the stage relative to the body tube and objectives.   The controls of both instruments are now placed below the stage level.

ago one is struck by the large number of accessories which often necessitated a second box as large as that of the microscope itself; most of these accessories were used for varying the type of illumination, and with the better appreciation of the principles underlying the microscope theory they naturally were all rendered obsolete. Although the

Fig. 7.8. Diagram illustrating some of the various components which can be added to a modern basic microscope stand.

modern instrument comes with few accessories it is so well engineered that it proves an easy matter at any time to replace certain parts such as the body, the stage or the condenser with components of a different type which may be required for some particular purpose. Some idea of the various range of fittings available may be gained from Fig. 7.8 which shows the basic microscope stand and some of the variant arrangements which may be bought and set up at any time for the accomplishment of special tasks.

The whole design of the modern microscope stand is extremely functional, all its parts being arranged for ease of manipulation. In this respect our present microscopes show a marked advance over the older stands; although the best of the old microscopes would do the job just as well as a modern microscope, the latter is much easier to use and adjust. Some flexibility, however, has had to be sacrificed in order to achieve this ease of operation and it is not now the practice to make each individual microscope stand universal in function. If polarized light is required, or if phase-contrast or some other special technique is needed, then it is more usual nowadays to employ an instrument specially designed for the job rather than proceed to adapt a standard biological microscope by means of added accessories.

In its basic design, the microscope has changed remarkably little since the nineteenth century, each improvement tending to be in detailed construction rather than representing a radical rethinking of the whole design. Recently, however, one of our leading manufacturers (Vickers Instruments) has produced an instrument which represents a breakaway from traditional microscope design. This microscope, known as the "Patholux", is shown in Fig. 7.9, from which it can be seen that the traditional limb is replaced by a very solid casting, which has considerable rigidity and carries the stage and the optical system.

It can be seen from the figure that the limb now takes the form of a box frame, perhaps one of the most stable of all engineering constructions; the stage is very large and rigid and is firmly fixed, the focusing movement being once again applied to the lens system. The operating controls are arranged on the base panel and it has been found by ergonomic study that this placing allows the maximum of comfort allied to operating efficiency. The coarse and fine focus controls are concentric and it is interesting to note that in this microscope, for perhaps the first time for a hundred years, the rack and pinion mechanism for the operation of the focusing has been abandoned; in its place a sturdy lever and scroll mechanism has been substituted. There is an integral light source and the whole instrument has been designed to be as adaptable as is consistent with the maintenance of the primary functions of the microscope stand. This microscope may be compared with the instrument shown in Fig. 7.10 which represents the conventionally designed instrument from the same maker, with the focusing movement of the instrument being applied to the stage and with the standard type of base and limb.

FIG. 7.9. A modern trend in microscope design. The Vickers "Patholux" microscope.

With the rethinking of the engineering of the microscope stand,
changes, although less striking, have also been made in the optical
system. For a long time after the introduction of apochromatic
lenses it was thought that the ultimate had been reached; this, as
so often in the past, proved to be a mistaken view. Improvements
have taken place in the methods of mounting the objectives on the
instrument, so that the modern microscope now carries three, four or

even six lenses so arranged that any one may be instantly brought into use. This change of objectives by simple rotation of a nosepiece is not, of course, a new development; as we have seen it was used in the eighteenth century by Benjamin Martin among others. The modern revolving nosepiece, however, is a piece of high precision engineering

Fig. 7.10. The Vickers research microscope model "M15b". The light control unit is seen in the background.

so that the centration of each lens to the optical axis of the microscope is guaranteed.

In the past eighty years or so many devices have been introduced to enable single objectives to be changed very quickly. All of these "objective changers", as they are termed, incorporate some device for centring each lens individually and they achieved a high popularity for high resolution work in which the exact centration of the lens was very important. A further advantage in addition to the exact centring of a whole "battery" of objectives was that the fine adjustment slide only had to bear the weight of one objective at any one time. Modern manufacturing methods, often involving much more robust slides and the use of ball-bearing mechanisms, have, together with the more accurate centring of the revolving nosepiece, rendered the single objective changer much less necessary, although for some purposes, especially in polarization microscopy the very exact alignment which they allow is sometimes essential.

One important feature of the modern objective which has been developed along with the revolving nosepiece is their adjustment so that all the objectives on one nosepiece are approximately in focus when this is rotated. This is called "parfocality" and is very valuable as in routine diagnostic work it is very often necessary to inspect an object with several different powers in rapid succession; much time and temper (not to mention accidents to the objectives!) are saved if the nosepiece can be rapidly rotated and the new lens will still be approximately in focus.

One danger which is always present, especially with the higher powers in which the lenses have a very short focal length and consequent short working distance, is that the objectives may inadvertently be racked down into the slide during the focusing movement. In the past many valuable lenses and preparations have been ruined by this; even a very slight knock is often sufficient to displace the front element of some oil-immersion lenses. In recent years a very simple device has been adopted to prevent damage in this way. The lenses of the objective are arranged so that they can slide in a cylindrical fitting in the upper part of the mount, against the pressure exerted by a weak spiral spring. In normal use this spring keeps the lens fully extended in the correct working position, but if the front lens is accidentally brought into contact with the slide then the full pressure exerted by the focusing screw is absorbed by compression of the spring, the lens elements of the objective sliding into the mount; the result is that no damage to the mounting of the lenses can take place with normal usage.

In addition to these improvements in the mounting of the objective, there are some other improvements which are worth noting. First, there is the much more extensive use of the mineral fluorite. The use of natural fluorite by Abbe and other makers has already been mentioned, but pieces of natural fluorite large enough for optical use are now very rare indeed. This placed a very severe restriction on the use of this substance for the components of microscope lenses. In recent years, however, it has been discovered that the mineral can be recrystallized and obtained as discs which may be several inches in diameter and without flaws and so perfectly suited to optical work.

This "synthetic fluorite" (and the use of crystals of lithium fluoride which may be synthesized in the laboratory) has enabled this substance to be used extensively in the construction of microscope lenses; by its aid the designer has been able to obtain superior corrections at a very reasonable price. The "fluorite" lenses have corrections intermediate in quality between the achromatic objective and the very expensive apochromat and are usually referred to as "semi-apochromatic" objectives. They possess the improved spherical correction associated with apochromats and are especially valuable for photomicrography. Both fluorite and apochromatic objectives, despite their very high degree of spherical and chromatic correction, do suffer from a rather marked curvature of their field. This means that the only area in sharp focus at any one setting of the fine focus control is very limited. If the centre of the field is sharp, then the edges are out of focus and vice versa. For visual examinations, especially where one is working at high resolution, this is not a great drawback, as it is natural to bring the object of interest to the centre of the field for examination; the expert microscopist is also constantly manipulating the fine focus, so that field curvature is often passed almost without notice.

With the development of photomicrography as a means of recording the microscopic image this defect has assumed a much greater importance. Only one plane of focus can be recorded at any one time with the camera and the out-of-focus areas around the periphery of the field then become very objectionable. To some extent this fault may be overcome by using sufficient camera extension (or a high-power eyepiece) so that only the sharp central portion of the image is recorded on the plate; this solution may, however, involve the use of excessive magnification so that the resultant picture suffers from the effects of "empty" magnification in which blurring ensues and no further detail is rendered visible. The solution to this problem has been provided by the optical designers who have computed lenses which not only have very good corrections but also provide a truly flat field. This has been achieved only at the expense of making a very complicated objective and at the expense of a certain amount of resolution. These "plan-apochromats", as they are called, may now be obtained with various focal lengths, but as they combine the corrections of an apochromat with the additional quality of a flat field, naturally their cost is extremely high.

It seems a pity that with all the current trends in microscope design leading to instruments which are easier to use and which are better engineered, the ultimate resolution of the optical microscope is getting ever harder and harder to attain. In the latter years of the last century skilled microscopists such as Nelson, van Heurck and Woodward, to name but three, could easily resolve the most difficult test objects available, such as Nobert's artificial rulings. One version which Nobert produced in about 1875 had twenty bands of rulings, each band containing a series of parallel scratches on a glass slip which were closer together than those of the preceding band.

The author, in collaboration with G. L'E. Turner of the Oxford Museum of the History of Science, has recently examined a specimen of one of these plates by means of the electron microscope. This technique, which enables a very accurate measurement of the band spacing to be made, has shown that of the twenty bands on the plate, only the first eleven could possibly be resolved with the optical microscope, the spacings of the final nine bands being too close to be resolved. Records exist which show that Nelson exhibited the resolution of the tenth band of this plate to the Royal Microscopical Society in 1881, and a few years earlier Woodward in America had succeeded in photographing a similar band; these photomicrographs are of superb quality and they would be hard to equal today!

Examinations of these test plates with modern lenses show that the performance of the optical microscope is *in this respect* not equal to that of the microscope of sixty years ago. It is true, however, that the modern lenses do not have such a high aperture as the older objectives (the views of one modern writer on this subject have already been quoted, see page 268); although the modern lenses excel in the general quality of their corrections and especially in the flatness of their field, they do not possess the ultimate resolving power of the best of the older apochromats. To a large extent, of course, this is conditioned by the demand. In the microscopy of 1880–1920 or thereabouts the work was often carried out at the limits of resolution; with the advent of the electron microscope which extends the optical limits of resolution at least a hundred times, and with the development of interest in the study of the living cell by special optical methods, the demand for direct optical microscopy at the very limits of resolution has dropped. With this fall in demand, so the equipment which is currently available has changed and lenses which would give a superb performance at the extremes of resolution are no longer required or indeed available.

To a certain extent the reliance on the electron microscope for obtaining the ultimate resolution is unfortunate. Although this is an invaluable technique it does involve a very complex preparative cycle and the cells which can be studied by its aid are very dead! This means that the information provided by the electron microscope requires very careful interpretation in order to relate it to the knowledge provided by the methods of conventional microscopy; there has been a tendency in recent years to rely overmuch on the electron microscope alone and it is hard to escape the conclusion that the practice of careful microscopy at the highest level of resolution has suffered in consequence.

In an earlier chapter the use of reflecting or catoptric systems has been mentioned. In the eighteenth century interest in them was largely centred on the efforts to obtain microscope objective systems which were free from chromatic aberration. More recently such systems have been reinvestigated. This is for two reasons: first, the lack of chromatic aberration in a mirror system allows it to be focused in visible light and then used in either the ultra-violet or the infra-red regions of the spectrum without the necessity to refocus. Examination of biological material with light of these wavelengths has provided valuable information, especially about the distribution of the nucleic acids within the cell.

The second great advantage of a mirror system is that for a given focal length, much longer working distances are possible than can be obtained with a lens system. For the same power a mirror objective introduces less spherical aberration than a lens, so it is feasible, therefore, to construct an objective of relatively high N.A. with the further advantage that the curvature of the field may often be easily eradicated with a mirror system. Catoptric objectives do, of course, possess disadvantages, such as the fact that it is often necessary to occlude the central portion of the aperture by the secondary mirror, and the fact that many of the more modern and more successful systems involve the figuring of aspheric surfaces. These cannot yet be produced by mass-production methods and so such microscope objectives have not been produced as a commercial proposition, although several of the prototype microscopes made by Burch in Bristol gave very valuable experience in the construction methods involved and provided interesting information about the possibilities of this system.

The development of mirror objectives which has made the most headway and has proved very useful in biological and industrial work is due to Dyson; it is a very simple unit-magnification mirror system which serves to project a real image into the front focal plane of a normal microscope objective and so obtain a long working distance. This is shown diagrammatically in Fig. 7.11. The increased working distance enables the introduction of instruments for carrying out micro-surgery experiments on a single cell, or it allows the examination of such objects as the filament of a thermionic valve through the glass of the envelope of the valve while this is actually functioning.

One of the great aims in microscope design over the last hundred years has been a desire to introduce compactness into the design so the instrument could be made portable for use in the field. We have seen that the "chest" microscope of Nairne (p. 121) was designed with this

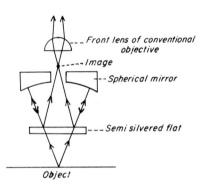

FIG. 7.11. A diagram of the optical system of the Dyson mirror attachment for obtaining long working distance.

end in view and that Adams produced a portable version of his "Vari-able" microscope (see p. 143). Most of the leading makers in the nine-teenth century also included some form of small microscope, often made to fold up for ease of transport, in their catalogues. Most of these stands, however, ingenious though they were, represented no new departure in design but were merely a simplification of the basic large stand with the elimination of non-essential components and the provision of various devices for packing the whole into a confined space. In 1934 a new microscope was announced which represented a fresh approach to the whole problem of design of a portable micro-scope. This instrument was produced by McArthur especially for diagnostic field work. He stipulated that any portable microscope must be light, occupy very little space and be capable of operation when held in the hand. In addition such a microscope must be easy to set up and be capable of producing work of exactly the same quality that a larger laboratory microscope could achieve.

McArthur pointed out that the majority of the previous attempts to produce a portable microscope had merely been modifications of the conventional instrument and had resulted in the production solely of a *collapsible* microscope, which was inevitably a compromise between lightness and rigidity with all the subsequent inconveniences of setting

(a) The McArthur portable microscope.

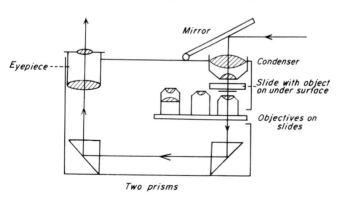

(b) A simplified section of this instrument to show the three objective lenses on a slider, together with the prisms and the eyepiece.

FIG. 7.12.

up. In consequence, he produced a radical departure from the standard design by using a standard objective which was set to look upwards at an inverted slide. The eyepiece was mounted in the normal way but between the objective and the eyepiece were interposed two reflecting surfaces so that there was no conventional tube; instead the body was machined from a single casting. This is shown clearly in Fig. 7.12 from which the size of the instrument may be gauged.

The separate objectives were mounted on sliders which not only enabled a very quick and precise change from one power to another but also provided very accurate centring of the lenses. This slider was made with an L-shape and was fitted with provision for upwards and downwards movement in a dovetail; this was actuated by a screw and lever mechanism in order to provide the means of focusing the lenses. There was no coarse adjustment on this instrument, as with an inverted slide and parfocal objectives the need for this device is no longer felt. In actual practice it is found that the fine focus only needs a very slight amount of adjustment between the different lenses. McArthur claimed that the use of the inverted specimen slide also led to other advantages, such as a more readily accessible condenser and easy location of objects on the slide. As the body was made in a single casting the whole arrangement showed a very great rigidity and the objects of portability and ease of operation were secured.

Since its first inception this microscope has been considerably developed and now it forms a complete system of microscopy, with provision for fitting built-in illumination, photomicrographic attachments and a whole host of other accessories. Such is the rigidity of the construction that actual instruments have been run over by a motor car and dropped from an aeroplane without in any way impairing their performance. Although primarily designed for diagnostic field work, for example, in the study of malaria in the tropics, it is now proving to have a whole new field of applications especially in some industrial concerns where by means of the incident light attachments it may be placed directly onto a metal or other surface in order to examine the surface structure.

With the development of the apochromatic objective it seemed that the optical advances possible in the light microscope had approached the limit; indeed apart from the developments listed above, which did not affect the resolving power of the instrument, little real progress in the optics of the microscope was evident for several decades. In 1934 however, a paper was published by F. Zernicke on a new method for testing telescope mirror systems. In the following year the same worker extended this to microscope objectives and he initiated the method of "phase-contrast" microscopy which has revolutionized biological microscopy by allowing the direct study of transparent objects.

In the latter years of the nineteenth century great interest was shown in Abbe's theory of microscopic vision and experiments on the diffraction spectra produced by an object grating were carried out by several workers, including Abbe himself. In particular, Bratuscheck noted the possibilities of obtaining enhancement of the contrast of a grating formed by the deposition of strips of soot on a slide by attenuating the direct light or, as it is sometimes called, the zero-order spectra in the back focal plane of the objective (see Fig. 6.14). He showed that under certain conditions the contrast between the bars and the strips of the grating might even be reversed. In 1905, both Conrady and Rheinberg showed that control of contrast in the image could be obtained by controlling the phase of the spectra in the back focal plane of the objective. These experiments were thought to be of theoretical interest only and were not pursued as no possible practical application was envisaged at that time. The objects used in such studies were very artificial, and as they were illuminated by light from a distant source it was thought that there was no relevance to the every-day microscopy of biological objects.

With a microscopic object not only must the detail in the image be resolved but also it must be rendered visible; this is normally achieved by changes in the intensity of the light waves which pass through the object (see Fig. 7.13). Such changes in the amplitude of the light waves are produced by the absorption of some of the light in the specimen, a phenomenon which is greatly enhanced if the latter is coloured either naturally or by means of staining procedures. If staining is not possible for any reason, then visibility may often be achieved by modifying the illumination system, either by the use of very oblique light or by dark-ground techniques in which the light is so oblique that no direct light falls within the acceptance angle of the objective and only the light diffracted from the object contributes to the formation of the image.

Biological specimens, such as living cells, are normally very transparent and often it is not possible to stain them without causing their death and possibly altering their structure. Such objects form a large part of the interest in biological microscopy and therefore until some method of adding contrast to their image could be developed the

microscope could not realize its full potentialities in terms of resolution on living biological material.

Fortunately, however, such biological material does usually exhibit
differences in refractive index between its various component parts
and the mounting medium. Although the cells do not change the

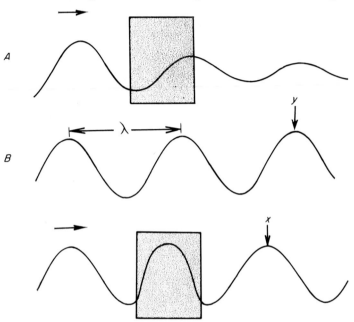

FIG. 7.13. A diagram to show the effect of two types of object on the
light waves passing through them.

(a) An absorbing object causes a change in amplitude of the wave
only.

(b) A transparent object causes no change in the amplitude of the
waves, but alters their phase with respect to the original beam.

Note that the crest of the wave x is retarded relative to that of wave y.

amplitude of the light passing through them, they do affect the light
waves. Because of these differences in refractive index, there is a difference in the optical path of light which passes through the specimen
compared to that which passes around it. In consequence the light
waves which pass through the object and its component parts will be
changed in phase (Fig. 7.13). Our eyes are completely incapable of
perceiving such changes in phase of light and so this type of specimen

is, therefore, normally invisible. Zernicke's method was the first practical way of making such phase differences into observable differences in amplitude and so by optical means making transparent objects visible through a microscope.

With biological objects the difference in optical path introduced by the object is small. It depends on the thickness of the object and upon the difference in refractive index between it and he medium, but in most cases the phase difference between the direct light (the zero-order beam) and the first-order diffracted light is about one quarter of a wavelength; this is usually expressed in the form $\lambda/4$. Zernicke's simple but ingenious idea was to introduce a further $\lambda/4$ path difference between the direct and diffracted light so that the total difference of phase between the two beams was increased to half a wavelength; at this value destructive interference between the wave fronts would occur, so causing the desired differences in amplitude. As Zernicke wrote in 1942:

> By the phase-contrast method transparent details of the object which differ in thickness or in refractive index, appear as differences of intensity in the image.

The desired additional retardation between the diffracted light and the zero-order beam was introduced by the inclusion of a "phase strip" into the optical system. Zernicke at first used straight phase strips but he also studied other shapes such as the cross and the annulus or ring form. A diaphragm of a similar shape to the phase strip in use is placed in the back focal plane of the condenser so that it will, by the principle of the conjugate focal planes of the microscope, be imaged directly in the back focal plane of the objective. It is at this point that the phase strip or phase plate, as it is called today, is mounted. The phase plate consists of a plane parallel piece of optical glass which has an area corresponding to that covered by the image of the diaphragm either raised or recessed. The depth of the recessing is such that the difference in optical path through the recessed area is less by a quarter of a wavelength than that through the remainder of the glass phase plate. Such a system is shown diagrammatically in Fig. 7.14. It will be obvious that all the direct light (D) from the annular diaphragm will pass through the condenser and the objective and be imaged on the recess in the phase plate (P) which is in the back focal plane of the objective.

The phase plate, with its recess, is shown in cross-section in the upper part of the diagram (Fig. 7.14) and the direct light (DL) is shown passing through the area of the annular recess. The diffracted light (which it will be remembered originates at the object and which is, therefore, retarded by $\lambda/4$ with respect to the direct light) will not be restricted to this area of the phase plate as it is not conjugate with the focal planes of the condenser or objective and will, therefore, pass through the whole area of the phase plate. This is a much larger area, indicated by the unlabelled arrows in the diagram, and in so doing it will have to

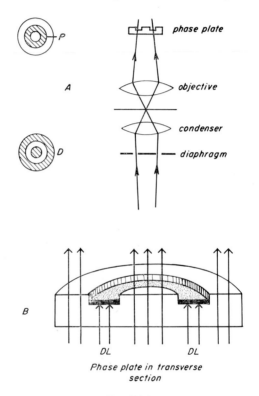

Phase plate in transverse
section

Fig. 7.14.

(a) The optical arrangement of a phase-contrast microscope. The annular diaphragm (D) and the phase plate (P) are shown on the left.

(b) An enlarged section through a typical phase plate. The direct light (DL) passes only through the groove in the plate whilst the diffracted light traverses the whole structure. An absorbing layer is deposited in the groove of the phase plate to reduce the intensity of the direct light with respect to that of the diffracted rays.

pass through a greater thickness of glass which will introduce a corresponding extra degree of retardation. As this thickness is so calculated to give the extra $1/4\lambda$ which is required to make the direct and diffracted light interfere destructively, the necessary contrast will be introduced into the image. Zernicke further introduced a layer of absorbing material into the phase strip which served to reduce slightly the intensity of the direct light and so still further improve the contrast. This description of the principle of the phase-contrast microscope is, of course, extremely simplified and interested readers are referred to the standard books on microscopy for a fuller explanation.

Zernicke obviously realized the tremendous implications of his method very early on, perhaps as early as 1932, before the original paper was even published. Patent rights were secured in collaboration with the firm of Carl Zeiss, who proceeded to experiment on practical methods of producing and exploiting the invention. A phase-contrast microscope was in fact produced by Zeiss in the early years of the Second World War, but such instruments did not become generally available until after the cessation of hostilities. In 1941, Köhler and Loos produced a long and detailed paper on phase-contrast theory and its applications. This was reprinted in translation in a textile journal in this country in the following year; in the paper the authors comment that

> the field of application of the phase-contrast method seems to be quite large — at any rate, larger than could be foreseen at the beginning of the development.

They proceed to list many of the possible uses stressing the valuable information which can be obtained by this means from thin unstained preparations of biological material, although the most important feature, that this method is particularly successful with *living* material, is only hinted at with reference to the study of living trypanosomes in a blood film. In this country, C. R. Burch was engaged in research on the new system of microscopy and in 1942 he published a paper in collaboration with J. P. P. Stock on experiments they had carried out with straight strip phase plates. This paper gave full details of the methods for constructing experimental phase plates and, equally important, it included some results showing the application of this method to the study of unstained living leucocytes and their interactions with bacteria in pus.

On the Continent other workers were using phase-contrast systems for the study of living cells; one notable piece of work was the use of this new method by K. Michel to obtain by time-lapse techniques a remarkable cine-film of the divisions and changes which occurred in the development of the sperm cells of the grasshopper. When this film became widely known to the biologists it, more than any articles or demonstrations, convinced them of the tremendous potentialities of the phase-contrast method for the study of the activities of living cells. Although early work was carried out with slit and cross shaped phase plates, it very soon became apparent that the annular shape of phase plate possessed considerable advantages as this shape had a complete axial symmetry and it did not introduce any undesirable asymmetry into the image as did the other forms of plate.

After the end of the war microscopes based on the phase-contrast principle became available commercially and research both into the applications of the system and into its theory proceeded very rapidly. It was realized that phase-contrast does introduce a slight loss of resolution but this is far outweighed by the visibility of detail which it confers on unstained or living material. In 1946, Bennett, Jupnick, Osterburg and Richards published a comprehensive paper on this new method of microscopy; they concluded that the method would have great application in biology for the study of tissue cultures and for the observation of various processes such as ciliary action, amoeboid motion, cyclosis and many others. They stressed, however, that the advantages of phase-contrast would not be limited to the study of living biological systems. In industrial and chemical work the observation of crystals, fibres, emulsions and particles would be greatly facilitated as this method would render visible detail in transparent materials which were previously invisible with direct microscopy in transmitted light.

The phase-contrast microscope has the tremendous advantage of simplicity and it has now become established as a routine laboratory instrument. It has fully justified its early promise and many valuable discoveries have been reported by its aid. The image is not perfect, however, the edge of the object being surrounded by a very prominent halo, for example. This is due to shortcomings in the optical system whereby the separation of the direct and diffracted light is effected; some of the diffracted light does in fact pass through the area of the phase plate which is intended to receive the direct light and it is this mingling which gives rise to undesirable optical effects.

To a large extent these defects have been eliminated in a further development which is known as the interference microscope. As we have seen the contrast arises in the phase microscope by interference between the direct light and the diffracted light which arises at the object and which has undergone a retardation in phase. In the interference microscope the destructive interference takes place between two wave fronts which are produced within the microscope optical system itself. One set of waves is allowed to pass through the object and is subjected to modification by it, whilst the other wave front (which is referred to as the reference beam) passes along a different course which does *not* include the object. Most of the interference microscopes actually use some form of beam-splitting arrangement so that the whole aperture of the objective may be utilized.

Many types of interferometer have been devised at the microscopic level. These have been especially valuable in the measurement and control of surfaces in optical components and it is surprising that these devices were not developed for microscopic use much earlier than in fact they were. F. H. Smith, to whom we owe the development of a really practical interference microscope, believes that this may be attributed to the general lack of interest in such methods for increasing the contrast of objects by optical means which was so apparent in the attitude of most biologists in the early years of this century. They were well provided with a host of synthetic dyes and their whole attention was concentrated on the study of the appearance of the fixed and stained cell at the maximum limits of resolution rather than on the study of the low-contrast images which were obtained from living material. It was probably due to this conservative attitude that Zernicke's invention received so little attention for so many years.

When the desirability of studying the living cell finally became obvious it was realized that optical methods for the enhancement of contrast were needed and development then began not only on the phase-contrast system, but also on the interference microscope. There were many types of interferometer available for use. Most of these were only applicable to reflected or incident illumination and so although they proved very satisfactory for the study of surfaces for assessment of smoothness of finish and so on, they were of very limited application in biology. The study of the transparent objects which form the bulk of the material examined by the biologist obviously needed some form of interference microscope which would work with transmitted light; one of the obvious solutions was to use a double beam system with in effect two duplicate microscopes with matched condenser and objective systems. One of these carried the object whilst the

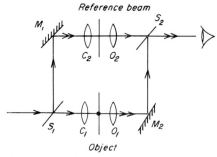

Reference beam

Object

(a) An idealized "round the square" interference microscope system. S1 and S2 are semi-silvered surfaces which reflect and transmit equal amounts of the light falling on them. C1 and C2, and O_1 and O_2 are matched pairs of condensers and objective lenses respectively; M_1 and M_2 are totally reflecting surfaces.

(b) The optical construction of the Leitz interference microscope which utilizes the same principle.

Fig. 7.15.

other had a blank reference slide. This idealized system has been called the "round the square" microscope and is shown in Fig. 7.15(a).

In this microscope a beam of light is divided by means of semi-silvered reflecting surfaces and passes through the two microscopes. The specimen introduces a phase change into the light which passes through it and after the recombination with the reference beam which has traversed the other arm of the square the desired interference takes place. Such a microscope was not considered feasible for many years owing to the expense of duplication of the optical systems and the difficulties in alignment of the system, but recently the firm of Leitz has developed a form of interference microscope working on this principle. The ray diagram of their instrument is shown in Fig. 7.15(b) from which it may be seen how closely this system approximates to the ideal "round the square" interference microscope. Such a system with its complete physical separation of the two beams by means of beam-splitters using semi-reflecting surfaces has many advantages and for some purposes works rather better than the other current instruments in which the separation of the beams is effected by some form of birefringence crystal.

As far back as 1930, Lebedeff realized that a practicable form of interference microscope could be made if the two beams could be made to pass through the same microscope objective but with the reference beam displaced to one side so that it did not pass through the object but through an adjacent clear area of the slide. Lebedeff achieved this by using a device, originally due to Jamin, which utilizes the birefringent properties of a calcite plate to separate light into two beams, the ordinary and the extraordinary rays. One of these served as the reference beam, whilst the other was passed through the object. By adding a half-wave plate together with a second calcite plate identical to the first one, in front of the objective the two separate beams could be recombined and the phase-change introduced by the object allowed to interfere with the unchanged reference wave fronts. Lebedeff actually built a microscope using this system and it proved to work well with low powers.

In 1947, F. H. Smith working completely independently, developed the same idea; it was marketed in conjunction with Messrs. Bakers and this proved to be the first really practicable interference microscope which was efficient at all powers. This microscope also used birefringement elements to separate and recombine the two beams. It is not possible to go into a detailed optical description of Smith's microscope here; such information is available in the technical literature. It will suffice to mention that Smith produced two variants of the system, one involving a lateral displacement of the reference beam with respect to the object, the so-called "shearing" system, and the other involving a "double-focus" arrangement whereby the reference beam is brought to a focus below the level of the object and so the latter is surrounded

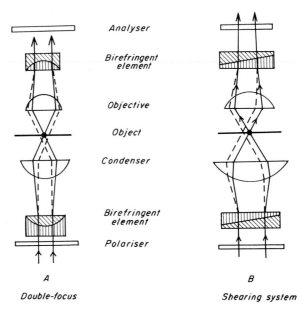

Fig. 7.16. The optical principles of the Smith interference microscope system using birefringent material to effect beam separations.

(a) The double-focus variant, in which the reference beam is brought to a focus at a different level from that of the object beam.

(b) The "shearing" type, in which the reference beam is displaced laterally with respect to the object.

by an annular cone of the reference light which does not actually traverse it. This will be clear from the diagrams of the two systems which are provided in Fig. 7.16.

This interference microscope possesses several advantages over the simpler phase-contrast instrument, in that, for example, the image is not surrounded by a troublesome halo. Also in the phase microscope the contrast is only adequate in those regions where there is an abrupt change in optical path difference, such as at the edge of an object; in the interference microscope on the other hand gradual changes in optical path difference are equally well shown. This makes the interference microscope a particularly valuable tool for morphological studies of cell inclusions which are small (and therefore show little phase change) or which have a refractive index very close to that of the surrounding cytoplasm. If the instrument is used with white light then the interference often removes only a portion of the wavelengths which are present so that the image appears in the subtractive colours of Newton's scale. This again is a feature of great advantage for morphological work, as the eye is very sensitive to changes in colour whereas small changes in greyness as might be produced with the phase-contrast microscope would probably pass unnoticed.

The most important advantage of the interference microscope, however, is probably the fact that the optical path difference introduced by the object may be measured directly and very easily. This measurement allows a calculation of the refractive index of the inclusion and also determination of its dry mass. Such information is yielding valuable data at the present time about many of the vital activities of the living cell, as it is possible by the use of phase-contrast and interference microscopy coupled with time-lapse cinematography to build up a picture of the changes which take place throughout all the stages of, say, a single division cycle of a cell in tissue culture.

With the development of such techniques which enable contrast to be added to the image of cells or living biological preparations by optical means, whole new fields of study are opened to the biologist; it is by the use of new methods, as those which have been mentioned above, that the optical microscope is contributing very greatly to scientific research at the present time. The emphasis has changed completely from that which prevailed only a few years ago, and much less interest is shown in trying to work at the ultimate limit of resolution. After all, there are now better methods available for providing a better resolution of structural detail, methods which surpass the maximum provided by the optical microscope by more than a hundredfold.

Up to the middle of the present century the optical microscope was regarded entirely as a tool for studying the fine details of the morphology of an object, which in the case of a cell meant a preparation which had been killed and prepared by an elaborate schedule and stained with the synthetic dyes. With the coming of the electron microscope the optical study of structure has receded in importance and the optical microscope is being used for important studies of the living cell and organism; more and more the microscope is being used as an analytical tool to provide information about the chemical and physical components of the cell. It is in this new role, probably allied to new developments in mechanical or automated devices for integrating and processing the information which the microscope records, that the optical microscope has found a new part to play in the search to elucidate and interpret the structure of the biological world. In addition, the importance of the optical microscope will continue as a routine tool of investigation and diagnosis in biology, as a means of assisting in quality control and assembly operations in industrial fields, and in countless other applications.

Often in the past the comment has been made that the optical microscope had reached the peak of its development; each time so far the speaker has been proved completely wrong. It would be a foolish man who, in the present technological age, predicted that the optical microscope had finally reached the end of the road.

CHAPTER 8

THE SEARCH FOR GREATER RESOLVING POWER; THE ULTRA-VIOLET AND THE ELECTRON MICROSCOPE

By the beginning of the twentieth century it seemed that optical research, largely stemming from the work of Abbe, had taken the resolution of the optical microscope as far as it was possible to go. From his theoretical studies it was clear that the resolution of the microscope (R) was given by the general relationship

$$R = \frac{0 \cdot 6\lambda}{N.A.}$$

where λ was the wavelength of the light used to illuminate the system and N.A. referred to the numerical aperture of the objective. For various practical reasons the maximum possible upper limit of the numerical aperture of the objective had been attained some time in the latter years of the nineteenth century; hence if the system were to give a greater resolution then it must be achieved by using light of shorter wavelength. This was, of course, attempted many times and slight improvements in resolution were obtained by skilled microscopists such as Woodward and van Heurck who habitually used deep blue light for their photomicrographs.

These tendencies were carried to their logical conclusion in 1904, when Köhler and von Rohr of Zeiss designed a microscope intended to operate in the ultra-violet region of the spectrum. This instrument used the radiation generated by a spark (actually a cadmium arc was used) and it was based on the standard vertical microscope which this firm was manufacturing at that time. According to Abbe's theory, a microscope operating with radiation of a wavelength of 2750 Å would be expected to show double the resolution which it would afford with light of wavelength 5500 Å and objectives of the same numerical aperture. In effect, a lens of N.A. 1·25 specifically designed for operation in ultra-violet would be equivalent in resolving power to an objective with a working aperture of 2·50 operated in green light at 5500 Å.

Although this twofold increase of resolution obtained by the use of ultra-violet radiation is very well in theory, there are some practical drawbacks to the regular use of such short wavelengths in practice. Not least is the fact that the eye is not sensitive to radiation in this region of the electro-magnetic spectrum. This means that all focusing must be carried out with an artificial aid such as an eyepiece fitted with a fluorescent screen to convert the short wavelength radiation into visible light. The final image has to be recorded on a photographic plate and all the observations made on the final print. It is, of course, possible to focus the instrument in visible light and then change to illumination with ultra-violet but if this is done then the focus of the object has to be altered by a predetermined amount in order to compensate for the fact that the focus of the ultra-violet rays is not equivalent to that for visible light. This disadvantage, inherent in all lens systems, may, however, be avoided if a mirror objective is used; this is one field in which the reflecting microscope has a valuable role to play.

A further disadvantage of using short wave-length ultra-violet radiation in the microscope for increasing the resolving power is that the glass of which the lenses are made will only transmit such radiation freely down to a wavelength of about 3000 Å; below this figure glass is not suitable as a material for lenses. This difficulty may be avoided by making the lenses out of synthetic fluorite or even better, of fused quartz. This latter substance was in fact used by Köhler and von Rohr in their original microscope and it is still favoured today for lenses which are intended for critical work in the far ultra-violet. Not only are the various optical glasses opaque to the shorter wavelengths of ultra-violet, but so are also the normal mounting media and immersion oils, and hence substitutes have to be found. It proved possible to mount the specimens in water or castor oil or in glycerine jelly, whilst glycerine was found to be suitable for the immersion medium between the coverslip and the front element of the lens. Again, the coverslip and the actual slide on which the specimen is mounted must be made from fused quartz, as also must the substage condenser, so it is apparent that if serious work is intended in the far ultra-violet it is a matter of some complexity, not to say expense!

It is thus evident that microscopy with light of very short wavelengths presents many problems; in consequence of the very complex nature of the equipment, it followed that this method of obtaining more resolution was restricted to very special research problems. Several firms have produced and marketed ultra-violet microscope outfits at various times in the last fifty years, but it seems fair to say that in only a very few projects did the contributions to knowledge so obtained really justify the trouble and expense involved. After all, the increase in resolution over the ordinary optical microscope was only a factor of two. Again it was found that the ultra-violet microscope was of no help in the study of living cells, as the intense ultra-violet radiation soon caused cell damage and death.

At the present time ultra-violet microscopy is no longer in any demand as a means of increasing the ultimate resolution of the optical microscope. Other valuable information has been derived from its use, however; studies initiated in the late 1930's by Caspersson, and since continued by him and his pupils, utilized the heavy absorption of certain wavelengths of ultra-violet which is characteristic of compounds such as nucleic acids, to locate by photometric means their distribution within the cell, and to follow changes in them during certain activities such as division of the cell.

Today, ultra-violet (or deep blue light) is more commonly used in what is termed "fluorescence microscopy". Here the short wave-length radiation is used as a source of energy to stimulate substances present in the tissue on the slide. These compounds (which may be already present or which may be added during the preparation of the specimen) absorb the energy and re-emit it at a longer wavelength, i.e. in the visible spectrum, in the form of fluorescence. For this type of microscopy the requirements are much less stringent; usually the source is a mercury arc lamp provided with suitable glass filters to absorb the visible light and isolate the desired band of shorter wavelengths.

As the radiation is only acting as an "exciting" agent it is possible to use the longer wavelengths and so the optics of the microscope may be made out of glass. It is necessary to ensure that all the ultra-violet light which is not absorbed in stimulating fluorescence in the section is prevented from passing up the microscope and entering the eye, so that such instruments invariably contain a selective ultra-violet absorbing filter in the optical system somewhere between the objective and the eyepiece. This protects the eye from the damaging effect of ultra-violet radiation and does not detract from the efficiency of the instrument since the important information is contained in the fluorescence, which is, of course, light in the visible region of the spectrum.

The fluorescence microscope has assumed a great importance in medical research today, for by its aid it has proved possible to locate the sites of antibody production in the body. This is done by coupling fluorescent dyes (which serve as labels) to the compounds which, when applied to cells or tissue sections, link in their turn to the proteins known as antibodies which form one of the body's main defence mechanisms against disease. Such specialist uses of the fluorescence microscope are, however, beyond the scope of this book; they form a striking development from the system which was developed by Köhler and von Rohr in the early years of the century in a simple quest for more resolution.

Abbe himself realized that the limit of resolution was set by the finite wavelength of light, and although he was aware of the possibilities of better results from the use of shorter wavelengths, he was not very optimistic about their successful use. It is ironic that the basic discoveries which paved the way for the eventual development of what must surely be regarded as one of the greatest advances in microscopy since the invention of the compound microscope itself, had already been made by German physicists about 1858 or 1859.

It had been noted by various workers that if electrodes were sealed into a glass tube which was then evacuated, rays which possessed curious properties were emitted from the cathode. Plücker in 1859 showed that these cathode rays were propagated in a linear fashion whilst ten years later Hittorf proved that they could be deflected by a magnetic field and concentrated by an axially symmetrical field. One other property of these rays which was important for their experimental study, was that although they themselves were invisible, they were capable of affecting a crystalline substance and causing it to emit light. Such substances, often sulphides of metals, are known as phosphor and are much used today in the manufacture of fluorescent light tube and television screens.

Crookes, working in England, was attracted to the study of these rather mysterious cathode rays and in 1879 he provided a much better proof that they were transmitted in straight lines. It was left to J. J. Thomson, however, working in the Cavendish Laboratory in Cambridge, to provide about 1897 the first theoretical and experimental studies on the quantitative aspects of these rays and to enunciate the concept that they were composed of streams of negatively-charged Particles which are now called "electrons". The cathode rays excited a great deal of interest and studies were now in progress in many laboratories all over the Continent. In 1899, Wiechert showed how an electron beam could be concentrated by means of a solenoid instead of a permanent magnet and a few years later Wehnelt demonstrated in 1903 that the same phenomenon occurred with an electrostatic field. This is in fact still used in modern electron microscopes in the first stages of the electron "gun" to begin the initial collimation of the beam; the metal cylinder around the heated tungsten filament (which is used as the source of the electrons) is often referred to as the "Wehnelt shield".

An important theoretical study by C. Stoermer in 1907 resulted in the calculation of the trajectories of electrons through a solenoid, but for some reason this important work was not recognized for many years and it fell to de Broglie in 1924 to launch the science of electron optics by introducing one of its most important concepts — that the electron could be regarded not only as a negatively-charged particle but also as a wave. His work was of the greatest importance and it proved a tremendous stimulus to others; it led directly to the studies of Busch who in 1926 showed that the magnetic coil which focused the electron beam could be regarded as analogous to an optical lens. Busch derived the equations for such lenses but he did not put his knowledge to practical use in the construction of a lens.

Great interest was aroused in this field and development followed rapidly. Gabor in 1927 discovered that by concentrating the magnetic field from a solenoid by casing the latter in soft iron a practical electron lens could be made. This was applied in several fields which had been opened up by de Broglie's pioneer studies, such as the application to electron diffraction by Davison and Germer in 1926–7 and somewhat later by G. P. Thomson, and to the construction of the instrument for observing the effects of a fluctuating electric potential which became known as the cathode-ray oscillograph. Examples of this were built by Gabor and Brücke in Germany, and by Zworykin in America.

These early oscillographs were of the so-called "cold cathode" type in which the beam of electrons was generated by the application of a high potential between two electrodes sealed into a vacuum tube. The actual electrons were emitted from the cathode and accelerated down the tube by a voltage of about 50,000 volts (50 kV) applied to the perforated metal anode lower down the tube. A collimated beam of electrons thus issued from the hole in the anode into the actual column or tube forming the body of the instrument. One of these early oscillographs is shown in section in Fig. 8.1.

After passing through the anode, the collimated beam of electrons was then further concentrated by passing through the field of one of Gabor's electro-magnets called the "concentration coil". It then passed

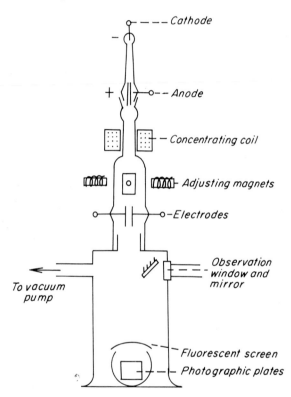

Fig. 8.1. A sectional diagram of Gabor's cold-cathode oscillograph. Notice the provision for internal photographic recording of the image.

between sets of metal plates (sealed into the tube) to which the fluctuating voltage under study was applied, before passing on down the column to affect a fluorescent screen. Usually there were two sets of these deflector plates arranged at right angles to each other. If a regular oscillating voltage was applied to one set of plates, the electron beam would be deflected and register as a line on the screen. If now the voltage to be studied was applied to the other plates then the result would be to cause the straight line recorded on the screen to become curved according to the fluctuation of the voltage under study.

Such instruments had, of course, to be operated at a pressure very much below that of the atmosphere, in order to prevent stoppage of the electron beam by collision of electrons with air molecules; in practice the whole column was connected to a complex pumping system which was in continuous operation throughout the working of the oscillograph. In order to obtain permanent records of the events on the screen, photographic plates were usually included at the bottom of the column in some form of cassette which could be introduced into the beam instead of the fluorescent screen. Not only were these instruments the forerunners of our present day oscilloscope, which is one of the most valuable tools of the physicist and electronic engineer, but they also paved the way towards the first electron microscope.

Although Busch's pioneer work provided the beginning of electron optics and drew the parallel between the trajectories of light waves through a glass lens and electrons through a solenoid, strangely enough it did not suggest that the construction of an electron microscope would be a practicable possibility. This was left to the group of workers in Berlin, which included in addition to Gabor and Matthias, two men whose names are now closely associated with this new development. These were Knoll and Ruska. The Berlin group began a systematic investigation of the possibilities of electron lenses about 1928 and very soon an instrument was built which used an electromagnetic lens to form the image of an aperture in a metal disc although without introducing any magnification.

The next step taken by Knoll and Ruska was to add a second lens and so produce what was in effect the first electron microscope which gave an image magnified about seventeen times. This first true electron microscope (Fig. 8.2(a)), developed between 1930 and 1931, also used a cold-cathode discharge tube to generate the electron beam which was allowed to enter the tube of the microscope proper through a small hole in the anode exactly as in the oscillograph. In addition to the concentration coil or condenser lens, a magnetic imaging lens was included together with provision for an electrostatic lens. This instrument was only capable of forming an image of the cathode of the discharge tube. In the diagrammatic section (Fig. 8.2(b)) the discharge tube, the lenses (which are mounted outside the vacuum) and the transparent fluorescent screen at the bottom of the column may all be seen together with the external photographic apparatus. Development of this apparatus soon enabled emission pictures to be obtained at a magnification of about 400×.

(a)   (b)

Fig. 8.2.
(a) Knoll and Ruska's first electron microscope of 1931.
(b) A sectional diagram of this instrument. Note that the photo-
     graphic apparatus is outside the vacuum system, the image being
     recorded through the glass fluorescent screen let into the base of
     the column of the microscope.

At about this time other German workers were thinking along similar lines; one researcher named Rüdenberg even obtained patents, filed in 1931, which anticipated several of the design features which were later common in electron microscopes. Rüdenberg later emi-grated to America and continued work in this field and in 1936–7 several American patents were granted to him in respect of the design of electron microscopes. In the early 1930's there was some doubt whether the electron microscope could ever be made into a practicable scientific instrument. It was true that images had been obtained, but they were only of self-emitting objects; it was generally felt that

FIG. 8.3. Ruska's electron microscope of 1933. Note the cold-cathode discharge tube at the top and the pipes carrying cooling water to the electro-magnetic lenses.

any attempt to obtain an image by transmission of the electrons through a specimen would result in hopeless failure, either through vacuum damage to the object or to the heating effects of the intense electron bombardment. Difficulties were also foreseen because at that time it was not easy to obtain, let alone maintain, the high degree of vacuum required and to provide for the current in the magnetic lenses to be maintained with the required degree of stability.

Despite these apparent obstacles other workers entered this field and in 1932 L. Marton successfully built and operated a simple electron microscope with magnetic lenses. Ruska also persevered and by 1933 he had built another microscope (Fig. 8.3) which may for all practical purposes be regarded as the direct ancestor of all existing electron microscopes. This 1933 microscope retained the cold-cathode tube for generating electrons which were accelerated by 75 kV applied to the anode. There was a single condenser lens and two separate magnifying or imaging lenses, which were known as the objective and projector lenses respectively. This new instrument of Ruska's was designed to accept specimens which were mounted in a horizontal metal disc which could be rotated mechanically (from outside the vacuum) around an axis slightly off-set from that of the column so that each specimen in turn was brought into the electron beam. All the lenses of this microscope were shrouded in soft iron and were provided with water cooling in order to maintain thermal stability; this is a feature still found in present-day electron microscopes. The pipes carrying the cooling water to the lenses are a prominent feature of the microscope shown in Fig. 8.3.

At first the photography of the fluorescent screen was carried out from the outside, but subsequently this was modified and an internal camera was included. With this microscope Ruska obtained transmission micrographs of a piece of aluminium foil and of cotton fibres. Although these were carbonized in the intense beam, the picture still showed a resolution of about 500 Å. In 1934, Driest and Müller working in Berlin with the improved version of this microscope and using internal photography, succeeded in producing photographs of the leg and wings of a housefly at a resolution of around 400 Å. This microscope, although appearing crude by present day standards, worked and produced pictures by transmitted electrons of objects at a resolution about five times better than it was possible to obtain with the light microscope. At the end of 1934, however, the future of the instrument was still not certain, and research was dropped for lack of immediate support.

At this stage it is convenient to leave the story of the development of this embryonic electron microscope in order to describe briefly the similarities and differences between the electron microscope and the optical instrument and to indicate the special requirements of the electron microscope. Basically the two systems are composed of analogous components; from Fig. 8.4 it can be seen that the light source of the optical microscope corresponds to the source of electrons (the electron "gun") in the electron microscope. Both instruments have a condenser to concentrate the radiation on the specimen, and the primary magnification in both types of microscope is produced by an objective lens.

In Fig. 8.4, the optical microscope is shown arranged to project an image by means of the eyepiece which consists of two separate lenses. In the electron microscope these lenses are represented by the separate intermediate and projector lenses respectively. In the optical microscope it is customary to arrange the system with the eyepiece

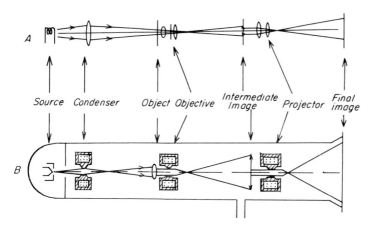

Fig. 8.4. A block diagram comparing the lens arrangements of the optical microscope (a) and the electron microscope (b).

projecting an image upwards onto, say, a photographic plate which is held at the top of the bellows extension of a vertical camera. For reasons of convenience in construction and stability imposed upon it by the long tube, the electron microscope usually has the electron gun at the top of the column and the final viewing screen and the photographic plates are located at the lower end of the column.

Despite these basic similarities which are apparent from the block diagram (Fig. 8.4) there are several fundamental differences. First, as has already been mentioned, the whole column of the electron microscope must be evacuated to a pressure of somewhere around 1×10^{-4} torr (a torr is the unit of vacuum, equivalent to 1 mm Hg) in order that the mean free path of the electrons is increased to about

2·5 metres. This then allows them a clear path down the length of the column (which is usually about 1·5 metres long) without suffering unnecessary scattering on the way by collision with air molecules. Secondly, in the optical microscope the greater part of the total magnification of the system is produced by the objective lens, the eyepiece only contributing in a minor fashion to the final enlargement of the image; this is not so in the electron microscope, where the production of the magnification is more equally distributed between the objective and the intermediate and projector lenses.

In the optical microscope the lenses are, of course, of a fixed focal length and adjustments are made by changing the positions of the lenses, particularly the objective lens, with respect to the specimen. In the electron microscope, however, the situation is exactly the opposite as the lenses are fixed in position and the adjustments of focus and magnification are effected by altering the strength of the lenses by varying the current which is passing through the windings. Again, in the optical microscope the lenses are now highly corrected for chromatic and spherical aberration, as we have seen, but in the electron microscope no such corrections are possible at the present time in the same way as is possible with the optical counterpart.

In present day electron lenses the spherical aberration can only be minimized by accurate workmanship and by "stopping down" the aperture exactly as Hooke did in his microscope of 1665. This, of course, imposes a severe limitation upon the resolution of the instrument. Again, it is only possible to circumvent chromatic aberration by using an electron beam of very high stability, in which all the electrons have the same wavelength, that is, by effectively using "monochromatic" electrons. It is for this reason that the high tension accelerating voltage must be controlled to such rigorous limits. This again, together with the necessity for accurate stabilization of the lens currents in order to obtain a stable image leads to the proliferation of electronic equipment which is such a characteristic feature of the power supply box of an electron microscope, and which contributes largely to the very high cost (up to £15,000) of these instruments today.

Although the spherical and chromatic aberrations of an electron lens can be controlled and brought within acceptable limits by the means listed above, in actual practice the aberration which causes more trouble to the user is that known as astigmatism. In the case of optical lenses this may be present but the user can do nothing about it, whereas part of the skill of the electron microscopist lies in the facility with which he can detect and correct astigmatism in the objective lens. Astigmatism is characterized by the lens showing two focal planes for axes which are separated by 90 degrees.

If an object such as a hole in a carbon film is imaged with an electron microscope the image will possess a different appearance according to

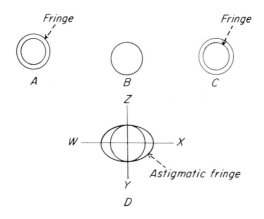

FIG. 8.5. Diagram to illustrate the appearance of a hole in a carbon film when imaged by the electron microscope. (a) Overfocus; the Fresnel fringe is *outside* the hole. (b) At focus; the fringe is not now apparent. (c) Underfocus; the fringe is now *inside* the hole. (d) The appearance of the hole when the lens is astigmatic. The plane Y–Z is in focus and no fringe is seen here, but the lens is overfocused in plane W–X and there is thus a prominent elliptical fringe around the hole.

whether the lens is above focus, at focus, or below focus. The different appearances which are illustrated in Fig. 8.5 A–C, are marked by the changes in the position of what is known as a "Fresnel fringe" around the edge of the object. If the lens is above focus the fringe is outside the hole, at focus the fringe is not visible at all, whilst below focus the fringe now appears as a bright rim to the inside of the hole. If the lens is perfect these fringes will be absolutely symmetrical.

If on the other hand the lens suffers from astigmatism, which may be due to imperfections in the actual manufacture of the lens, to inhomogeneities in the iron of which it is made, or to "contamination", which is a deposit which accumulates on it or on the objective lens aperture during use, then there will be a marked ellipticity in the fringe; this is shown in the lower part of Fig. 8.5 at D. The lens is in focus along the plane Y–Z, and the fringe is not perceptible but along the plane W–X the lens is overfocused so that there is a bright fringe outside the rim of the hole. Such astigmatism, it was discovered in 1946, may be compensated by adding a neutralizing field to cancel out the error and the skilled user of the instrument is always checking this compensation and adjusting it as necessary. This facility, and the need for correction of astigmatism during operation, then marks a point of difference from the optical instrument.

A final point of difference which must be mentioned, as it is of importance when one considers the methods for the preparation of specimens for study in the electron microscope, is the actual method of image formation. In the optical microscope the basic image-forming mechanism is one of absorption, in which the object reduces the amplitude of the light passing through it and thereby introduces the necessary contrast. In the electron microscope, however, the contrast in the image is largely due to the differential scattering of electrons by the atoms constituting the actual specimen. The scattered electrons are thrown out of the axis of the instrument and are blocked by coming into contact with the movable objective aperture.

The actual absorption of electrons plays a very limited role in image formation in the electron microscope; the amount of scattering which takes place is very much dependent upon the actual amount of matter present in the object, in other words, by the number of atoms present multiplied by their atomic number. If a heavy metal can be incorporated into the specimen, then the final image contrast will be much enhanced. This may be done by adding the metal either at the fixation stage, by the use of such substances as osmium tetroxide, or at a later stage in the preparation techniques when salts of uranium or lead may be used as "electron stains". As the sections of biological material which are used in the electron microscope are so very thin (being only of the order of 500–800 Å thick), the use of these contrasting agents becomes very desirable, in order to achieve an acceptable image contrast.

The necessity to operate the electron microscope at a high vacuum to some extent proved a limiting factor in the early days of its development, as the production and maintenance of a high degree of vacuum was not then very easy. With the improvements in vacuum technique, in pump design and other technological aspects, this factor has assumed a smaller importance. The other great technological stumbling block in the development of the electron microscope was the need for such accurate control of the accelerating voltage and lens currents. In the early days of the instrument's development (up to about 1940) this often resulted in the proliferation of bulky and inconvenient systems of storage batteries, with all the maintenance problems which the use of storage cells involves. About 1940 the American firm of RCA led the way and introduced electronic stabilization of the power supplies and succeeded in reducing the physical size of the power supply units. Electronic techniques moved very rapidly during the Second World War and the knowledge gained in this way has since been utilized in improving the power supply and stabilization of the electron microscope.

To return to the further development of the instrument; many workers became interested in this new tool about 1934 and it was regarded as an instrument of great potentiality for providing an alternative to the optical microscope for examining objects at a high level of resolution. In particular, L. Marton in Brussels was responsible for the design and construction of a two-stage magnetic instrument. This machine was designed to operate with an accelerating potential of 90 kV and for the first time specimen chamber and photographic plate air-locks were fitted to the column. These, a feature of all present-day instruments, made it possible to change specimens much more quickly and allowed the use of internal photographic plates to become a practical reality.

Marton was convinced that biological material could be examined successfully with this new instrument and in 1934 he published the first electron micrograph of a biological specimen. He used a 15-micron thick section of the leaf of the sundew, *Drosera*, which he had prepared by impregnating it with salts of osmium. He saw that although some sort of an image was obtained, the sections would have to be much thinner and that it would be essential to mount them on a support film if adequate results were to be obtained. Gradually it proved possible to reduce the electron beam falling on the specimen and so minimize damage from this cause. Soon, Marton managed to obtain a resolution better than that obtainable with the optical microscope. It was obvious though that the real advance would have to come in the preparation of the specimens if all the potentialities already discernable in the new type of microscope were to be exploited to the full.

In this country the initiative was taken in 1935 by Professor L. C. Martin of Imperial College, London, who persuaded Metropolitan-Vickers to manufacture an electron microscope. This instrument, which came to be known as the E.M.1 was described in detail by Martin and his associates Whelpton and Parnum, in a paper published in 1937, although the instrument was in operation during the preceding year. The general pattern of the microscope was modelled on that of Ruska and its design was to some extent conditioned by the desire to examine an object first with the optical microscope and then *immediately* change to examination with the electron beam and study the same part of the same specimen. In order to achieve this the optical microscope was actually embodied in the construction of the electron microscope. Provision was made for the object to be examined with the optical microscope whilst it was in the vacuum of the electron microscope by arranging that the axes of the two microscopes were parallel. The object holder was fitted into a rotating plate which could be accurately rotated by means of a tangent screw; the amount of angular rotation could be checked by observing with a micrometer microscope a graduated circle let into the upper side of the object disc. In this way the object of interest was located in the field of the optical microscope and then by rotating the disc through exactly 180 degrees, the same object came automatically into the axis of the electron microscope. In addition to the tangent screw mechanism which controlled the rotation, there was also a provision for adjusting the position of the object in a radial direction.

The whole instrument stood over six feet high and is shown in Fig. 8.6. The actual column of the microscope is seen in the centre of the illustration, with the cold-cathode discharge tube arising from its upper end, above the expanded part of the casing which contains the rotating object holder plate. The column is strengthened and mechanical vibrations are minimized by the addition of lateral girders, one of which is clearly seen at the side of the column.

The beam of electrons was generated in the cold-cathode discharge tube, which was maintained at a relatively low vacuum, and then entered the actual column of the microscope itself through a hole 0·004 inch in diameter in the aluminium anode. The microscope column was maintained at a high vacuum by means of a large diffusion pump — visible in the illustration at the base of the column in the centre; this large pump was backed in turn by a smaller diffusion pump and a rotary or vane pump. There was a condenser lens and two stages of magnification as in Ruska's instrument; the actual image could be viewed on a fluorescent screen either at the intermediate position, using only one stage of magnification, or by using both stages and observing the picture on the screen at the base of the column. Photography was internal and plates could be inserted into the vacuum of the tube at either of these positions.

FIG. 8.6. The electron microscope of Martin *et al.* (1936) installed in Imperial College, London. This machine was built by Metropolitan Vickers and was known as the E.M.1. Note the stabilizing girders at the side of the column, the cold-cathode discharge tube (c.c.t.), the object-holder chamber (o.h.c.), the objective lens (obj.), the upper viewing port (v.p.) and the vacuum pumps (p).

Figure 8.7 shows, in simplified form, a section through part of the upper end of the electron microscope column, with the specimen disc and the optical microscope with its external illuminating apparatus. The lens of the optical microscope (of 0·57 inch focal length and an N.A. of about 0·28) was mounted entirely outside the vacuum system. At its lower end the tube of this microscope was provided with a prism, so that the optical axis was turned through a right angle and the image

Fig. 8.7. A simplified section through the object-holder chamber of the E.M.1. Note the optical microscope aligned with its axis parallel to that of the electron microscope.

could be observed in comfort. The illuminating system for this microscope was made to dismount very easily and the specimens could then be loaded into the rotatable disc. When the holders had been dropped into the apertures in this disc, the lamphouse was replaced and the whole microscope evacuated once more. The specimens could be radially aligned by means of a clever cam arrangement worked from the knob attached to the centre axis of the disc and, as has been mentioned, rotated by the tangent screw.

This microscope had a very long column, and so it proved necessary to add smaller coils surrounding the tube in addition to the actual magnetic lenses. These accessory coils served to neutralize the earth's magnetic field which would otherwise have exerted some effect on the beam. At the same time it proved expedient to add extra deflection coils, so arranged that their field acted in a direction at right angles to the compensation coils. These deflector coils allowed some control over the positioning of the electron beam. No vacuum valves were provided on this microscope, which was regarded by its makers as a highly experimental instrument; as Marton wrote:

> The question of the provision of vacuum taps of large bore to isolate the diffusion pumps from the instrument was considered. Admittedly such taps will save a great deal of time if microscopical work reaches a stage in which vacuum must be let down frequently for changes of object, but for the present it was decided to dispense with them.

In fact, although Marton had pioneered the use of airlocks in 1934, it was some years before these were universally adopted on electron microscopes; several of the commercial models available after the war were designed with a small pumping volume and no airlocks. When a specimen or a plate had to be changed it was necessary to let the whole volume up to atmospheric pressure, although as the volume was small, it usually reached the operating pressure again in a matter of a few minutes.

Successful photographs were obtained with the E.M.1, operating with an accelerating potential of 20 kV. In the original paper pictures were published of a test object which consisted of a strand of resistance wire 0·0008 inch thick. The photograph taken at the level of the intermediate screen was at a magnification of about 100×, with a resolution of better than 1 micron, whilst that from the final screen had a magnification of 780×. In this case, however, owing to the low power of the projector lens in use, there was considerable pin–cushion distortion evident in the final image.

Although the E.M.1 did not surpass the resolution of the optical microscope, it is noteworthy as the first electron microscope to be made by a commercial firm, and also as an instrument which provided valuable experience in this field; unfortunately, owing to the outbreak of war, further developments were postponed for some years.

In Germany, Ruska now working in collaboration with von Borries, had entered into association with the electrical firm of Siemens and Halske to develop an electron microscope for commercial production. They designed a prototype which was in operation by 1938 and the first production model was installed in the following year in the laboratories of I. G. Farben. This microscope is shown in Fig. 8.8; by this time the cold-cathode had been superseded by a heated tungsten

FIG. 8.8. Siemens's first commercial electron microscope (1939).

filament as a source of electrons, but the stable lens current was still furnished from storage batteries. The general resemblance of the modern Siemens instrument to this microscope of 1939 may be seen by comparing Fig. 8.8(a) with Fig. 8.11(b), which shows the current model, the Siemens Elmiskop IA. It is worth recording that the Siemens electron microscope of 1939 was the first to be placed in serial production and which could regularly surpass the optical microscope in resolving power.

In the early part of 1940 two interesting electron microscopes were constructed. One, described as a "Universal" microscope, was built by Ardenne and was intended to incorporate all the variants in design and function which were current at that time; the other was designed by Marton, now working in America, and was constructed under his direction by RCA. This microscope, which constituted this company's first essay into this new field, was known as the type "A" and never came into commercial production; however, it marked the beginning of the use of highly stabilized power supplies furnished by electronic means, which are now universal features of all electron microscopes. The RCA type "A" was very shortly followed by the type "B" instrument in which the electronic power supplies were made more reliable and were reduced in size. This was so successful that the power supplies could be incorporated along with the vacuum system into the console of the instrument, instead of requiring a separate cabinet of their own. The type "B" microscope, which was largely due to the efforts of Zworykin, Hillier and Vance, proved to be the first commercial instrument available in America, coming onto the market in 1941. It proved to be the forerunner of a long and continuing series of very successful high-quality electron microscopes.

Progress up to this point in the design of electron microscopes had been rapid. During the ten years or so since Knoll and Ruska demonstrated their first microscope, the main trends had been towards proving the practicability of the instrument and exploring the feasibility of obtaining high resolution by means of electrons. The early electron microscopes were experimental, laboratory-made and often rather crudely constructed; stress was placed on the design of critical operational components and little attention was given to the accessory apparatus or to equipment which did not contribute directly to the production of the image. In consequence, these microscopes were not easy to operate and definitely came into the class of laboratory prototypes which were not suitable for commercial manufacture.

When the future of the instrument seemed assured, and there were indications that a high resolution would ultimately be attained, the engineers began to design electron microscopes in which more reliance was placed upon the ease of operation, actual reliability in use, and simplicity of construction. The electron microscope was at this stage emerging from a laboratory "string and sealing wax" gadget into the hard world of a rugged, commercially-built instrument intended for long years of reliable service. In this respect the RCA type "B" machine led the way, being particularly advanced in the design of the vacuum system.

Up to this date all the instruments had been designed with the axis of the column vertical, with the electron gun at the top and the viewing chamber and photographic plates at the bottom. This led, of course, to simplicity in construction and to a minimization of problems due to the weight of individual items in the column; in addition it made the processes of mechanical alignment somewhat easier. With the production of the electron microscope on a commercial basis it was soon realized that there was a future market for small, compact instruments which had a more limited resolving power than the large machines.

Such microscopes, with a resolution of about 250 Å, say five times that of the optical microscope, were intended largely for use in industry as microscopes for routine operations such as quality control and the like. RCA, in particular, were soon developing such a microscope and with these instruments the design began to be modified. The column was made smaller, the lens systems were much simplified by the omission of some of the lenses and sometimes by the use of fixed-focus permanent-magnet lenses. This allowed the column to be placed horizontally or to be inclined downwards away from the operator's desk, with consequent reduction in the size of the whole equipment. Very often, too, these microscopes were intended for use with only a restricted range of magnifications limited to several predetermined values which could be selected by means of a switch.

At the same time developments in the main-stream of electron microscope design were leading towards the production of instruments with still higher resolutions. One feature which appeared in instruments produced around 1942–3 was developed by Marton and von Borries and Ruska independently. This was the use of three stages of magnification instead of two. In the two-stage microscope the lenses (the objective and the projector) were separated by three to four times the actual length of a lens, with the result that the column was rather long and in consequence there were troubles due to the lack of mechanical rigidity. By the introduction of a third lens (the so-called intermediate lens) the column was rendered much shorter and the versatility of the microscope was substantially increased. With a two-stage instrument the magnification could only be varied over a range of about 5:1

without changing the position of the specimen with respect to the objective, whereas with the newer three-stage microscopes using an intermediate lens this ratio was increased to over 100:1. At the same time the use of three stages allowed the instrument to be set up very easily for obtaining the electron diffraction pattern of a small selected area of the specimen. This feature is of great value in some physical applications as it allows precise information to be obtained as to the nature and configuration of crystalline materials present in the specimen.

In 1944, RCA produced a successor to the type "B" model which became known as the EMU; largely developed by P. C. Smith and R. G. Picard in its early form it had only a two-stage column. The main importance of this microscope lay in the incorporation of many engineering improvements; further refinements were added over the years as they became available. It was claimed by the makers that the EMU microscope gave a resolution of "better than 100 Å", and in actual practice in many laboratories it was resolving about 20 Å. At this period electron microscopes usually operated with an accelerating potential of around 50 kV, but a general feeling was developing that for some applications, especially in metallurgy, it would be preferable to increase this figure. Marton constructed a microscope for Stanford University which he designed to work with a maximum accelerating voltage of 100 kV and with provision for adjusting the high tension in steps of 10 kV down to a minimum limit of 30 kV. This microscope was also provided with a double condenser lens system and with the now standard three-stage column. It seems to have performed satisfactorily, but no actual resolution figures are quoted in the literature.

In England, progress in the development of commercial electron microscopes was delayed by the aftermath of the war, but Metropolitan-Vickers were at work on the design and construction of a new model, the E.M.2, which appeared on the market in 1945. It retained some of the features of the E.M.1, its pre-war ancestor, but was much improved and incorporated the latest advances in vacuum technology such as the use of rubber gaskets rather than the old fashioned metal-to-metal grease seals. The electrons were generated by a heated tungsten filament instead of from a cold-cathode discharge tube; the high tension and the lens power supplies were also stabilized electronically, a practice which was now universal.

This microscope (Fig. 8.9) incorporated airlocks for the specimen and the camera so that the speed of operation of the instrument was greatly increased. Magnifications of up to 10,000× were available on the screen of the instrument, and further enlargement of the photographic plates was, of course, possible; this microscope was to some extent a compromise instrument in that many desirable features, such as the ability to

Fig. 8.9. The Metropolitan Vickers E.M.2. The electrical controls for the lens circuits are located in the small console to the left of the microscope.

take stereoscopic micrographs, were sacrificed in the interests of producing a dependable and easy-to-use microscope.

These features were, however, incorporated into the E.M.3 (Fig. 8.10) which was developed about 1947 and came into production around 1949. With the design of the E.M.3 we find for the first time a British microscope designed to incorporate the intermediate lens. In this new instrument the lens windings were now outside the vacuum of the column and mechanical adjustments and alignment controls were provided which worked through vacuum seals. Airlocks were not installed on this microscope, and in order to maintain a rapid rate of

Fig. 8.10. The E.M.3 of 1949. The common convention of placing the microscope column on a desk which also carries the controls has now been established. The cabinet in the background contains the electronic power supplies and stabilizers.

specimen and plate change the pumped volume of the column was kept as small as possible. The whole microscope column had to be brought up to atmospheric pressure in order to change either the specimen or the plates but the microscope was back at the working pressure within a matter in minutes. It was considered that this method of construction, by avoiding the complication of airlocks, simplified the whole and rendered it more reliable in operation.

The E.M.3 was provided with a continuous coverage of a very wide range of magnifications, with dark-field, with provision for taking stereo-micrographs and with full facilities for selected-area electron diffraction. The E.M.3 could compete on even terms with the best of the electron microscopes available at that time, and had an average resolution of 35 Å with a best performance of somewhere around 25 Å.

All the early electron microscopes were troubled by the presence in their lenses of the aberration known as astigmatism, which has already been described. This, which caused asymmetries of the Fresnel fringes formed by diffraction at the edges of the objects, was due to errors in the magnetic field of the objective lens. It was evident that until such an aberration could be effectively corrected the resolution of the electron microscope was severely limited and really high resolutions would be unattainable.

In 1946, Hillier and Ramberg made one of the significant discoveries in electron microscopy when they discovered the way in which a magnetic lens could be compensated for astigmatism. This was achieved by the so-called "stigmator" which acts by introducing a compensating asymmetry into the magnetic field of the lens in order to neutralize the unwanted errors. Such compensation is now an indispensable feature of every objective and condenser lens and is brought about either by adjusting soft iron correcting slugs on the top of the lens by mechanical means, or in the more refined instruments by applying a potential to one or more of a series of insulated pins or sectors mounted on the lens. The electrostatic field so introduced acts in exactly the same way as a magnetic field and cancels out the unwanted components which are causing the aberration. By this means it is possible not only to compensate for the inherent astigmatism of the lens, but also for that astigmatism which arises during use from the build-up of carbonaceous contamination upon the movable objective aperture. Such deposits are non-conducting and so they charge up under the electron bombardment and they in their turn act as electro-static lenses and introduce astigmatism into the image.

It is worth mentioning at this point that electrostatic electron lenses can be constructed and this was realized very early in the development of the electron microscope. Efforts were made to develop an instrument which used electrostatic lenses instead of electro-magnets and the first microscope was devised and built in Germany by H. Mahl around

1939. Several commercial electrostatic microscopes have been built, especially in France, but they never seriously challenged the popularity of the electro-magnetic types.

When the objective stigmator had been perfected as a consequence of the work of Hillier and Ramberg, serious efforts were made to develop the electron microscope to give a really high resolution. In Germany, Siemens had produced in 1950 their model ÜM100 (Fig. 8.11(a)), which (as its name implies) provided for the use of accelerating voltage up to 100 kV; this instrument was the predecessor of their Elmiskop I (Fig. 8.11(b)) which was introduced in 1954 and is still current in a modified form. This microscope has a double condenser system, an advantage in that greater intensities can be obtained on the screen at high instrumental magnifications and that a much smaller area of the specimen is irradiated with electrons at any one time so reducing the contamination. It has the usual three stages of objective, intermediate, and projector lens, and was capable of a point-to-point resolution of better than 10 Å, which was at that time a quite astounding figure to be attained routinely from a production microscope. There were several microscopes in electron microscope laboratories around the world, which were specially "hotted-up" to give high resolutions, but their use and maintenance was a very highly skilled business. With the advent of the Elmiskop I such resolutions became possible as a routine. Some idea of the improvement in the resolution

Table 5. Some electron microscopes and their approximate resolving power

Date	Instrument	Approximate resolving power
1934	Ruska	*ca.* 500 Å
1934	Driest and Müller	*ca.* 400 Å
1936	Marton *et al.*, E.M.1	better than 1 μ
1939	Siemens first commercial model	100 Å
1940	RCA type "B"	25 Å
1940	Siemens	25 Å
1944	RCA type EMU	*ca.* 20 Å or better
1945	Metro-Vick E.M.2	100 Å or better
1950	Metro-Vick E.M.3	average 35 Å; best 25 Å
1953	Siemens ÜM100 e	10 Å
1954	Siemens Elmiskop I	*ca.* 9 Å
1956	A.E.I. E.M.6	Prototype 10 Å; later improved to *ca.* 5 Å
1964	A.E.I. E.M.6B	3 Å

FIG. 8.11.

(a) The Siemens ÜM 100 (1950).

Fig. 8.11.

(b) The Siemens Elmiskop IA (1964). This is their current production model and resembles fairly closely the model I which was introduced in 1954.

(*Siemens Werkbild*)

attained with the electron microscope may be gained from the figures given in Table 5.

Two years later the British E.M.6 (Fig. 8.12) was announced; this was a microscope intended to have not only a high resolution, but also to be very versatile, covering all the possible requirements of both the biologist and the physicist, whilst remaining at the same time easy to operate. Much of the research which had been carried out in the

FIG. 8.12. The A.E.I. E.M.6 microscope. The general layout of the column and control panels is well shown in this picture.

post-war years was embodied in the design of this instrument and it showed a considerable advance over the old E.M.3.*

In particular, the new E.M.6 differed from its forerunner in that it had the double condenser system and an electrostatic beam alignment device which materially helps in the initial adjustment of the microscope after replacing the filament and makes the operation much easier. This same beam alignment device also allows for reflection electron microscopy to be carried out without the necessity of tilting the whole electron gun and condenser system mechanically. Reflection microscopy is especially valuable in metallurgy for the study of the surface of metal specimens and for observing such effects as that of local wear between two metals in contact. The high-tension circuits of the E.M.6 were redesigned and a novel feature at that time was the incorporation of automatic switching so that the lens currents were changed if the accelerating voltage was changed. This automatically refocused the microscope and made it very easy to carry out observations at differing accelerating voltages. The E.M.6 was first marketed in 1958 and although it has now been superseded by the E.M.6G as a general purpose microscope, very many E.M.6 microscopes are giving excellent service at the present time.

Until very recently the general concept in the design of electron microscopes has been towards the provision of a single high resolution instrument which would serve equally well for the biologist, who mainly requires high quality transmission electron micrographs, and for the physicist or engineer. These workers often demand not only transmission micrographs but also reflection pictures, selected-area diffraction, and even facilities for the incorporation of experimental apparatus such as goniometer or heating or cooling stages inside the microscope itself so that the behaviour of their specimens may be studied whilst they are being heated or bent. Designing a universal instrument, as the optical microscope makers had discovered in the eighteenth century, is a very difficult task and only too often something has to be sacrificed so that the resulting compromise is not very acceptable to anyone.

This problem has been recognized by Associated Electrical Industries (AEI), the successors to Metropolitan-Vickers in electron microscope

*It may be noted that the E.M.4 was designed and produced between 1950 and 1953 as a small, compact microscope with a purposely limited resolution, whilst the E.M.5 (which never entered into production) was an experimental high-voltage microscope intended for use with thick biological sections.

manufacture in England, with the result that their most recent instruments are now intended for either the biologist or the worker in the physical sciences. Their general microscope (the E.M.6G) has all the provisions for fitting such attachments as experimental stages and includes a built-in goniometer stage as standard. It has been realized that the operator today is primarily interested in the information to be obtained from the use of the electron microscope and not in carrying out time-consuming and difficult instrumental adjustments. In consequence these modern microscopes tend to have their controls made as simple as possible, and as many as possible of the lens adjustments have been pre-set in order to keep the number of adjustments during actual operation down to a minimum.

The counterpart of the E.M.6G, intended for the biologist, is the E.M.6B; the biologist requires an instrument with maximum resolving power so that structures at the macromolecular level may be examined and also a microscope which will give maximum contrast in the image. This is needed in order to counter one of the chief difficulties of biological electron microscopy which is that the contrast of the material is so often very low. By specializing the instrument it has proved possible to produce a lens of low chromatic aberration (which will in itself tend to improve the image contrast) and to simplify the controls still further, so that the microscope may be used by operators who have had the minimum of training.

Much biological electron microscopy depends on the careful selection of the areas to be photographed, an operation which can only be done by the actual scientist involved in the experimental work. Such scientists often are not really interested in the electron microscope on its own account and so to them a machine which is simple to operate is a great advantage.

The E.M.6B which is now in commercial production is proving a very popular microscope indeed and has consistently resolved image detail of about 5 Å, whilst values of 3 Å can be obtained from suitable specimens. Contamination of the specimen, due to carbon deposited on it, is a great problem in modern electron microscopes due to the high beam intensities often used. This contamination is probably due to the electron beam striking stray molecules of pump oil in the column. It is essential that such contamination, which seriously obscures image detail, must be kept to the minimum and it has been the practice to keep the beam intensity to a low value and to photograph any interesting detail rapidly before the contaminating layer has had time to form.

In the design of the E.M.6B the makers have had this particular problem well in mind and by the addition of a cold trap which is filled with liquid nitrogen, the region around the specimen may be brought to such a low temperature that the formation of the carbonaceous deposit is inhibited. As the designer writes in a technical description of the instrument published in 1964:

> The freedom from contamination allows a field of view to be examined and photographed at leisure. The operator is able to relax and get on with the job of obtaining micrographs without having to worry about continual incidental adjustments to the instrument.

At the present time there are many high-resolution electron micro-scopes on the market and it is not possible to enumerate them all here. With any of the current instruments, such as the Siemens Elmiskop IA, the E.M.6B or G, the Dutch Philips EM200, and several of the microscopes now being manufactured by the Japanese, it is easy to obtain instrumental resolution extending down into the range of macromolecular sizes.

The design trends of electron microscopes since 1948 may be conveniently summarized under three headings. First, there was a trend which as mentioned above is now (1965) beginning to reverse. This was the demand for the production of a high resolution instrument which should have the utmost flexibility in operation, or in other words, approach as closely as possible to the "Universal" electron microscope. This demanded a very wide range of magnifications and the provision of a host of auxiliary features, many of which were not used by the eventual purchaser of the microscope. Secondly, there was a trend towards the production of a very simplified electron microscope which was intended for routine use. Such microscopes as the E.M.4, produced by Metropolitan-Vickers in 1954, and the RCA EMC instrument belonged to this category. Although these particular instruments are today obsolete, some, such as the Akashi "Tronscope", the JEM "Superscope" and the small Tesla microscope, might be placed in this category.

The "Superscope" carries the concept of the simplified electron microscope to its ultimate expression. The instrument is of very small size and is entirely self-contained in its cabinet which would almost fit underneath a laboratory bench. It has switched magnifications and a simplified vacuum pump system which has dispensed with the con-ventional water-cooling of the diffusion pump. The third main trend in the development was perhaps most marked and attracted the greatest amount of attention; this was the production of instruments which would routinely provide the highest possible resolution and image quality. This was initiated by the Siemens Elmiskop I in 1954 and was continued by the E.M.6 and the Philips EM200.

It is probably true to say that the very rapid development of the electron microscope from the first instrument of Knoll and Ruska to the accomplishment of modern resolutions of the order of a few Ångstrom units is a triumph of modern instrument technology. It is striking when one considers that a comparable development of the optical microscope took over two hundred years whilst barely thirty years has elapsed since the first instrument of Ruska was operational. The main stages in the achievement of such resolutions are summarized in Table 5. It is, of course, this tremendous resolution which constitutes the main advantage of the electron microscope, and justifies the expenditure by laboratories and universities of £15,000 or thereabouts for a modern high-performance instrument. Such resolution had led in biology to a complete rewriting of our concepts of the structure of tissues and cells. This is illustrated in Fig. 8.13(a) and (b). The former represents the appearance of a piece of mammalian pancreas when observed with the highest resolution of the optical microscope. It is evident that relatively little structure can be made out inside the actual cells; there is the nucleus and indications of some granular bodies at one end of the cell but that is about all.

With the electron microscope on the other hand (Fig. 8.13(b)) the same type of cell shows a wealth of detailed structure in the cytoplasm. Membrane systems fill the bulk of the cytoplasm, and various organelles such as the mitochondria and lysosomes show complex internal organization which was not even suspected with the optical microscope. At very high magnifications (Fig. 8.13(b) inset) the resolution is such that these membranes of the cell, the "endoplasmic reticulum", are seen to be covered with particles about 150 Å in diameter; these particles are now known to consist of nucleoprotein and are involved in the processes of protein secretion which are carried out by this particular cell type.

Such high resolution is very valuable to the cell biologist but it cannot be attained without some sacrifices, which do to some extent limit the value of the electron microscope in cell biology. First, as the microscope operates at a vacuum of about 1×10^{-4} torr inside the column, it follows that living cells cannot be studied with this instrument.

FIG. 8.13.

(a) A high-power optical micrograph of the exocrine cells of the pancreas. Although the nucleus is clearly seen, little structural detail can be made out in the cytoplasm.

(b) An electron micrograph of the same type of cell as in (a) above. Notice that a great deal of detailed structure is now resolved in the cell cytoplasm. The inset shows, at a much higher magnification, the ribosomes which are attached to the cytoplasmic membranes of this type of cell; the resolution of the electron microscope is so great that such magnifications still present us with more useful information.

Not only would the water contained within the cell destroy the vacuum, but as it was "boiled off" with explosive force the whole structure of the cell would be disintegrated. Again, as the electron beam has a very poor penetrating power, a thickness of water such as would occur in a living cell would prove to be an impenetrable barrier to the electrons. It is necessary, therefore, to kill the cell, embed it in plastic material and then cut it into very thin slices which are inserted into the microscope as the specimen. The electrons are able to traverse sections of such material of up to 1000 Å thickness and form some sort of an image, but for high resolutions it is necessary to work with sections of material which are considerably thinner than this.

Such electron microscope images suffer from the drawback that they are entirely two-dimensional; if one is studying an 800 Å-thick slice of a cell which may itself be over 40 microns in thickness, it is obvious that in order to survey all the structures present in three dimensions about 480 sections would be required. For various technical reasons sectioning so much material is a very difficult feat, and it is only in very recent years that microtomes have become available which will perform sufficiently well; then each section has to be inserted into the microscope and photographed and the photographs used to make a three-dimensional reconstruction of the object. It is apparent that such a task is full of technical difficulties and has very seldom been attempted.

The lack of penetration of the electrons might be overcome in future years by increasing the accelerating voltage applied to the electrons. It might then become possible to include the living cell in some sort of culture chamber which is outside the vacuum of the microscope column and admit the beam to the specimen via thin windows above and below the chamber. Efforts to develop microscopes working with such high voltages are in progress at the moment, in Cambridge and in Toulouse in France; only time will tell whether it will prove feasible to utilize the tremendous resolution of the electron microscope on the living cell in this particular way.

The electron microscopist, obliged to use only dead material, is always aware of the possibility that the structures which he is examining so carefully are entirely artificial, being produced by the action of the fixative or some other part of the preparative process on the cell. It is very difficult to exclude all such possibilities entirely, as the objects of interest are usually well below the limits of resolution of the optical microscope, so their existence cannot be verified by reference to the direct observation of the living cell. Such indirect evidence as there is suggests that the appearances now current do in fact bear a genuine relationship to the structure present in life, but it is always essential to bear the possibility of artifact formation well in mind.

Again, the living cell is a dynamic entity and what we are examining in the electron microscope is the end product of a whole series of highly artificial operations. These show us the cell as it was *at the time that it was killed* by the chemical fixing agent. It seems not unlikely that as the cell goes through its cycle of activity the ultrastructure would undergo considerable changes. With the restriction on the examination of living cells in the electron microscope the possibility of obtaining accurate information about the dynamic activities of the cell is not very great. It is perhaps legitimate to compare the problem to the difficulty of obtaining reliable information about a cyclical microscopic process by the expedient of taking a series of still photographs at intervals. Such photographs may be strung together in sequence to present some impression of the activity, but the information gained is limited and not comparable with that which could be obtained from a continuous record as might be provided by a cine-camera. With the electron microscope it is only possible to produce large numbers of photographs from material taken at various stages and hope that these can be linked to give some sort of valid impression of the whole process. It is obvious that any development which would allow the examination of living cells in the electron microscope would be an extremely valuable help in the problem of seeking to interpret the relationship between structure and function in the cell.

Finally, in biological work, as has already been mentioned, the electron microscopist is faced with the problem of obtaining sufficient contrast in the image. The use of heavy metals in some form or other does improve the position considerably, but the use of such methods suffers from the drawback that the deposition of heavy metals in the tissues tends to be non-specific; this gives a picture which is, therefore, entirely lacking in chemical information. It is hoped that future developments in specimen preparation technique will lead to the production of micrographs in which the electron densities are directly related to the presence of certain specific chemical groups. By the exact localization of some of the compounds involved in the make-up of the cell a further step forward would have been taken in our laborious process of piecing together the relationship between the chemistry of the cell, its structure and its function.

The very rapid development of the electron microscope itself has been stressed in this chapter; equally rapid and equally important has been the complementary developments and improvements in the methods of preparing material for study with this instrument. The early electron microscopes were much used for the study of particles, either inorganic, such as dust or metallic oxide smokes, or biological particulate matter, such as the bacteria and viruses.

In the case of inorganic particles little more need be done in order to examine them than to arrange for their deposition on a suitable support film which is attached to a specimen grid. In order to add sufficient contrast to biological material, however, it was usual to deposit a layer of heavy metal upon the material by the use of what is called "metal shadowing". The object, mounted on the support film, is placed in a bell jar which contains a tungsten wire filament which carries the metal to be deposited. The air in the jar is pumped out and then a heavy electric current is passed through the tungsten wire. This vaporizes the metal (usually gold palladium alloy or some other heavy metal such as platinum) which settles onto the specimens. If the filament is arranged to lie to one side of the specimen then the deposit of metal is concentrated on one side and this serves to throw the objects and in particular their surface structure into sharp relief. By this method much information about the size and shape of the specimen may be obtained.

At the present time the method has been to some extent superseded by the technique of "negative staining" in which the particle is surrounded by a deposit of electron-dense material dried down from a solution of a substance such as potassium silico-tungstate. The heavy metal contained in the deposit cannot penetrate the particle and so outlines it, sharply delineating any surface irregularities.

The problem of preparing homogeneous material was much more difficult. With thin cells, such as might be found in a tissue culture, some success was obtained by growing them directly onto the support film carried by the electron microscope grids. The cells were fixed by chemicals and then dried before examining them in the electron microscope as whole mounts. By this means Porter was able to show the system of canals (called by him the endoplasmic reticulum) inside the cytoplasm. Later work has confirmed the existence of this system and has emphasized its importance in the transport and synthetic activities of the cell. Such a method of study, however, is limited in its scope and the degree of resolution which can be attained is severely limited by the thickness of the cells. Attempts were, therefore, made to adapt the techniques of the optical microscopist, especially that of embedding the cells in a supporting medium and then cutting them into very thin slices by a microtome.

In 1950, Hillier and Gettner succeeded in obtaining sections $0 \cdot 1$ to $0 \cdot 2$ micron thick by using a modified histological microtome. Such sections, which were obtained from material which had been double-embedded in a mixture of celloidin and paraffin, showed a resolution of about 200 Å when they were examined in the electron microscope. (It may be mentioned, for comparison, that the normal section thicknesses used for optical microscopy range from 5 microns upwards to over 100 microns in special cases.) A great step forward in the art of preparing sections for the electron microscope came when Newman, Borysko and Swerdlow introduced the use of plastics as embedding agents, chiefly using polymerized butyl methacrylate for this purpose. In this way, Palade managed to obtain sections $0 \cdot 05$ micron thick, which showed a correspondingly improved resolution.

About the same time, the first microtome especially designed for cutting thin sections for the electron microscope was designed by Claude and Blum. This machine embodied several of the principles which were found in nearly all subsequent microtomes. Perhaps the most important was the "bypass" principle in which the block containing the tissue to be cut only passed the knife edge on the actual cutting stroke, being deflected on the return movement. Other innovations were the continuous mechanical advance and the use of a trough filled with liquid attached to the knife edge; this received the sections as they were cut and allowed them to form a ribbon which could then be picked up on a specimen grid. From this microtome the famous Porter-Blum model was developed and marketed in 1953. This, together with the introduction some years later of the epoxy resins, led to a tremendous improvement in the quality of sections. These new resins have many advantages over the methacrylates formerly used for embedding materials in order to produce thin sections for electron microscopy. With the aid of the epoxy resins even finer cellular detail could be preserved and pictured, so that the resolutions attained with sectioned biological material improved by leaps and bounds.

It is not possible in a book of this type to enter into all the recent technical advances in specimen preparation for electron microscopy. Methods are changing and improving all the time and progress in this field, although rapid, still lags behind the actual progress in instrument design. One innovation, however, must be singled out for comment and mentioned with the Porter-Blum microtome as contributing to the very rapid spread of biological electron microscopy; this was the discovery in 1950 by Latta and Hartmann that the edge of a piece of broken plate glass could be used to cut much better thin sections than any steel knife. Perhaps more than any other single technological advance this has helped in the preparation of acceptable material for study in the high-resolution microscopes of today.

With the development of the high-resolution electron microscope, the story of the microscope has been brought up to date. There can be no doubt that the end of the road has not yet been reached, even though resolution of a few Ångstrom units, which would have seemed fantastic twenty years ago, let alone at the turn of the century, are now commonplace. There are many fields of active development in optical microscopy, some of which have been indicated in Chapter 7, and even better prospects for the future of electron microscopy. As yet, the design of electron lenses is in its infancy and the search for increased aperture and better corrections still goes on. By this means the resolving power of the electron microscope will be pushed gradually nearer and nearer to the figure of $0 \cdot 1$ Å, which would be expected on theoretical grounds. Alternative methods of recording the image are under examination in which the use of visual focusing on a screen and recording on a photographic plate may be dispensed with in favour of throwing the image onto the tube of an image intensifier and its subsequent presentation by electronic means. Again, quantitation at the electron microscope level is only just beginning.

Something has already been said to indicate the scope for future methods which would yield chemical information at the resolutions of the electron microscope and for methods which would be applicable to the study of the living cell. Variants of the straightforward electron microscope are being developed at the present time. Such instruments, for example the scanning electron microscope in which a focused beam of electrons is systematically passed over the surface of the object and a picture is built up on a television type of monitor by recording the electrons scattered from the specimen, are now in production. Again much fascinating work is taking place with the electron probe micro-analyser in which a focused beam of electrons is used to irradiate a small area of the surface of a specimen. This excites the production of charac-teristic X-rays from the elements present in the specimen: these X-rays may be recorded and analysed to give much valuable data about the chemical composition of the specimen under study. As yet this technique has only limited application to biological material but in future years the applications of this type of instrument are sure to increase as our techniques become more sophisticated.

A whole new world of structure, hitherto entirely unsuspected, has been revealed to us by the rapid development of the electron microscope in the last thirty years. Who can foresee what awaits us in the next thirty years?

FURTHER READING

(I) BOOKS

The following represents a selection from the many available on the history and construction of the microscope (references to very early books or rare works in Latin have not been given).

ADAMS, G. 1746 *Micrographia Illustrata, or the microscope explained*, London.
ADAMS, G. 1777 *Ibid.*, 4th edn.
ADAMS, G. 1787 *Essays on the Microscope*, London.
BAKER, H. 1753 *Employment for the Microscope*, London.
BREWSTER, D. 1837 *A Treatise on the Microscope*, Edinburgh.
CARPENTER, W. B. 1901 *The Microscope and Its Revelations*, 8th edn, ed. Dallinger, W. H., London.
CITTERT, P. H. VAN 1934 Descriptive Catalogue of the Collection of microscopes in charge of the Utrecht University Museum.
CLAY, R. S. & COURT, T. H. 1932 *The History of the Microscope*, London.
DISNEY HILL, A. N., HILL, C. F. and WATSON BAKER, W. E. 1928 *The Origin and Development of the Microscope*, Royal Microscopical Society, London.
FRISON, E. 1954 L'Évolution de la partie optique du Microscope au cours du Dixneuvième siècle. Communication 89, Rijksmuseum voor de Geschiedenis der Natuurwetenschappen, Leiden.
HALL 1966 *Introduction to Electron Microscopy*.
HARTING, P. 1866 *Das Mikroskop*, 2nd German edition, Braunschweig.
HEURCK, H. VAN 1893 *The Microscope*, Trans. from the French by E.Wynne Baxter. London.
HOOKE, R. 1665 *Micrographia*, London.
MARTIN, B. 1742 *Micrographia Nova*, London.
QUEKETT, J. 1848 *Practical Treatise on the Use of the Microscope*, London.
ROOSEBOOM, M. 1956 *Microscopium*, Leiden.
STAR, P. VAN DER 1953 Descriptive catalogue of the simple microscopes in the Rijksmuseum voor de Gescheidenis der Natuurwetenschappen, Leiden.
VICKERS, A. E. J. (ed.) 1956 *Modern Methods of Microscopy*, London.

(II) ARTICLES

Many valuable articles on all aspects of microscope design and development will be found in the *Journal of the Royal Microscopical Society* from the middle of the nineteenth century onwards. Other specific articles which may be consulted are:

ABBE, E. 1879 On Stephenson's system of homogeneous immersion for microscope objectives. *J. Roy. Micr. Soc.*, p. 279.

ABBE, E. 1887 On improvements of the microscope with the aid of new kinds of optical glass. *J. Roy. Micr. Soc.*, p. 20.

BEDINI, S. A. 1960 Seventeenth century Italian compound microscopes. *Physis*, **V**, 383.

BENNETT, A. H. 1943 The development of the microscope objective. *J. Opt. Soc. Amer.*, **33**, 123.

CLAY, R. S. 1938 A review of the mechanical improvements of microscopes in the last forty years. *J. Roy. Micr. Soc.*, **58**, 1.

COLE, F. J. 1938 Microscopic Science in Holland in the seventeenth century. *J. Quekett Micr. Club.*, Se 4, **1**, 59.

HOOKE, R. 1679 Lectiones Cutlerianae. Reprinted in "Early Science at Oxford". Ed. R. T. Guntler, Vol. 8.

HUGHES, A. 1955 Studies in the history of microscopy I. The influence of achromatism. *J. Roy. Micr. Soc.*, **75**, 1.

HUGHES, A. 1955 Studies in the history of microscopy II. The later history of the achromatic microscope. *J. Roy. Micr. Soc.*, **76**, 47.

KINGMA BOLTJES, T. Y. 1940–41 Some experiments with blown glasses. *Ant. van Leeuwenhoeck. J. Microbiol. and Geology*, **7**, 61.

LISTER, J. J. 1830 On some properties in achromatic object glasses applicable to the improvement of the microscope. *Phil. Trans.*, **130**, 187.

MALIES, H. M. 1946–48 The microscopes of Powell and Lealand. *The Microscope*, **6**, 95.

MALIES, H. M. 1955 The microscope during the last hundred years.
1. *The Microscope*, **10**, 113.
2. *The Microscope*, **10**, 149.

MAYALL, J., Jnr. 1885 The Cantor Lectures on the history of the microscope. *J. Roy. Soc. Arts.*, 34.

STEPHENSON, J. W. 1878 On a large angled immersion objective without adjustment collar; with some observations on numerical aperture. *J. Roy. Micr. Soc.*, p. 51.

NAME INDEX

SUBJECT INDEX